P9-BZW-353

PERSONAL MENTAL HYGIENE

PERSONAL
MENTAL HYGIENE

By
DOM THOMAS VERNER MOORE
O. S. B., M.D., Ph.D.

Professor of Psychology and Psychiatry
Catholic University of America

WITHDRAWN FROM
State Teachers College Library
J. EUGENE SMITH LIBRARY
EASTERN CONN. STATE UNIVERSITY
Willimantic Conn.
WILLIMANTIC, CT 06226

GRUNE & STRATTON
NEW YORK
1944

NIHIL OBSTAT
  JOHN J. JEPSON, S.S., PH.D., CENSOR DEPUTATUS, BALTIMORE
NIHIL OBSTAT
  J. EDWARD RAUTH, CENSOR DEPUTATUS, CONGR. ANGLIAE O.S.B
IMPRIMATUR
  ✠MICHAEL J. CURLEY, ARCHIEP., BALTIMORE

PRINTED BY WAVERLY PRESS, INC., U.S.A.

COPYRIGHT, 1944

GRUNE & STRATTON, INC.

381 FOURTH AVENUE, NEW YORK CITY

FIRST PRINTING DECEMBER 1944

SECOND PRINTING JANUARY 1945

THIRD PRINTING MAY 1945

FOURTH PRINTING APRIL 1946

31.32
77864

PREFACE

THE PRESENT work is termed *Personal Mental Hygiene* because it is intended primarily for the individual. It is written in the hope of presenting various attitudes of mind, ideals, and principles which may be of value to the individual confronted with the difficulties of life. Attitudes of mind, ideals, and principles can often soften the conflicts of life and give stability to the personality so that it may not be crushed and overwhelmed by the emotional burdens that from time to time will be placed upon it. And yet psychiatry too often neglects ideals and principles and attempts to attain its ends by adjusting the mechanisms to be found on the emotional plane without rising to anything of an intellectual or spiritual character. I was once asked by an educated layman why it is that one can never turn to a psychiatrist to point the way to the higher things in life and I had to admit that this is too often true, but tried to argue that there is no reason in the nature of the science of psychiatry itself why it should be so. Unfortunately it is so and that too at a time when psychiatrists are stepping forward to act as the guides of human beings in the conflicts and perplexities of the present crisis in modern life.

If one attempts to deal with all human difficulties on the emotional plane, he will have to give up as hopeless and insoluble many problems of life which have a solution in that intellectual and spiritual sphere which extends far beyond the limits of all possible emotional adjustments.

The present work has attempted to point out the possibilities of the ordinary emotional adjustments and at the same time to bring into psychiatry the higher things in human life without which the mind of man sinks to an animal level.

Because the book has been written to be helpful to the individual, the workings of the mind and its adjustments to life have been illustrated by an analysis not only of clinical material, but also of various historical and literary personalities.

v

8 9 4 7

It is an attempt to familiarize the reader with the possibilities of emotional adjustments to the difficulties of life and also by a number of examples to provide a knowledge of wholesome attitudes of mind, ideals, and principles, some of which he can take over, make his own, and use practically in the difficulties he now experiences or may encounter in the future.

THOMAS VERNER MOORE

Washington, D. C., October, 1944

CONTENTS

CHAPTER I

THE CONCEPT OF MENTAL HYGIENE AND MENTAL DISORDER

THE TERM hygiene has been in the English language since the sixteenth century in the sense of the science or art of preserving health. In the seventeenth century hygiene along with physiology and pathology was looked upon as one of the three major parts of medical theory.[1] As early as 1843 William Sweetser wrote a book entitled *Mental Hygiene, or an Examination of the Intellect and Passions Designed to Illustrate Their Influence on Health and the Duration of Life.*[2] But the concept of mental hygiene is much more ancient. Roger Bacon (1214?–1294) wrote a book entitled *Libellus de retardandis senectutis accidentibus et de sensibus conservandis*[3] and the later English translation tells us that it treats of how to preserve the youth, strength, and beauty of body, and the senses and all the faculties of both body and mind.[4] And so one could search antiquity and find that from earliest times human beings have been interested in the hygiene of the body and of the mind.[5]

The concept of hygiene has from the earliest times been that of a science which has to do with the preservation of health or physical well-being. And as early as the thirteenth century, as the title of Bacon's work indicates, one associated therewith

---

[1] Salmon, *Syn. Med.* III. i. 322: "The speculative part of medicine is threefold: to wit, in Physiologia, Hygiene and Pathologia" (in James A. H. Murray [ed.], *A New English Dictionary*, Oxford, 1901, vol. 5, p. 493, under "Hygiene").

[2] New York: J. and H. G. Langley.

[3] Oxoniae, 1590. For a modern critical edition, see A. G. Little and E. Withington, *Fratris Rogeri Bacon, De retardatione accidentium senectutis . . .*, British Society of Franciscan Studies, Oxford: Clarendon Press, 1928, vol. 14.

[4] London, 1683.

[5] Some idea of the interest of older writers in mental and physical hygiene can be obtained by examining the list of books prior to 1800 under "Hygiene" ("Literature of") in ser. 1, *Index Catalogue*, Library of the Surgeon-General's Office, U. S. Army, Washington, D. C.: Gov't Print. Off., 1885.

1

the concept of the preservation of mental health, that is to say, of the senses and faculties of the mind.

At the present time we lay special stress on the concept of the individual who possesses senses and faculties of the mind; and so we would like to define mental hygiene as a practical science which studies the human personality and its deviations from ideal perfection with a view to their prevention. We use the phrase "deviations from ideal perfection" rather than "mental disorders" because minor blemishes of character are well worth while avoiding and also correcting after they have been incurred.

The most common blemishes of character derive from an inadequate control of the emotions, and concern in particular all those displays of temper and antagonism that cause difficulty in our interpersonal relationships. Small as these things are, if they are uncontrolled, allowed to become habitual, one's rapport with one's fellow men deteriorates and one is eventually regarded at least as of unsound mind; and one may spend some time or the remainder of one's life in a hospital for patients suffering from mental disorders.

This leads us to a consideration of the disorders of the mind. There is a group of these disorders which may be regarded as fundamentally and essentially faults of character and major defects of the personality. This group of mental disorders is sometimes referred to as the essential psychoses and embraces the various forms of what are known as manic-depressive insanity and dementia praecox or schizophrenia.

It may seem at first sight strange to some to have manic-depressive and schizophrenic mental disorders spoken of as outgrowths of personality defects. This view is based on the following lines of evidence.

A study of the symptoms of the mental disorders demonstrated that they hang together in groups or syndromes. The ultimate reason for this is that a mental disorder must necessarily be a disorder of something. This something in the essential psychoses is a special form of emotional behavior due to the disturbance of a specific type of emotional function.[6]

The next problem was to see whether or not the symptoms of the patient's mental disorder were in any way bound up or associated with his prepsychotic mental temperament. This was found to be the case.[7]

Let us look for a moment at what type of mental disorder you are likely to develop in case you become insane. The following groups of traits in the individual's character before his mental trials were positively associated with the presence of the mental disorder indicated:

ANXIOUS, SAD TYPE OF MANIC-DEPRESSIVE INSANITY

Tendency to changes of mood
Tendency to worry
Scrupulosity
Tendency to express anger by rather violent action
Subject to peculiar abnormal fears
Tendency to overdo
Not timid nor retiring
Cocksure of self
Does not mope
Does not easily give up and quit
Does not like to be alone
Does not like to study

MANIC TYPE OF MANIC-DEPRESSIVE INSANITY

Quick to make friends
A good mixer
Likes to be with others
Prefers outdoor activities
Thinks of suicide when in trouble
Has difficulties with the family
No tendency to sadness
No tendency to spells of the blues
Rather quick in flow of words

---

[6] Cf. Thomas V. Moore, *The Essential Psychoses and Their Fundamental Syndromes,* Studies in Psychology and Psychiatry from the Catholic University of America, Washington, D. C., vol. 3, no. 3, 1933.

[7] Cf. T. V. Moore, "The Prepsychotic Personality and the Concept of Mental Disorder," *Character & Personality* **9:** 169-87, 1941.

Marked tendency to be overactive and to overdo
Marked sociability in the sense of not being timid nor retiring

PARANOID DEMENTIA PRAECOX

Peculiar ideas in early life
Peculiar outlook on life
Visionary
Suspicious
Peculiar personality
Different from others
Slow to make friends
Poor mixer
Makes good progress in school
Likes to read
Easily gives up and quits
When angry does not show it by loud voice and violent actions

CATATONIC DEMENTIA PRAECOX

Unlike the paranoid the catatonic dementia praecox patient shows *no* tendency to have
Peculiar ideas in early life
Peculiar outlook on life
Visionary trends
But he
Often loses his temper
His movements are rather slow
Tends to have a loud manner when angry
Does not think of suicide when in trouble
Does not tend to be scrupulous
Tends to cry easily
Generally gets along well with outsiders

These character traits are not signs of impending insanity but rather of a character type. If one of the character types indicated is your type, then when the stress and strain of life impinge on your personality, or organic factors of some kind undermine stability, you will be more likely to develop the type of insanity indicated rather than any other form of major mental disorder.

But you may ask: Are there any character traits which indicate a weakness of mental constitution, so that if your temperament abounds in these traits it indicates a weak personality which is more likely to break under the stress and strain of life?

Some light on this problem was obtained by studying the character traits of 110 normal individuals and the prepsychotic character of 112 patients in mental hospitals.

This enabled us to find out what character traits tended to be relatively more common in mental patients than in the group of normal individuals who so far at least had never manifested any major form of mental disorder.

The following table gives the positive coefficients of association found:[8]

Symptom		Symptom	
Different from others	.814	Slow walker	.343
Churlish, crabbed, gruff	.810	Sulks and pouts	.331
Spreads gloom	.795	Refuses to talk	.327
Peculiar personality	.757	Prefers indoors	.325
Peculiar ideas in early life	.712	Tendency to overdo	.319
Slow to laugh	.689	Keeps promises	.308
Poor mixer	.619	Scrupulous	.280
Slow to make friends	.608	Difficulties with family	.258
Likes to be alone	.607	Likes to study	.227
Cold	.545	Slow speech	.222
Tired	.538	Suspicious	.206
Peace-disturbing	.450	Loud voice	.187
Peculiar outlook on life	.444	Goes off by self	.178
Gives up and quits	.443	Easily angered	.176
Mopes	.415	Standing in class	.172
Sad	.393	Tendency to worry	.079
Loud manner when angry	.391	Delirious	.077
Slow movements	.378	Difficulties with outsiders	.067
Cocksure of self	.351	Actions when angry	.003

Traits with a coefficient above .500 may be looked upon as bad signs. In general the words by which they are designated tell roughly what is meant by the trait in question. "Different from others" has the highest coefficient of association with the appearance of a mental disorder. What is meant by it is indicated by the following examples:

[8] *Op. cit.*, Table 12.

"Never had anything to say when friends visited the family. Hung back and wanted other person always to speak to her first."

"He wanted to avoid other members of the community lest they should find some reason to talk about him."

"No activity, insanely jealous when first married. To get him to shave or shine his shoes required a long argument."

"Never friendly. One day he would speak to people and the next would talk to nobody."

"So quiet she was almost dead. Seemed to think she had to always hide behind her mother."[9]

When we look at these traits they seem to point to the fact that the psychotic patient fled from reality into his psychosis. Had he mixed with the world and taken in good part the knocks and blows in the warfare of life, had he attempted to come out of himself and be kindly and sympathetic and to be all things to all men, his mental disorder might never have developed.

There are indeed other than mental factors in the onset of a mental disorder, some of which we can do little to control. But it would be well worth while for anyone to examine our table and see if he can locate among the traits with the higher coefficients any of his personal character defects and then do what he can to overcome them.

All this suggests an important definition of the essential psychosis: A mental disorder is an abnormality of human behavior dependent to a very large extent on the original constitution of the individual with all its complex mental and physical constituent elements. Emotional trends have a basis in the central nervous system, and a mental disorder is more likely to develop in a person in whom the neurological basis of emotional experience exists from early years in a condition of abnormal lability.

[9] *Op. cit.*

1. THE INCIDENCE OF INSANITY

We may now ask: Is a mental disorder a rare event and, if not, how often does it occur?

Malzberg has pointed out the fallacy of the conclusion that insanity is on the increase because the number of patients in mental hospitals increases from year to year. A patient remains in a mental hospital on an average for five to six years; consequently, given hospitals with ample facilities to receive patients, and let us say a stable rate of incidence of insanity, the annual admissions for some years must exceed the total number of discharges and deaths. When the hospitals are crowded, there will be a tendency to build more hospitals. "One concludes, therefore, that no legitimate influences with respect to the relative increase in mental disease can be drawn from data with respect to the number of patients under treatment in hospitals."[10]

If one could actually count all new cases of mental disorder occuring in the course of a year and do this year after year or at stated intervals, it would be possible to get true knowledge of the rate of increase of insanity. Not having such a statistic for the total population, one turns naturally to the data on first admissions to mental hospitals. Here there are two difficulties:

a) New and better hospitals are ever being constructed and the relatives of mental patients are more willing to send to a hospital a member of their family who is mentally disturbed.

b) The importance of early care for the insane has been stressed in various ways and through numerous channels in recent years.

[10] Benjamin Malzberg, "The Increase of Mental Disease," *Psychiatric Quart.* 17: 489, 1943. In his argument Malzberg seems to lose sight of the fact that, given an average stay of six years for patients in mental hospitals, and supposing a constant rate of incidence of insanity, the hospital population would increase for six years and then remain at an approximately constant level and not go on increasing indefinitely.

Consequently data based on all the hospitals in the United States are likely to be fallacious. It is generally admitted, however, that in at least two states in the United States there have been adequate hospital facilities for several decades and in these states there have been frequent attempts to enlighten the general public on the necessity of care for the mentally ill. These two states are New York and Massachusetts. Though the New York sample is not perfect it may nevertheless serve to give a fairly correct estimate of the tendency of insanity to increase or decrease or remain constant, as the case may be.

Malzberg made use of the New York data to throw light on this problem. The outstanding features of this study are: "Taking mental disorders as a whole there has been a slow upward trend over many years. The slope of the trend is not sufficiently steep to justify the alarmists, who ascribe the increase in mental disease to the rapid multiplication of defective stock."[11] This is not due as is commonly said to the fact that the proportion of elderly people in our population is continually increasing.

The most marked rise in any form of mental disorder is that of psychoses associated with cerebral arteriosclerosis. The rate standardized for sex and age has about trebled in the last three decades. Considering that smoking is a factor in diseases of the arteries, this very marked increase in arteriosclerotic insanity may be due in large measure to the great increase in the prevalence of smoking that has taken place in this period. The ratio of incidence for the period from 1920 to 1940 is

$$\text{for men,} \quad \frac{72.24}{24.85} = 2.91$$

$$\text{for women,} \quad \frac{56.15}{16.81} = 3.34$$

Alcoholic psychoses were at a minimum in 1920–1921, at which time prohibition was at maximum efficiency. With more

[11] *Op. cit.*, p. 503.

successful bootlegging and the later repeal of prohibition, the alcoholic insanities increased till their rate is "now higher than at any time in the recorded history of the New York State Department of Mental Hygiene."[12]

If one examines the incidence of alcoholic insanity in New York one will notice a general downward trend from 1909 (the first available report) till the advent of prohibition. One may look upon this downward trend as due to the various total abstinence movements common in the United States prior to prohibition. It was not good custom to drink at one's office during business hours. High school students did not drink at their evening social events. One would not be offered a cocktail as a routine procedure at a private social function in the evening. With the advent of prohibition, every housewife prided herself on having some good old-time stuff or her own home brew which guests were supposed to test and admire. The children heard the parents extolling the wonders of old whiskey and their mother's original concoctions. And it was hard to persuade them to forego entirely what their parents admired and enjoyed themselves. And so the high school student commenced to carry a bottle to the evening dance. A man had at his business office a cabinet kept well stocked by his bootlegger and visitors were usually invited to have a drink. Total abstinence movements became unpopular. Sermons were no longer preached in many churches on the moral beauty of sobriety. And so, as soon as the prohibition laws were successfully evaded, alcoholic insanity started to increase and is now more frequent than it has ever been before.

Syphilitic insanity, however, is waning, owing to vigorous attempts by boards of health all over the country to prevent the spread of syphilis and also to the success of the malaria and fever therapy of paresis.

Manic-depressive insanity for some reason dropped in 1940; but there has been a gradual increase in the number of de-

---

[12] *Op. cit.*, p. 503.

Average Annual Standardized Rates of First Admissions to All Hospitals for Mental Disease in New York State During the Years 1919-21, 1929-31, 1939-41 per 100,000 Corresponding Population, Classified According to Sex and Specified Type of Mental Disorder[13]

	Male			Female			Total		
	1920	1930	1940	1920	1930	1940	1920	1930	1940
Senile*	25.13 ±0.99	26.13 ±0.89	30.75 ±0.85	32.91 ±1.04	31.48 ±0.97	36.11 ±0.74	31.74 ±0.78	31.58 ±0.69	37.20 ±0.66
Cerebral arteriosclerosis*	24.85 ±0.98	50.91 ±1.24	72.24 ±1.30	16.81 ±0.81	35.36 ±1.03	56.15 ±0.92	21.31 ±0.64	44.44 ±0.82	66.67 ±0.88
General paresis**	21.50 ±0.51	17.66 ±0.41	12.93 ±0.33	4.67 ±0.24	4.83 ±0.21	4.24 ±0.14	12.94 ±0.28	10.90 ±0.23	8.49 ±0.19
Alcoholic***	5.61 ±0.28	13.47 ±0.38	17.60 ±0.41	1.64 ±0.15	2.55 ±0.17	3.76 ±0.19	3.58 ±0.16	7.95 ±0.21	10.60 ±0.22
Manic-depressive**	12.39 ±0.39	13.74 ±0.36	7.18 ±0.25	23.26 ±0.53	21.24 ±0.45	15.27 ±0.27	17.70 ±0.33	17.39 ±0.29	11.11 ±0.22
Dementia praecox**	36.18 ±0.66	35.77 ±0.59	38.87 ±0.58	27.81 ±0.58	27.90 ±0.52	36.51 ±0.42	31.72 ±0.44	31.57 ±0.39	37.56 ±0.40
All psychoses***	114.84 ±1.18	133.21 ±1.14	145.17 ±1.12	103.35 ±1.12	102.63 ±1.00	126.31 ±0.78	109.13 ±0.81	118.23 ±0.76	136.65 ±0.76

* Population of New York State aged 45 years and over on January 1, 1920, taken as standard.
** Population of New York State aged 15 years and over on January 1, 1920, taken as standard.
*** Population of New York State aged 20 years and over on January 1, 1920, taken as standard.
[13] From Benjamin Malzberg, "The Increase of Mental Disease," Psychiatric Quart. 17: 497 (July), 1943.

mentia praecox patients. The accompanying table from Malzberg's study summarizes the findings above.

On the basis of first admissions to mental hospitals in Massachusetts, New York, and Illinois, Dorn calculates that of the 2,144,800 infants born in 1938, from 110,000 to 120,000 will eventually be committed to hospitals for mental disease. That gives us an incidence of from 5.12 to 5.59 per cent.[14]

Some years ago Ogburn and Winston pointed out that according to New York statistics, out of 84,450 persons alive at 15 years of age, 3907 or about 1 in 22 will go insane and spend some time in a mental hospital.[15] Furthermore, they pointed out, not all the insane are in hospitals and they estimated that roughly there is about one chance in ten of going insane in the course of a lifetime.

One might attempt to study the comparative rates of insanity in different nations and countries; but variations in the concept of insanity, in the ease with which patients are sent to mental hospitals, and the extent of hospital facilities are all so different in the various countries of the globe that any conclusions would be difficult to draw.[16]

[14] Harold F. Dorn, "The Incidence and Future Expectancy of Mental Disease," *Pub. Health Rep.* **53**: 991–2004 (Nov. 11), 1938; Reprint 2001, p. 14.

[15] William F. Ogburn and Ellen Winston, "The Frequency and Probability of Insanity," *Am. J. Sociol.* **34**: 822–31, 1929.

[16] For a comparative study of the insanity rates of the countries of Europe, cf. H. M. Bersot, "Les aliénés en Europe," *Ann. méd.-psychol.*, ser. 15, **2**: 88–96, (June), 1936.

For the situation in France, cf. G. Ichok, "Etude sur la population française: Les psychopathes," *Biol. méd.* **28**: 245–90 (May), 1938.

For the German statistics, cf. "Irrenstatistik der Gesellschaft deutscher Neurologen und Psychiater" (Psychiat. Abt., 1936), *Allg. Ztschr. f. Psychiat.* **107**: 162–63, 1938, with two large tables inserted.

On the Jews in Palestine, cf. L. Halpern, "Some Data on the Psychic Morbidity of the Jews and Arabs in Palestine," *Am. J. Psychiat.* **94**: 1215–22, 1938.

For the situation in Russia, cf. Ira S. Wile, "Present Problems of Mental Health in Russia," *Ment. Hyg.* **22**: 25–56, 1938—an excellent study based on printed documents obtained in a journey through Russia from Leningrad to the Black Sea.

Regarding England under war conditions, cf. Aubrey Lewis, "Incidence of

Seeing that insanity is after all such a frequent calamity in mental life, let us look for a moment at the financial burden it imposes on society.

2. THE COST OF MENTAL DISORDERS TO THE STATE

Horatio Pollock has made it possible for us to estimate the cost of insanity to society. Naturally any measurement of this cost is limited to monetary values. The cost in worry, anxiety, and unhappiness is over and above the pure financial loss to society. The mental costs are beyond the possibility of measurement, but we can get some idea of the bill that has to be paid in dollars and cents.

Pollock's study was made possible by a book by Dublin and Lotka of the Metropolitan Life Insurance Company, entitled *The Money Value of Man.*[17] This book naturally does not deal with spiritual values but merely with what a man is worth

---

Neurosis in England under War Conditions," *Lancet* **1243:** 175–83 (Aug. 15), 1942.

For a critique on surveys of the incidence of insanity in various localities, cf. Paul Lemkau, Christopher Tietze, and Marcia Cooper, "A Survey of Statistical Studies on the Prevalence and Incidence of Mental Disorder in Sample Populations," *Pub. Health Rep.* **58:** 1909–27 (Dec. 31), 1943; Reprint 2434.

[17] Pollock gives the following table from Dublin and Lotka, which gives the economic value of a man at various ages, assuming that his maximum earning capacity will be $2000 a year.

Age (years)	Value	Age (years)	Value
0	$7,000	40	$20,350
10	14,950	50	13,800
20	23,850	60	6,700
30	24,450	70	400

"The economic value of an average woman was not calculated in this study, but is assumed by the authors in an earlier study to be half that of a man": Horatio M. Pollock, "Economic Loss to New York State and the United States on Account of Mental Disease, 1931," *Ment. Hyg.*, 16, p. 294. If a male child at birth is worth about $7000 to the state and a female child $3500, a family allowance to encourage the procreation of children would be well worth while financially.

in the sense of what he is likely to earn and spend. The financial loss due to insanity falls under two headings:

a) Cost of maintenance and treatment of the mental patient.

b) Loss of the patient's monetary value due to cessation of his earnings.

Let us first take a look at the economic loss due to preventable mental disorders of males.

PSYCHOSES	FIRST ADMISSIONS	ESTIMATED ECONOMIC VALUE OF AVERAGE PERSON OF SAME AGE	PERCENTAGE OF ESTIMATED VALUE LOST ON ADMISSION	ECONOMIC LOSS DUE TO MENTAL DISEASE
General paralysis..........	744	$12,667,380	75	$9,500,535
Cerebral syphilis...........	80	1,311,630	60	786,978
Alcoholism	530	8,518,905	50	4,259,453
Drugs, etc.................	17	262,710	50	131,355
Total....................	1371			$14,678,321

Thus annually the definitely preventable mental disorders cause a financial damage in New York State of almost fifteen million dollars.

The total loss for 1931 in New York State due to all forms of insanity is estimated by Pollock as $54,542,784 for males and $20,455,673 for females; and for males and females including certain cases in private hospitals the total loss for New York State was estimated as $84,425,269. The total estimated loss in the United States, for males and females together, was estimated at $742,145,956.[18]

It is quite clear therefore that anything that can be done to reduce the incidence of insanity will be a financial contribution to the American public, to say nothing of the spiritual and intellectual values involved.

[18] H. M. Pollock, "Economic Loss to New York State and the United States on Account of Mental Disease, 1931," *J. Am. Statist. Assoc.*, new ser., **27:** 179–87, 1932. Cf. also *Ment. Hyg*, vol. 16, p. 294.

CHAPTER II

THE MENTAL HYGIENE OF EMOTIONAL LIFE

W E HAVE now obtained a general concept of the disorders of the mind and a knowledge of the frequency of their occurrence. We enter next upon the task of studying what we can do to keep our own minds from succumbing at some time to a mental disorder.

There are a number of mental disorders that we can certainly eliminate if we seriously make up our minds to avoid the causes which lead to them. Here we have the groups of syphilitic and alcoholic mental disorders and drug psychoses. Though there is such a thing as *syphilis insontium* or accidentally acquired syphilis, it is so rare that one can say that there is no danger of syphilis if one leads a chaste life, but considerable danger if he indulges in extramarital contacts. Certainly no one will develop an alcoholic psychosis if he practices total abstinence. And in all probability one will avoid arteriosclerotic insanity if he does not smoke. Eliminate these and we have already ruled out the possibility of about 20 per cent of all forms of mental disorder.[1]

Seeing too that a sober, industrious life is a great contribution to mental peace and happiness, we can say that chastity and sobriety will contribute a great deal to mental hygiene. But this is mental hygiene only indirectly. What we are now in-

---

[1] Taking the following as forms of insanity brought on by one's own fault, we have the percentages of first admissions in mental hospitals in the United States as given in *Statistical Abstract of the United States, 1942:*

Paresis..................... 6.8	Alcoholism..............	6.7
Other forms of syphilis of	Alcoholic insanity........	4.6
central nervous system... 1.2	Psychoses due to drugs..	0.5

Total.. 19.8

Arteriosclerotic insanity provided for 11.6 of the first admissions in the United States in 1940.

terested in is the hygiene of the mind properly so called, namely, the management of our mental life so as to avoid mental disorder.

Let us start this investigation with a study of our emotional life and its management. For there can be no doubt that both acute and chronic emotional strain have something to do with the origin of mental disorders.

The following table comparing the ages of first admissions to mental hospitals in Russia in 1935 and in the United States in 1933 may be analyzed to show the influence of mental stress and strain on the incidence of mental disorder:

Age	Percentage of new admissions to Russian psychiatric hospitals, 1935	Percentage of first admissions to state mental hospitals in the U. S., 1933
Under 20	11.12	5.0
20–39	60.79	37.2
40–49	16.05	19.3
50 and over	9.39	37.7
Age unknown	2.69	1.7

Ira S. Wile, who prepared the table, points out that the first group "represents persons born since 1915, who were subjected to the stresses of the war and of the revolution, to pestilence, famine and reconstruction.

"The second, group born between 1895 and 1915, spent their early lives amid pre-revolutionary conditions. They were subjected to the destructive struggle for existence against famine, pestilence and so on. . . .

"The third group were born between 1885 and 1896. All of them had attained their maturity prior to the revolution."[2]

The relatively large number of juvenile psychoses in the mental hospitals of Russia may merely mean, as Wile suggested, that care and help are given to the young but denied to the old. It might, however, mean that the stress and strain of life lead

[2] Ira S. Wile, "Present Problems of Mental Health in Russia," *Ment. Hyg.* 22:41, 1938.

to mental disorder.   And there is much evidence which points in this direction.[3]

If emotional strain is a factor in the origin of psychotic conditions and various abnormalities of the mind and individual behavior, it seems reasonable to conclude that anything we can do to lessen emotional strain will be a contribution to mental health.

Let us first have a look at the psychology of our emotional life.

Human emotions are normally mental reactions to our appreciation of a situation.   In man the appreciation of a situation involves intellectual insight into the present episode and all its ramifications.   Animals in virtue of past experience have a certain sensory estimation of a given situation and react to this appreciation of their plight with emotions whose resonance is more or less similar to that in human beings.

We have said that a human emotional reaction involves *normally* an intellectual appreciation of a situation, because the study of pathological states of mind indicates that some emotions have nothing to do with insight and appreciation.   There is a center in the brain which, when stimulated, produces the external signs of a violent emotional experience, and it seems also that these external signs are *sometimes*, though not always, accompanied by actual conscious emotional experience.[4]   This center can be stimulated electrically or by chemical agents or by substances produced in the body itself, such as adrenalin. It seems reasonable therefore to suppose that substances such as adrenalin circulating in superabundance in the blood can stimulate the emotional centers and the patient may not only experience an acceleration of the heartbeat or muscular tension or cry, but also feel for example an emotion of anxiety and sadness.[5]

    [3] Cf. T. V. Moore, *The Nature and Treatment of Mental Disorders*, New York: Grune and Stratton, 1943, pp. 76 ff.
    [4] Cf. *ibid.*, pp. 248 ff.
    [5] The distinction between emotions caused by a mental reaction in a dif-

Every violent emotion is accompanied by a pouring of adrenalin into the blood stream. Therefore one who stews over his emotions will intensify and prolong the emotion itself and the bodily resonance which accompanies the emotion.

It therefore seems possible to exert a control over our emotions:

   a) By looking at a baffling or unhappy situation calmly and reasonably;

   b) By endeavoring to accept as quietly as possible all emotional states whether caused by our insight into the seriousness of a situation or by physiological conditions over which we have no control.

How can we exert this control? By an attempt to understand our emotional mechanisms, thus enabling us to control them, and by learning to take various attitudes in the presence of trials and disappointments which will enable us to see things from a more wholesome point of view. Thus we shall eliminate many violent emotional states of tension which might well lead on to a mental disorder.

In the course of this book the reader will find a number of mental attitudes which will be of value in meeting emotional situations.

Let us now turn to an understanding of our emotional mechanisms.

One important principle to realize in studying the mental hygiene of the emotions is that emotional states are not always transitory flashes that flare for a moment and are seen no more.

---

ficult situation and those due to internal physiological conditions of an ill-defined nature is implicitly recognized by the "Classification and Definition of the Clinical Entities of Psychiatry" given in the *Statistical Manual for the Use of Hospitals for Mental Diseases* published by the National Committee for Mental Hygiene. The manic-depressive psychoses are put under the heading "Psychoses Due to Unknown or Hereditary Causes, but Associated with Organic Change." Under the heading "Psychoneuroses," the *Manual* distinguishes the reactive depression which is a response "to obvious external causes such as bereavement, sickness and financial or other worries." Cf. T. V. Moore, *op. cit.*, p. 302.

There is a spontaneous tendency for the individual to hold on to his emotion and persevere in the affective type of reaction he is manifesting.

The emotion is associated with a blind, unreasonable drive to perpetuate itself. All mental functions have a drive to exercise themselves. We have eyes and not only see but also look and want to keep on looking. We have ears and not only hear but have a drive to listen. We have intellects and as Aristotle says in the opening words of his metaphysics, all men have a natural craving to know. We have emotions and our emotions too have a tendency, specific to themselves, to flow over into action and maintain the current of that flow.

But besides the specific drive peculiar to the function, all sorts of extraneous factors enter into the situation and tend to perpetuate the emotion. As we have pointed out elsewhere[6] there are various advantages, strange to say, that a patient reaps from his emotional disability. Such an advantage acts as a final cause which makes it, from some point of view, worth while for the patient to maintain his emotional disability. The emotional disability does not indeed contribute to the true welfare of the patient, but it has a specious value, inasmuch as it enables him to avoid an unpleasant kind of effort, or to hold on to something he might otherwise lose. Furthermore, it generally seems to the patient that he is prevented from, let us say, doing an unpleasant duty simply because he is mentally sick. He feels no guilt for shirking a clear moral responsibility. The result is that he pities himself and makes no effort to get out of his emotional difficulty. He may even seek help from a psychiatrist, but in so doing seems to expect that the psychiatrist will by some magic process bring about a complete cure without any effort on his part. He even fights against getting well. It would seem that he would like to demonstrate that a cure is impossible and that he has done everything in his power to bring it about and the only thing left for him to do is to

6 *Op. cit.*, p. 109.

settle down to his emotional disability and so hang on to the hidden advantage which his emotional disability secretly provides.

Let us consider the following case. A patient developed a tremor of her hand which led to a fear that if she lifted a full cup or glass she would spill the contents. This led to her avoiding meals in public places and later she became tense in any social gathering and resigned her position. Finally she even had a hard time eating alone. She consulted a psychiatrist, who explained to her that her fear of trembling was the result, not the cause, of her trouble, that it might have taken other forms, as fear of going to a movie or going up in an elevator, having a panic in church, dropping the baby, etc. At first she thought these would be silly fears. But after a bit she could not go to a movie, or go up in an elevator, she got panicky in church, feared she would kill the baby, and developed many other fears besides. The psychiatrist told her she was not to force herself to do anything, but to do only what she felt like doing. He suggested that she quit going to church till she felt like it and that she should allow herself a little more sexual freedom. She felt she could not follow his advice and so he suggested that she should go elsewhere. We are interested at the present in seeking an illustration of how an emotional disability may have an advantage to the patient.

In one of the interviews when we were attempting to find out the reason why the emotional condition persisted, she remarked that the mere thought of doing anything good made her panicky. "Therefore," she said, "I should never do anything good."

"What advantages," I asked, "do you reap out of your fear which leads you to avoid doing anything good?"

She remarked: "It's good not to have to do anything someone else tells you, such as wash the dishes. One would be free to indulge in various pleasures that are not right. You can blow off when you get angry. No one wants to line up and be good anyway."

"Suppose," I remarked, "you regained the emotional control
you once had, would you have to line up?"

"I sure would and it would be harder now."

"Does the desire to remain in your condition shift the responsibility and make you think 'I can't get out'?"

"It sure does that."

And so we see that a phobia which was at first restricted to a
small definite field broadened out and prevented the patient
from doing a number of things she did not want to do and
finally produced a state of mind in which the patient felt that
the danger of arousing her phobia justified her in refusing to do
various more or less unpleasant chores.   And so she held on
to her phobia lest she should have to "line up and be good."
She did not in any sense throw overboard the moral law.   But
like most neurotic patients she remained miserable on the horns
of her dilemma without taking up any decisive line of conduct.

It is much easier for any patient to take himself in hand
than it is for the psychiatrist to persuade him to be active in
his own behalf when he does not want to be.   Therefore perhaps the study of mental hygiene may be helpful by enabling
one to understand himself and manage his emotional life with
full intellectual insight.

Let us now consider a group of emotional drives which many
often experience, perhaps all at some time or other, and which
cause a great deal of trouble in human life.   These are depression, anxiety, anger, and hatred.

Chapter III

DEPRESSION

THE HUMAN mind is like the stock market, which though peaceful at times, is ever being disturbed by bull movements in which the stock soars to unwonted heights, and bear movements in which values are depressed to alarming levels.

A depression is a bear movement in the stock market of the mind. A student for example is unable to answer the question posed by a professor and immediately commences to feel blue, glum, depressed. A young girl's boy friend does not come when he said he would come and leaves her all alone without any explanation and the bottom drops out of her stock market completely. Anything that tends to a lowered estimation of one's self or that frustrates cherished ambitions leads easily in some people to pure depression, but in persons of a different temperament such things lead to anger.

Depression is normally a sporadic event. The emotional pendulum swings to the opposite extreme. One solves a baffling puzzle or a mathematical problem or answers a question and displays his information, and there is a sudden bull movement in the stock market of the mind, all because of an enhancement of the feeling of personal value due to some trivial cause.

The life of a normal man is a scene in which bull and bear movements are continually taking place. One man differs from another not in the presence or absence of elation and depression, but in the degree, duration, and frequency of their occurrence. There is room for a study here of the normal variations. On the basis of a study of the normal character in college girls, I can say that depressions may last in these college students from a few minutes to days on end and may come on several times a day or only a few times a year.

One consoling thought in the midst of a depression is to

realize the fact that depressions are transitory. One need but wait and they will pass. In the meantime it is the part of wisdom to refrain from making any decision or taking an important step during a spell of depression. Such things must be postponed if it is in any way possible. Don't resign your job. If you must write that letter, don't mail it. Lock it up for a month, and then you will say: "Thank God I did not mail that letter!"

Is there anything like regularity in the cycles in which depressions recur? Rexford B. Hersey[1] finds that there is.

He used the accompanying rating scale for emotional tone, by which twenty-nine male workers of the Pennsylvania Railroad system were studied. At the high end of the scale we see such traits as elated, happy, cheerful and at the low end sad, apprehensive, worried. "Regularly recurrent fluctuations in emotional resistance have been found in every one of the 29 cases studied—without exception."

Rating Scale of Emotions[2]

Happy—elated..   +6
Happy—minus..   +4 to +5
Cheerful or hopeful..   +5
Interested—joking, cooperative...............................   +3 to +4
Neutral plus: pleasant feeling tone................+1 to +3, usually +2
Neutral indifferent: tension, equilibrium mixed......+1 to −1, usually 0
Neutral minus: unpleasant feeling tone, no definite negative emotions clearly defined.............................−1 to −3, usually −2
Peevish, suspicious, uninterested............................   −1 to −2
Angry...   −2 to −3
Disgusted...   −3 to −4
Sad...   −4 to −5
Apprehensive..   −5 to −6
Worried...   −6

---

[1] Rexford Brammer Hersey, *Workers' Emotions in Shop and Home*, Philadelphia: Univ. Penn. Press, 1932, p. 349. Hersey was invited by the Oberländer-Trust to repeat his studies in Germany. In every one of twelve workers in Germany the same recurrent fluctuations were found. See his study, *Seele und Gefühl des Arbeiters*, Leipzig: Konkordia-Verlag, 1935, p. 136.

[2] Scale used by R. B. Hersey in *Workers' Emotions in Shop and Home*, p. 339.

In the highs a worker's drive toward activity was in general greater. In general, production is greater, though at times the man may stop to tell the other men how to do their work (a typical hypomanic tendency). Work seems to require no conscious effort. One is not troubled much by a sense of fatigue. The worker indulges in many more extraplant activities.

In the lows, it is often a drag to work. It is very difficult to carry on several activities at the same time. One likes to sit around and think. It seems to take more effort to do the same amount of work; and there is a greater tendency to feel tired or somewhat out of sorts generally.

There seems to be no difference in sleep or sexual activities characteristic of the two periods.

A study of only five healthy, intelligent women suggested that the manic-depressive cycle found with the men was also found with the women, but did not coincide with the menstrual cycle.[3]

The length of the manic-depressive cycle in men varied from 3.00 to 9.25 weeks. No definite cause could be found for the variations in span.

Donald A. Laird reports that he attempted to determine his span and found that his "emotional energy cycle is one of about six weeks."[4]

There are also physical causes that produce alterations in mood. Shakespeare seems to have had an insight into this when he wrote of "sleep that knits up the raveled sleeve of care." We have at present little knowledge of what these causes may be. There may be, however, an accumulation of products of metabolism that affect mood by way of cerebral centers and these may be eliminated by sleep and exercise. And so a nap, or at times a good vacation, may be the price of a brand-new outlook on life. Body and mind constitute one

[3] *Op. cit.*, pp. 350–66.
[4] "The Secret of Your Ups and Downs," *Read. Dig.*, August, 1935, p. 16 (from *Rev. of Rev.*, April, 1935).

unit substance, not two; and so the adage "A sound mind in a sound body" is based on an important philosophical truth.

Can one take any steps to prevent the appearance of a more or less serious depression? The following considerations will perhaps be of some value:

1. The normal prophylaxis against all forms of truly mental disorders is the establishment of a happy family with a number of children.

The fact that the insanity rate in the widowed is double that in the married and the rate in the single is somewhat higher than that in the married may be taken as evidence in support of this statement.[5]

Though the somewhat higher rate in the single might be explained in part at least by supposing that some of the single were so queer to start with that they just could not get anyone to pop the question, the double rate in the widowed can scarcely be accounted for except by supposing that the stress and strain of life in a broken home, or in no home at all, are greater by far than in one in which the family is intact.

Parents who are rearing a group of happy children have a sense of the value of accomplishment which is a matter of great importance in mental hygiene. A normal home is a stabilizing factor in emotional life which tends to prevent the occurrence of mental abnormalities.

Each child in the home has a certain insurance value for parental happiness. If there is only one child his premature death is a crushing blow from which at times the parents never recover. If, however, there are a number of children, the death of one child, though a great sorrow, is not an overwhelming calamity.

[5] The fact that the insanity rate in priests and religious is definitely lower than in the married indicates that a religious community or the priesthood may substitute in this respect for the protecting influence of the home. See T. V. Moore, "Insanity in Priests and Religious," (Am.) *Ecclesiast. Rev.*, November, 1936.

2. It is a matter of mental hygiene importance to have multiple interests in life.

It is fundamentally necessary to have a bread and butter plan of life. Any honest calling will suffice for this purpose; but it should be chosen in the first place with due regard to one's preferences and abilities. Very often the bread and butter plan of life is laborious and uninteresting. Or having been chosen for its glamor it loses its zest when the glamor fades out in the sunshine of experience. I remember a young naval officer who became disgusted with sounding the depths of the ocean in cold and rainy weather, resigned his commission, and became a farmer. It is not always possible, however, to change from one type of work to another. It is then that secondary interests are of importance. These secondary interests are sometimes termed hobbies. Scientific exhibits of medical societies often have a section set apart for the exhibition of the work products of physicians' hobbies. Sometimes a hobby, like the original by-product of a chemical industry, leaves its minor role and assumes major proportions. Thus Sir Walter Scott's bread and butter plan of life was for a career as a lawyer, but in importance for humanity as well as financially his side work as an author far outstripped what he did for the law or what the law did for him.

When thinking of a hobby one would do well to look for something which might become worth while in some way, not only to oneself, but also to others. I remember asking an eminent man if he played chess. He replied: "I used to play and enjoyed it immensely. But I commenced to think matters over and I concluded it was not worth while. After an interesting game of chess I had nothing to show for it—except perhaps a drive to play it all over in my head when I went to bed that night. So I decided to give up chess and read history. And now instead of a game of chess in the evening I turn to the study of a period of history. It is intensely interesting but perhaps not as absorbing as a game of chess, but after the evening I have something to show for the time I have spent. I have gained knowledge which is valuable in itself and may be very useful some time in conversation."

Those who are idealistic and would like to devote themselves wholly to art or literature might find it a safer procedure to get a bread and butter plan of life and take on art or literature as a worth while hobby. Perhaps eventually the side issue will become one's major interest and occupation.

3. It is very important to avoid unwholesome attitudes of mind such as "What's the use of trying, I am going to give up" or a tendency to feel sorry for oneself and badly treated, to shirk effort and personal responsibility, and after a deep slump brought on by some one or more of such attitudes to say to oneself: "Let us eat, drink and be merry today for tomorrow we die," and then in one way or another to give way to unwholesome excesses. One who seeks pleasure as a primary end is likely to fail in his attempts to attain his goal; but if he conceives of life as a time in which he is to make a contribution of some value to the welfare of mankind, on the way to attaining his goal he will find the pleasure he craves without having to do anything specific to attain it.

Should one have slumped into an unwholesome attitude of mind, he can do much more to get himself out of it by personal effort than can any psychiatrist, however skilful.

4. It is well to remember that idealism is the formal directing cause of many sources of pleasure and modes of activity. I remember an engineer who had many difficulties and failed to make a great success of himself in his profession. Instead of doing important works of considerable magnitude, he was sidetracked to the minor engineering feat of building concrete roads. What could be more dull and uninteresting? However, he thought to himself: "Whenever I go ahead and build a good concrete road, civilization follows with all manner of developments"; and so he took satisfaction in doing a service to

humanity. All honest work can be vivified by idealism. It is idealism that shows it to us in its true light. But in the false light of sadness and depression, the true beauty of its coloring is lost. Let in the light of idealism and depression vanishes.

Let us now take an example of a person who was subject to spells of depression and see how he attempted to manage them. And this time let us turn from the files of the clinic to the pages of history.

If we can judge by the detailed information collected by Carl Sandburg, Abraham Lincoln was subject to spells of depression from boyhood, and on the death of his fiancée, Ann Rutledge, went through a mental condition that approached at least a major psychosis.

"In growing up from boyhood to young manhood, he had survived against lonesome, gnawing monotony" and various hardships and illnesses. Perhaps lack of adequate interests and occupation explains the fact that "starting in his eleventh year came spells of abstraction. When he was spoken to, no answer came from him—'He might be a thousand miles away.' . . . This was one sort of abstraction he knew; there was another: the blues took him; coils of multiplied melancholies wrapped their blue frustrations inside him, all that Hamlet, Koheleth, Schopenhauer have uttered, in a mesh of foiled hopes. 'There was absolutely nothing to excite ambition for education,' he wrote later of that Indiana region. Against these 'blues,' he found the best warfare was to find people and trade with them his yarns and drolleries. John Baldwin, the blacksmith, with many stories and odd talk and eye-slants, was a help and a light."[6] Humor has at various times been pointed out as a defense reaction against the blues. The story is told of a man in France who had a depression and consulted a psychiatrist. After talking things over the psychiatrist seems to have been at his wit's end and finally said: "You are per-

[6] Carl Sandburg, *Abraham Lincoln, The Prairie Years.* New York: Harcourt, 1926, vol. 1, p. 76.

fectly healthy, my dear fellow, you need to be cheered up. There is a fine comedian in town. Go to hear him tonight. He would make anybody laugh."

"Well," said the patient, "I am sorry to say that I am that comedian."

But humor is helpful and Abraham Lincoln was helped in his depression in his earlier years by the stories and odd talk and eye-slants of Baldwin, the blacksmith; and later on it seems to have been a great relief to him to find people and trade with them his yarns and drolleries, though in these gatherings it was he who told most of the stories. It was a help, however, to make other people laugh, and perhaps when the crowd dispersed and he was again all alone with himself, there was a consciousness of having cheered others who might have been as blue as himself and so he was less sad because he had done a little service to humanity.

What looks like a serious depression came after the death of his fiancée. Carl Sandburg thus describes Lincoln's reaction:

"There was what they called a funeral, a decent burial of the body in the Concord burying ground seven miles away. And Lincoln sat for hours with no words for those who asked him to speak to them. They went away from him knowing he would be alone whether they stayed or went away.

"A week after the burial of Ann Rutledge, Bill Green found him rambling in the woods along the Sangamon River, mumbling sentences Bill couldn't make out. They watched him and tried to keep him safe among friends at New Salem. And he rambled darkly and idly past their circle to the burying ground seven miles away, where he lay with an arm across the one grave.

" 'Vain man thy fond hopes forbear.' As the autumn weeks passed, and the scarlet runners sent out signals across the honey locust and the sycamore tree where they had sat together on the Salem hilltop, and the sunsets flamed earlier in the shortening afternoons, the watchers saw a man struggling on a brink; he needed help. Dr. Allen said rest would help. They

took him to the home of Bowling and Nancy Green, at the foot
of a bluff climbed by oak-timber growths. A few days he
helped in the field at cornhusking; most of the time Nancy had
him cutting wood, picking apples, digging potatoes, doing
light chores around the house, once holding the yarn for her as
she spun.

"In the evenings it was useless to try to talk with him. They
asked their questions and then had to go away. . . . Slowly as
the weeks passed, an old-time order of control came back to
him—only it was said that the shadows of a burning he had
been through were fixed in the depths of his eyes, and he was a
changed man keeping to himself the gray mystery of the
change."[7]

It is interesting to note that "occupational therapy" was
used with such success in helping Lincoln out of his depression.[8]
Without it Abraham Lincoln might never have been president
of the United States.

Perhaps with no direct intention of treating his depression

[7] *Op. cit.*, pp. 189–90.

[8] In the days of Abraham Lincoln the possibilities of hospital care for mental
patients were very limited. The success of Nancy Green in seeing Lincoln
through his depression suggests that much more could be done in family care
for mental patients than is done in our day. Sometimes newspapers, representing the attitude of a misguided public, protest against the paroling of
improved patients from mental hospitals for family care in the community.
The public seems to take the attitude that the mental patient is to be locked up
and forgotten and should he be allowed any freedom in the community, it
would endanger the lives and property of the citizens. Horatio M. Pollock
("Is Family Care for Mental Patients Safe for the Community?" *Ment. Hyg.*
25: 620–23, 1941), from whom we have so many valuable statistical studies of
mental disorders, made a special study of patients paroled for family care to
see whether or not the practice constitutes a danger to the community. Out
of 2154 patients paroled to family care, only one was accused of a criminal
offense and even that accusation was not substantiated. If one took as a
basis of comparison the incidence of crime in the general population, one would
have expected more than 60 offenses during the year these patients were
paroled. It would seem therefore that paroled patients have been improved
in various ways by their stay in a mental hospital and that they do not constitute a menace to the community. Perhaps under adequate medical super-
vision some patients could be treated from the onset by intelligent family
care.

by occupational therapy, he nevertheless did so from childhood by work of a far different character from that laid upon him by Nancy Green. This was study.

"The farm boys in their evenings at Jones' store in Gentry-ville talked about how Abe Lincoln was always reading, digging into books, stretching out flat on his stomach in front of the fire-place, studying till midnight and past midnight, picking a piece of charcoal to write on the fire shovel, shaving off what he wrote, and then writing more—till midnight and past midnight."[9]

The passion for learning gave him a continuous interesting occupation without which monotony and the trials of life might have fed his tendency to sadness till it assumed the proportions of a psychosis. Study, for Lincoln, relaxed the strain and tension of life and became a powerful prophylactic against mental disorder.

"John Hanks, who worked in the fields barefooted with Abe, grubbing stumps, plowing, mowing, said: 'When Abe and I came back to the house from work, he used to go to the cupboard, snatch a piece of corn bread, sit down, cock his legs up, high as his head, and read. Whenever Abe had a chance in the field while at work, or at the house, he would stop and read.'"[10]

By private study he opened for himself his opportunities in life.

Once when having failed to run successfully a general store with his friend Berry, he found himself miserable, melancholy, and in debt. He could chase away the misery and the melancholy by telling comic stories to the boys. But he could not laugh away the debts. At this turn a friend offered him a position as deputy surveyor. The chief difficulty was that he did not know anything at all about surveying. But he did not have to go to work for six weeks. So Lincoln hunted up the schoolmaster, Mentor Graham, worked all day and nearly

[9] *Op. cit.*, p. 71.
[10] *Op. cit.*, p. 72.

all night, and at the end of the six weeks he had learned the essentials of surveying; he went to work and made good.[11]

One day while the store of Berry and Lincoln was still in existence, Lincoln, to oblige a man who was headed west in a covered wagon, paid him 50 cents for a barrel of trash. Emptying the barrel, he discovered at the bottom of it a copy of Blackstone's *Commentaries on the Laws of England*. A lawyer friend had once told him that the law student should read Blackstone first. He had once heard a lawyer address a jury and ever since nourished what he thought would be an impossible dream, to be a lawyer like the man who addressed that jury. So he started in and studied Blackstone.[12] "A little later he laid aside his surveying for a while to defend a girl in a bastardy case."[13] Somewhat later, having been certified to the Supreme Court as a man of good moral character, "he was licensed to write his name, Abraham Lincoln, Attorney-at-Law."[14] He moved to Springfield and the road was open to him to become president of the United States.

And so Lincoln managed his depression and became what he finally was by humor and hard work at intellectual occupational therapy. His partner in the country store, William F. Berry, reacted to the difficulties of life in a very different manner from that of Lincoln.

"As the store of Berry and Lincoln ran on through the fall and winter, business didn't pick up much and nobody cared much. Berry was drinking and playing poker; Lincoln was reading law and learning Shakespeare and Burns."[15]

The true philosophy of life leads us to work and to accomplish something of value. In so doing we treat the disorders of the mind before they can develop to serious proportions, and so therapy and accomplishment work hand in hand together.

[11] Cf. *op. cit.*, pp. 168 ff.
[12] *Op. cit.*, pp. 163 ff.
[13] *Op. cit.*, p. 176.
[14] *Op. cit.*, p. 204.
[15] *Op. cit.*, p. 162.

CHAPTER IV

ANXIETY AND SCRUPULOSITY

1. ANXIETY

IN THE last world war, a French soldier received the *Croix de Guerre* because he stood his ground and fired right and left at the enemy when his whole regiment fled. He seemed to have been utterly fearless in a situation of great danger. It was later found that he had general paralysis of the insane and just didn't know what was going on.

To be fearless and have no anxiety when in a situation of really grave danger is not the reaction of the normal healthy mind. The brave man is not without fear and anxiety in the presence of danger, but he does not show any signs of fear or anxiety and acts in a cool, reasonable, and efficient manner.

Sometimes a distinction is made very properly between fear and anxiety. When one is in the actual presence of danger he is said to be afraid; but when he merely anticipates a future danger and looks forward to it with various misgivings, he is said to be anxious.

Anxiety performs a useful psychological function. It makes us look before we leap and consider consequences. Were it not for anxiety we would rush into danger and get into trouble unnecessarily. A certain amount of anxiety is a sign of intelligence. But when anxiety has performed its function and we have taken the necessary look and carefully considered the pros and cons, it should, like a player who has played his part, leave the stage and appear no more. Unfortunately, however, it does not always play its part and cease.

Furthermore, many anxieties and sometimes the **most** troublesome ones are about things that could scarcely ever take place or are utterly impossible.

Jersild says: "That fear may be useful in promoting prudence and caution and thus serve as a protection against harm, is obvious, of course. But a large number of fears, appear, at first glance at least, to deal with spurious dangers. Moreover, in a great many instances, the effects of fear do not apparently lead to constructive efforts to master the environment. On the contrary, the fears often have an inhibitory effect, they often seem to promote retreat and withdrawal, they frequently seem to induce futile expenditure of time and energy, and operate as an extra weight that the individual must carry."[1] Jersild cites in a footnote Mark Twain's remark to the effect that he had had many troubles in his life, but most of them never happened. The things feared by neurotic individuals torment their minds for years on end, but "they never happen."

Let us consider the following case. A married woman in her early thirties came for help in the condition of unreasonable anxiety. The chief anxiety when she first came was a fear of rabies. Some six months before she sought help the newspapers began to give a good deal of attention to the possibility of developing rabies from bites of stray animals. The accounts in the newspapers merely awakened an anxiety which had been smouldering for three or four years. In this period, one of her children had been bitten twice by dogs. This led her to study up on rabies. She wanted the doctor to cauterize the place where the boy had been bitten and was somewhat disturbed when he paid no attention to her. For some reason the accounts in the newspapers and the number of dogs in the neighborhood made the fear of rabies become a tormenting obsession. She did not want her children to play outside the house. It was possible that they might touch a dog or cat and it was possible that the dog or cat they touched might have touched a dog or cat with rabies and the virus in the saliva of the infected animal might have been transferred to the dogs or cats that her children touched and if they had a microscopic

---

[1] Arthur T. Jersild and Frances Baker Holmes, *Children's Fears*, New York: Bureau of Publications, Teachers College, Columbia University, 1935, p. 328.

scratch the virus might get into the scratch and start to grow and her children might develop rabies. Her husband had a prescription filled for her at the drugstore. She remembered that she had been in the same drugstore during the previous week and had noticed that the clerk had his finger bandaged. And so the idea came to the woman that he might have touched a dog or other animal and so indirectly have gotten the virus of rabies in the cut on his finger and then have transferred it to the bottle containing her medicine and if she touched the bottle she might develop rabies and therefore she let the medicine stay where her husband had left it; and even though it was rather expensive, she made up her mind to get along with her ailment as best she could and so let the medicine absolutely alone.

The fear of rabies was merely the most recent form of a fear of germs that had tormented her for years. Nor was the fear of contamination by infectious material her only type of fear. Some years before, she had developed a fear that various men were irresistibly attracted towards her and being unable to approach her were driven to sin with others. "Even at the present time," she remarked, "I am not sure but what it is true."

She thinks that her basic fear is of dying and going to hell or of killing someone else by transferring to him the virus of rabies or some other disease and causing him to go to hell.

The fear of going to hell dated back to childhood. Her family went to a church where she heard the ministers preaching hell and damnation. It seemed as she looked back on her childhood that there was scarcely any other theme. She thought finally that heathens were better off than Christians and wished she had been born a heathen. As she got older she developed a persistent anxiety that unless she was perfect in all things, she would certainly go to hell. There was no distinction in her mind between big sins and little sins. One went to hell for any sin or imperfection whatsoever. Therefore she concluded that she had to strive to be perfect at all times and always be doing all she possibly could do to preach Christ and spread his kingdom. Any relaxation of the strain meant hell.

Granted that the preaching of hell was as constant and lurid as she seems to remember it, one must not think that her anxieties are adequately accounted for by the false type of preaching. The memory of the sermons was merely a mental experience to which she attached what we have several times referred to as a physiological anxiety.[2] Had she never listened to a sermon she would have found something or other in her past experience to which to attach her free-floating anxiety. A sane explanation of her difficulties from early childhood on might well have helped to prevent the intense anxiety of later life. Talking over her difficulties was of value. The principle that no poison is hurtful unless present in adequate amount, she found helpful. But it seemed that a pharmacological treatment[3] of her anxiety state was of more importance than psychological analysis.

2. SCRUPULOSITY

A special type of anxiety is known as scrupulosity. It is a dread of sin when in reality no sin at all is present. It is an ever recurring questioning fear about whether or not various acts of ordinary everyday life are somehow connected with sin or are really in themselves sinful, a tendency to worry about having committed a sin in the past and never having properly confessed it. One young girl who took a hopeful attitude about her scruples said: "I think scruples are unnecessary thoughts about certain things which will be answered in the course of time and that is what I am waiting for."[4]

Scrupulosity is a fairly common condition. In a questionnaire given to "four hundred students in a girl's private high

---

[2] Cf. p. 16.

[3] Cf. Moore, *The Nature and Treatment of Mental Disorders*, pp. 262 ff.

[4] Cited by Joseph J. Mullen, *Psychological Factors in the Pastoral Treatment of Scruples*, Stud. Psychol. & Psychiat. 1: 64, 1927.

school where the student body represents American-born students of very varied national descent"[5] Mullen found that 26.25 per cent answered affirmatively to: "Do you find yourself habitually scrupulous . . . anxious, uncertain, in doubt about conscience?" A study of the other answers and the examples given in the girls' accounts of themselves shows that most of these affirmative answers were given by really scrupulous individuals.

A check upon the students' own estimate was obtained by the question: "Have others judged you to be scrupulous?" Only 11.5 per cent answered this question affirmatively; as to those answering in the negative, it was clear from other statements that some were really suffering from scrupulosity. Sometimes scrupulosity is a silent inward suffering; and again, though clearly manifested, it may be ignored and the patient left to work out his own salvation as best he may.

If, however, we ask: "If not habitually scrupulous, have you ever suffered from a passing attack of scrupulosity?" we get 47.75 per cent of affirmative answers.[6]

It is quite probable that scrupulosity is a habitual mental disorder in about 25 per cent of Catholic high school girls. Quite possibly Catholic training colors the natural human trend to worry, in the sense that Catholics when anxious are more likely to be troubled about items of religious experience than those who have no religious training. The fact of having attended a Catholic parochial school rather than a public grammar school seemed, however, to have exerted very little differential influence on the development of scruples.[7] It is the experience of life that specifies what we are going to worry about. Though there are many experiences that produce anxieties, ordinary Catholic school experience does not seem to have any more anxiety-producing influences than are to

[5] Mullen, op. cit., pp. 29–30.
[6] Mullen, op. cit., p. 49
[7] Mullen, op. cit., p. 62.

be found in other schools, or if there are such factors in Catholic school experience there are also antidotes to anxiety which Catholic life naturally instils into the mind of the child. Thus one girl wrote: "My mother told me many stories of the Guardian Angel, this stopped my fear of the dark."[8]

Unfortunately, some parents and some teachers take the naïve attitude of attempting to secure good moral behavior by telling weird tales of the terrible calamities that happen to the bad boy or girl. These tales can be made lurid and terrifying and they do frighten young children. Many children rather enjoy the thrill of being frightened, forget the story, and no harm is done. But we must bear in mind the fact that there are children who are physiologically prone to excessive anxiety reactions and their tendency to fear and worry may be increased by listening to such stories. If frequently forced to listen to these tales of terror, especially when they are warned that the frightful experience may be their own if they don't look out, these more or less neurotic children may suffer for years from phobias that had their origin in someone's foolish attempt to frighten them into being good by "scaring them to death."

The frequency with which parents or teachers produce phobias in their children by attempting to frighten them into being good by tale telling may not be sufficiently great to show up in statistics, but some children might be spared a neurotic existence by wiser handling on the part of the parents.

The following account of a college girl of her fears and their origin will illustrate this point and I trust will discourage teachers from attempting to scare children into being good by tale telling.

I developed a terrific fear of walking down dark corridors, waking up at night, and being left alone in a house, besides other less frightening things. It seems strange to me because no one else in the family has such a fear and although to all outside appearances I have gotten over it, still I know I am even now deathly afraid of such things.

[8] Mullen, *op. cit.*, p. 34.

Although I can't remember clearly, Mother says that I had no apparent fear of anything until I was about eight or nine years old, when all of a sudden I developed a terriffic fear of going into the dark alone. So much so that I used to try to force my sister, who is two years my senior, to go to bed with me when I was sent. If she refused, I would cry and try to refuse also, which usually failed to get any result. Mother, however, knew how I felt and would, as soon as I calmed down, send Mary up to me. I was in about fourth grade at the time and as the year progressed, Mother says, my fear became greater. So much so, that I would wake up during the night crying and call for my father who would come and stay with me until I again went back to sleep.

Ghost stories frightened me so that I would be nervous and disturbed after hearing one. The very same story never seemed to have any effect upon the other children who heard it. Mystery stories today, if they are very realistic, scare me terribly. I have to free myself with all my strength to overcome the fear which I know full well in my mind to be unfounded. As a result, I avoid as many mystery stories as I possibly can.

But to return to the beginning of this fear. Mother tried to discover why I was so afraid of the dark, but in a childlike manner, feeling ashamed of myself, I would refuse to admit I was afraid. At very brave moments, usually the result of jibes from my brothers, I would disappear down one of our long dark corridors, or go to bed by myself. It would look convincing to them, but by the time I'd reach the room and put on the light, I'd have used most of my strength and be really quivering from fear. It was terrible, the agony I would go through doing such simple things, for although I fought against it, I couldn't seem to conquer it.

The reason for that I think is that the fear wasn't of physical things that could be readily proved not to exist but of supernatural things. It was a terrific fear of the devil and evil spirits which I felt were liable to come along and pounce upon me the minute I did something wrong, even a harmless thing like forgetting my prayers. It also involved a struggle inside of me because I felt perfectly sure that I didn't ever want to offend God, and yet there was the erroneous idea that I probably was, without being conscious of the fact.

It was an awful period to go through, but one whose intensity diminished in about two years. However, even now when I hear stories which are terrifying and deal with supernatural creatures of an evil type, something of that old fear returns.

The basis for all these fears, I think, in fact I know, was in a series of stories one of the Sisters I had in school told us. They all dealt with the devil, evil spirits, and hell, which might have been her method of frightening us into being good. One thing for sure, she frightened all of us so that none of us have ever forgotten her or her stories. The stories made such an impression on me that now about fourteen years later I have a vivid picture of her, my classmates, and myself and the stories, just as clearly as if they happened yesterday.

As an example of these stories, I'll offer this one which left a very marked impression. It concerned a young woman who had fallen away from the

Church and had for years been doing just about what she pleased. During the whole period, however, she never once forgot to say three Hail Mary's every night before she went to sleep. On one occasion, the devil appeared to her and woke her, saying that the first night she forgot to say the three Hail Mary's he would take her with him to hell. To make it worse, she told us he disappeared through the wall of the house, and left as a reminder a huge hole which could never be closed up. Now, you can readily understand the effect a story like that would have upon a group of children. We were scared out of our wits that any night we might wake up at night and see the devil standing there and hear a similar message delivered to us. That was why I became so frightened when I'd wake up during the night.

In all probability our patient was the only one who was so profoundly affected by the stories of this well-intentioned but misguided nun. Such an intense anxiety prolonged for so many years would not have been produced in one whose emotional centers were in stable equilibrium.

Have we any evidence of physiological factors having anything to do with the origin of scruples? To test the theory of Janet that scrupulosity may arise in a condition of "lowered psychic tension" and that lowered psychic tension may be produced by physical causes, Mullen introduced the question: "Did you ever happen to grow scrupulous during or after a siege of sickness?" Some will be surprised to learn that 39 out of 400 or about 10 per cent of our population developed scrupulosity during or after a spell of illness or an operation.[9] The evidence is not conclusive, but the frequency is great enough to be suggestive.

There seems to be something in Janet's concept of psychasthenia producing an incapability of throwing aside the persistent questions which are likely to arise in any mind as it runs through the gamut of possibilities and impossibilities. Such thoughts are easily disregarded by the normal mind and are soon lost in the wide range of its active interests. But the psychasthenic mind is easily fettered and chained to its scrupulosity. Jung adopted Janet's kindred concept of the *abaissement du niveau mental* as the fundamental reason why a schizophrenic patient

[9] Mullen, *op. cit.*, p. 55.

cannot carry a train of thought to its logical end.[10]   And more recently Alexander[11] has studied a group of patients in whom lack of interest and mental debility are presenting symptoms. He finds that they are much helped by atropine, a result to be expected if we look at the facts now accumulating on the physiological basis of emotional conditions and the pharmacological treatment of affective mental disorders.[12]

Another fact which suggests an organic factor in scrupulosity is that its origin seems to be associated with puberty.   At this period emotional experience becomes much more lively, owing to physiological changes.   The period at which scrupulosity first appears has its maximum at about the age of puberty and tapers off on either side of that age in rough agreement with the curve of error.

If one looks through a number of cases of scrupulosity and anxiety he will find some in which the condition seems dominantly mental in its origin and others which suggest a strong concomitant organic factor.

Among the mental factors one may mention psychic exhibitionism.   The penitent finds pleasure in going over his sins, in being looked at, and in getting attention.   Scrupulosity is at times a plea for lots of personal attention.   Again it is a defense reaction.   The scrupulosity incapacitates the patient in a situation he would like to get out of, but in which for various other reasons he would like to remain.

Some scruples are associated with compulsions and one may find that anxiety and compulsion have existed from childhood. One must at least consider the possibility that some patients have anxious temperaments and their fears are not to be explained by purely mental experiences in infancy.   If there are in the brain physiological centers of emotional expression, and if the irritation of these centers leads not only to emo-

[10] "On the Psychogenesis of Schizophrenia," *J. Ment. Sc.* **85**: 1999, 1939.

[11] Franz Alexander and Sidney A. Portis, "A Psychosomatic Study of Hypoglycaemic Fatigue," *Psychosom. Med.* **6**: 191–206, 1944.

[12] Cf. Moore, *op. cit.*, pp. 248 ff.

tional expression, but also to emotional experience, then a native lability of such centers may be the root of the anxious temperament.

Consider for a moment the following case. A religious was in a state of great anxiety when the time approached for him to take his perpetual vows. The anxiety centered about the

AGE OF ONSET OF SCRUPULOSITY

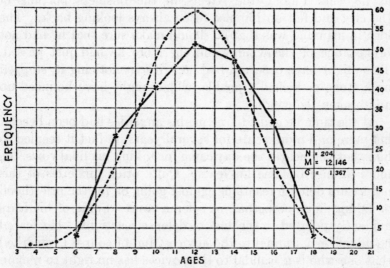

The unbroken line of the frequency polygon graphically represents the actual frequency. The broken superimposed curve indicates how closely the actual distribution approaches a normal distribution. Ninety-one of the 204 cases in which the subjects recalled the age of first onset of scrupulosity are found between the ages of 9 and 13, the period referred to as the preadolescent. (From Joseph J. Mullen, *"Psychological Factors in the Pastoral Treatment of Scruples,"* Stud. Psychol. & Psychiat. **1**: 67, 1927.)[13]

possibility of sin in all sorts of unreasonable ways. If for example he looked at a statue or a picture, he felt an impulse to look at it again. If he was busy about other matters, as was naturally ordinarily the case, the impulse became a drive and he felt that if he did not look at the picture again he would

[13] Mullen, *op. cit.*, p. 67.

commit a sin and that too a mortal sin. He was told that infringements of the community rules were imperfections but not sins, but he could not see how this could be and he felt illogically driven to argue that if they are sins they must be mortal sins. Asked about the origin of such difficulties, he recalled that when he was a young boy and his mind had not yet become sensitive to the idea of sin, he was much troubled as he walked along the streets in the business portions of the city and felt an impulse to be always looking back. The idea in his mind was that he should make sure that he had not broken one of the windows in the store he had just passed. This might have occurred had he, without noticing it, stepped on a stone or kicked a pebble, which might have bounced up and broken the window.

At the time he came to see me his anxieties had been becoming more and more acute for several years, in fact it seemed to him that the nearer the day came for taking his final vows, the more intense became his fears. Quite often anxieties of this nature are defense reactions against going on for the priesthood or taking final, perpetual, or solemn vows. Some of his fears evidently pointed to the line of defense reactions. He feared he might be a scandal to the novices, and of course I remarked that one who is a scandal to the novices has no right to remain in the community. He smiled and said: "That's just it." He feared he was an utter failure as a teacher and therefore he would be utterly useless to the community. And, therefore, it would not be right for him to take vows and throw himself as a burden on the community. And so we see that his anxieties and fears have a certain advantage to the lower self. In the meantime he dreams of how happy he would be, if he were to marry and have his own home and support himself by teaching. When he thinks of marriage, teaching appears as a hopeful means of support; when he thinks of his vows he sees himself an utter failure as a teacher.

Sometimes anxieties, as a defense reaction against the religious or priestly life, are situational and have no apparent connection with an anxious temperament. A seminarian is about to go up for ordination as a subdeacon. He becomes anxious about his future and asks to have the event postponed. It seems a great enigma to the authorities in the seminary, to whom he has not fully opened up his mind. He is intelligent and devout and has led an exemplary life. But for some years he has been turning things over in his mind. In his trips home he has become interested in a girl; he has talked over with her and her family the possibility of marrying her. It is quite natural therefore that he should hesitate about going on for the subdiaconate. It is a general rule that should scarcely ever be departed from that one who entertains serious doubts about going on for the priesthood should never do so till the doubts are entirely dispelled. Anyone too who is a prey also to anxiety and scruples should not go on for the priesthood. I have known cases of intense anxiety and scrupulosity suddenly to clear when the patients gave up their studies for the priesthood and returned to the world.

Sometimes anxieties may be physiological phenomena as far as their true causes are concerned. I remember a college student about to take his final examinations for his degree. He made up his mind that he would certainly fail and could not bear the thought of the shame and humiliation such a failure would bring on him. So he decided to leave college just as he was about to finish and get his degree. On being questioned, he said he had suffered with intense anxiety before every examination he had ever taken; but in his whole life he had never failed in any examination but had always done remarkably well. One would think that long experience would have toned down the anxiety. Had it been dominantly due to psychological causes this would have been the case. But if he was a person of an anxious temperament and the examination merely a present situation to which was hung his physiological anxiety, psychological experience might do little to

abate it. On the ground that adrenal cortical extract is a
parasympathetic stimulant and as such has a tendency to lessen
tension and anxiety, he was given a centimeter and a half of
eschatin hypodermically three times a week and urged to take
the examination come what might. He did so and, as usual,
passed with credit. Afterwards, he swore he would never
again be afraid of any examination. Perhaps explaining to
him that his anxieties were due to a physiological mechanism
tended to modify and soften the emotional resonance and experience. But there is grave danger that future tense situations will still provide a hook on which to hang the free-floating
anxieties of his temperament.

3. The Mental Hygiene of Fear and Anxiety

In the education of a child or of our own selves to take a place
as normal, strong personalities in the warfare of life, we must
rely far more on the delineation and love of ideals, on the
knowledge of careers and the possibilities they hold out, than
on an attempt to teach all about the pitfalls and blind alleys
of life.

We must not attempt to frighten. A fearful state of mind
is not a desirable thing. The first step in warding off the fears
of childhood and later life is to avoid producing any state of
anxious tension. That this should be a major factor in the
prophylaxis of anxiety is borne out by the careful study of
children's fears by Jersild and Holmes. "A large number of
the fears occurring between the ages of five and twelve years
fall under the heading of 'fears due to the apparently deliberate
efforts of others to frighten the child.'"[14]

It is a very different thing to attempt to frighten and to give
instruction in regard to possible dangers.

This holds not only in regard to practical physical hygiene
and the diseases of man, but also in regard to the realities of
eternal life.

[14] Jersild and Holmes, *op. cit.*, p. 334.

Mullen writes on this point as follows: "In the current literature many a case instead of blaming a predisposed constitution, taxes faulty religious instruction as a contributing cause of their abnormal fears. No doubt being puritanically brought up on brimstone and pitch could be harmful to an over-sensitive child. A stronger mind would think differently. Cardinal Manning tells how when a child he read the Apocalypse and remarks: 'And I never through all my life forgot the lake that burneth with fire and brimstone. That verse has kept with me like an audible voice through all my life and through worlds of dangers in my youth.' Charles Lamb blamed a luridly illustrated bible for his fears, and it would not be prudent to correct the first white lie of a child with the biblical story of Ananias and Saphira being struck dead for telling a lie. But we need have no such fear of Catholic truth unless it be ignorantly misinterpreted. Scientific catechetics calls for an integral but adapted exposition of the fundamental formulae of Christian Doctrine. The doctrine of eternal sanction for human sinfulness is not omitted, but this stern truth is not presented to the timorous child even as to the hardened libertine; nor does it hold first place. The child is taught to avoid sin 'most of all' out of a motive of love and friendship and devotion to the Saviour who suffers the little children to come unto Him. And it is the innocent child who can best be trained in the perfect motives of love and confidence, the filial spirit that excludes the contrary spirit of scrupulosity."[15]

Education instructs the intellect without disturbing the emotions. Because some individuals predisposed to anxiety develop an abnormal tormenting fear of germs from having taken a course in hygiene and bacteriology, it certainly does not follow that we should quit teaching the bacterial origin of various diseases. Individuals pathologically sensitive to anxiety will pick out the particular form their anxiety takes from whatever type of experience they may encounter. They can-

[15] Mullen, *op. cit.*, pp. 154–55.

not fly all experience but must learn to deal with their anxious trends as best they may.   On the other hand, teachers who seek to frighten rather than to enlighten the minds of their pupils should see their error and mend their ways.

There are some fears and anxieties that come from over-protection of a child so that he does not become familiar with and able to cope with many of the ordinary things of life. When such an individual is on the threshold of life he meets with many strange persons, strange objects, and strange situations.   The boy who does not know how to box, who cannot swim, who throws a ball like a girl, who has been kept away from games and sports lest he hurt himself and from other children lest they contaminate him, is likely to experience many timidities that will restrict his activities and limit his possibilities when he must fend for himself in the warfare of life.   Sports and wholesome contacts with other children should be helpful in strengthening the personality.   And some fears as we have seen[16] are persistent and aggravating simply because of the inherent weakness of the personality which is unable to rise above them and give full attention to the ordinary duties of everyday life.

Jersild says on this point: "Deficiency in ordinary motor-skills—through over-protection and lack of discipline—may also render the child more susceptible to fear in his social contacts: if he cannot climb, throw, fight, and tumble, he cannot keep pace with his playmates, he feels insecure in his social relationships, and shies away from contacts with people. Again, his deficiency may be in the field of social skills, in manners and techniques of courtesy, and such a deficiency likewise may result in feelings of insecurity in social relationships and fear of joining freely in social intercourse."[17]

That this is very true was brought to my attention by a case of amnesia.   A young girl entered into an amnesia and wan-

[16] Cf. above.
[17] Jersild and Holmes, *op. cit.*, p. 337.

dered away from home. When she came to herself she was in the mental ward of the city hospital. She had lost all memory of her previous existence and with that deprivation went the knowledge of how to behave at table and how to behave at church. She said she did not know what people did at social functions or in church and so she was afraid to go anywhere and stayed at home. Her plight illustrates what happens to many children whom no one teaches the rules of etiquette and social intercourse.

Once a child has become fearful and developed phobias about a number of objects or situations in his environment, there is one consolation: some of these will fade out in the sunlight of experience and with the ordinary development of his character. And we might say, the more normal and wholesome his environment, the more worth while the interests lying open to him, the greater the peace and affection in his family circle, and the less unreasonable anxiety is manifested by anyone around him, the more likely is it that any phobias he has developed will fade with his own maturation and the development of his own experience.

However, it would not be wise to suppose that all phobias will fade as the years roll on and so do nothing to try to correct them.

Let us first mention a few ways of dealing with a specific intense childhood fear which are *not* likely to be of much assistance.[18]

1. Keeping the child away from the feared object for a long time. Jones found this method unsuccessful even when the period of protection lasted for weeks or months.
2. Removing the feared object. Getting rid for example of a dog or moving to another neighborhood. As Jersild remarks, *in general* this does not help the child to master his fear, which should be our goal, but merely offers a temporary avenue of escape. One can, however, easily imagine a number of persistent annoying circumstances or objects from which any child should be removed if it is in any way possible.

---

[18] Cf. hereon Mary Coover Jones, "Elimination of Children's Fears," *J. Exper. Psychol.*, 7: 382–90, 1924; Jersild and Holmes, *op. cit.*

3. Explaining to the child the harmlessness of the object he fears. This seems to be the ordinary method which parents use in their attempts to free the child from its unreasonable fears. It is naturally the method to be used when an acute anxiety is produced by some harmless object. The child must be enlightened and informed about things and events in his immediate environment. But a chronic phobia does not ordinarily yield to verbal explanations. Thus a child in some way developed a fear of rabbits. The teacher in school worked out a project on rabbits and he and the children in his class became thoroughly familiar with rabbits and how innocent and harmless they are. He was then confronted with a rabbit and reacted with all his former terror.

As to the more useful methods of helping a child overcome his fears, one might mention in the first place stimulating and assisting the child in some way to approach the feared object of his own volition and to familiarize himself with it by actual contact or repeated experience. There are several ways of doing this. Mary Coover Jones found the most useful method to be what she terms social imitation. A child who is afraid of rabbits is allowed to go into a room where other children are playing with a rabbit. At first he is afraid, then curious, later touches the rabbit himself and finally enjoys letting it nibble at his fingers. Holmes urged the child to enter a dark room alone or to get a toy when it was in a box with a harmless snake or to go and see what made a loud noise, etc. If the child was afraid to do so she offered to accompany it and did go with the child or put in her own hand and got the toy. The urging and support by accompanying was repeated till gradually the child spontaneously approached the feared object and so conquered its phobia.[19]

Older children and adults sometimes take themselves in hand and force themselves to manipulate a feared object till familiarity breeds contempt. Jersild says that not many fears are overcome in this way.[20]

When an adult goes to a psychiatrist with a phobia the psychiatrist will often attempt to discover by analysis the

[19] Jersild and Holmes, op. cit., pp. 177 ff.
[20] Ibid., p. 333.

original frightening experience which gave rise to the fear in the first place. The discovery of the complex often gives an insight into the fact that "what troubled me then has no reason to bother me now" and the phobia fades out of existence. But if analysis fails to unearth the complex or is for some reason not attempted, it is still possible to help the patient overcome the fear "without resorting to a prolonged inquiry into forgotten events."[21]

[21] *Ibid.*, p. 343.

CHAPTER V

ANGER

PERHAPS the most common disturbance of the peace of the home and all other social units is the emotion of anger. Nevertheless, many pay little attention to correcting their faults of temper. If, however, everyone made a serious attempt to control anger and never to show the least sign of impatience, the world would be vastly more happy and a more comfortable place in which to live.

In an extreme form violent outbursts of anger are found in the manic type of manic-depressive insanity, in certain epileptic conditions, as a prodromal sign of *dementia paralytica,* in various forms of constitutional inferiority, and occasionally after a cerebral hemorrhage. But here one is more likely to find an irritability under slight provocation in a patient who before his "stroke" was kindly in manner and had a good control of his temper. Children who have recovered from *encephalitis lethargica* are often prone to temper tantrums. These facts indicate that irritability is sometimes due to a disturbance of neurological factors of control by means of which the visible expression of anger is ordinarily restrained. This concept is confirmed by Bard's study of dogs in which the cortex had been separated from the thalamic region. In these dogs every stimulus seemed to lead to an outburst of violent rage, termed by Bard "sham rage" on the questionable supposition that the "emotion" could not be conscious, seeing that the cortex had been isolated from the remaining parts of the central nervous system.

Now all these facts indicate that control is exerted over the manifestations of anger through neurological mechanisms which may be impaired or abolished by anything that attacks the neurological mechanisms.

On the other hand it is apparent that many eventually gain

good control over an original bad temper. There must therefore be a psychological or mental factor in the control of anger as well as an organic one. It is the role of mental hygiene to point the way to concepts and ideals that may help in the control of anger.

We may turn here to monastic teachings which for centuries have been concerned with developing harmonious interpersonal relations between all those who live together in a monastery. There is an essential similarity between the monastery and a family and between a family and many other forms of social units that consist of a number of individuals who live or work together. The normal attitude of mind in any social unit is one of friendly cooperation rather than one of competition. One is a true friend to every member of his group and to some extent also to everyone outside the group. When this friendly attitude of true charity develops, one is not easily angered by the words and actions of others. What is detestable, provoking, insolent in the behavior of one we dislike, becomes a mere amusing peculiarity in the conduct of a friend. Whenever we are provoked by another, it would be well worth while to pause and consider our fundamental attitude of mind towards the one who irritates us.

The mechanism of projection sometimes lies at the basis of one's irritability in one's dealings with a certain individual. One is said to *project* when he attributes to another or to others the feelings and attitudes of mind that he himself has towards them. One hates Mr. X, therefore (this "therefore" need not become conscious) because he has first hated X he commences in imagination to project into the mind of X a hatred of which X may be in no way guilty. And so sometimes it happens that we become provoked at and irritated by the innocent behavior of others which we see in a false light, and attribute to others antagonistic feelings which do not exist in their minds at all, but only in our own.

In this way, there develop what are termed *ideas of reference*.

Words, actions, gestures, conduct which have in reality nothing to do with the patient are seen by the patient in a false light and are looked upon as fully intended acts of persecution. One is likely to react to persecution, real or imaginary, with hatred, murmuring, anger, and antagonism. Ideas of reference show all degrees of abnormality from mere natural suspicions to perfectly unreasonable but nevertheless fixed and immovable delusions. It is good mental hygiene to discount heavily even suspicions that seem well grounded but which lead to an antagonistic, unfriendly attitude toward another.

In the fourth chapter of his *Rule*, entitled "Instruments of Good Works," St. Benedict has given a number of suggestions which have to do with our interpersonal relations. Most of them have to do with internal attitudes of mind, for out of the fulness of the heart the mouth speaks. If our interior attitude of mind is kindly and sympathetic toward all, our conduct will be but the natural expression of that inner all-embracing charity which should be the governing principle in all interpersonal relations. And so St. Benedict gives the following suggestions which we might well make use of in developing our inner attitude of mind towards others:

Not to harbor a desire for revenge

Not to foster guile in our hearts. (By this he means any kind of scheming to get another into trouble or to deceive a person in authority)

Not to make a feigned peace. (It sometimes happens that after an outburst of temper one makes up, but does so only externally. St. Benedict urges us to be perfectly honest in our forgiveness and to lay aside once and forever every shadow of a grudge or a desire for revenge)

Not to forsake charity

To love one's enemies

To bear persecution for justice' sake

To hate no man

To reverence the seniors

To love the juniors

To pray for one's enemies in the love of Christ

To make peace with an adversary before the setting of the sun

Certain other of these instruments seem to have to do with speech:

Not to give way to anger
To do no wrong to anyone, to bear patiently wrong done to oneself
Not to love strife

One way of attaining the correct idea of how we should feel towards others is to ask ourselves what must be the attitude of one of the saints in heaven to those about him. And the answer would be:

He has no antagonism towards anyone
He loves all without exception
He has respect for all
He thinks evil of none

But one might readily here interpose an objection: His companions are saints but mine are not. But let us conceive of our saint from heaven as disguised as myself and placed in my circumstances. Would not the following statements be true of his inner attitude of mind and govern his conduct?

He would love all because Christ loves each
He would therefore be friendly to all no matter how they treated him, because no living human being is excluded from the love of Christ

Even one who has not attained to the truths of Christianity should recognize the fact that all human beings constitute one universal society in which God the supreme intelligence rules over and labors with a world of intelligible beings. And if one recognizes this truth, universal cooperation should banish from the world all anger, antagonisms, and hatred.

But from the early years of Christianity there has been a special reason for banishing from the mind every attitude that makes a discord in the harmony of the social order. It is the concept that all those who take part in the Eucharistic banquet are thereby welded into one corporate body just as the grains of wheat are gathered from many fields, are ground and kneaded together and made into one bread, and drops from many grapes flow together and become one wine. St. Cyprian expressed the idea as follows:

"The Lord's sacrifice symbolizes the oneness of heart guaranteed by a persevering and inviolable charity, which should prevail among Christians. For when our Lord calls His body bread, a substance which is kneaded together out of many grains, He indicates that we His people whom He sustains, are bound together in close union, and when He speaks of His blood as wine, in which the juice pressed from many clusters of grapes is mingled in one fluid, He likewise indicates that we His flock are by the commingling of a multitude of persons made one."[1]

And the sufferings of this life, the friction of interpersonal relations, and death itself may be conceived of as a milling process by which we are ground into fine flour in order to be assimilated to the body of Christ. This concept is expressed in the words of the communion for the feast of St. Ignatius the Martyr, who was thrown to the lions in the early part of the second century: "I am the wheat of Christ. I shall be ground by the teeth of beasts that I may become pure bread." Such an attitude towards the trials of life is capable of making a situation that seems unendurable like a passing cloud, black and heavy indeed, but revealing in its wake a sunny sky.

This concept, which is found in more than one writer of the first centuries, derives from St. Paul, who wrote: "For we being many, are one bread, one body, all we who partake of one bread."[2]

It is because the world in general has lost sight of such truths that so many evils exist at the present day. Leo XIII called attention to this fact in 1902:

"If anyone will diligently examine into the causes of the evils of our day, he will find that they arise from this, that as charity towards God has grown cold, the mutual charity of men among themselves has likewise cooled. Men have forgotten that

---

[1] Ep. 96 ad Magnum, N. 5 (Al. 6), quoted by Leo XIII in his Encyclical on the Holy Eucharist (*Mirae caritatis*, May 28, 1902). See John J. Wynne, S.J. (ed.), *The Great Encyclicals of Leo XIII*, New York: Benziger, 1903, p. 528.

[2] I Cor. 10:17.

they are the children of God and brethren in Jesus Christ; they
care for nothing except their own individual interests; the
interests and rights of others they not only make light of but
often attack and invade."[3]

Since these words were written we have witnessed the attempt in Europe to supplant the law of charity by hatred, and
one nation has attempted to take over the land and goods of
its neighbors without regard to the interests and rights of those
it could conquer by force. But man cannot make morality
anything he chooses to have it and develop a living, workable
mode of existence. False principles do not work in practice
and we are now witnessing the inevitable collapse which had
to come sooner or later, once the principles of charity had been
utterly disregarded.

What we need fundamentally is a return of individuals and of
nations to the only principle on which the social order can be
based, and that is the law of charity—the love of God and our
neighbor as ourselves. We must enter life with the idea of co-
operating with others, not with the concept of crushing and
dominating all who stand in our path. If we really live this
ideal, anger will disappear as a character blemish and we shall
become a strong influence for good and the peace of every social
unit of which we become a part.

[3] Wynne, *op. cit.*, pp. 526–27.

CHAPTER VI

HATRED AND RACE PREJUDICE

1. THE PSYCHOLOGY AND PSYCHIATRY OF HATRED

THE CONCEPT of hatred involves more than that of an intense feeling of antipathy. Such feelings constitute what is sometimes termed dislike. But it is not necessary for us to hate a person whom we dislike. This can be made clearer by turning for a moment to the concept of love or charity. Here again we must distinguish between a feeling of being personally attracted to a certain person and genuinely loving or having charity towards that person. If you use a person who is attractive to you for the pleasure you get out of him and do nothing for his welfare, and discard him when you are "through with him," you cannot be said truly to love that person or to have genuine charity towards him. It is only when one effectively determines to do what he can to forward another's welfare and aid and abet his best interests—it is only then that one can be said to love a person. True love, therefore, is a matter of the will and not an emotional reaction. Now the opposite of true love is hatred and it, too, is a matter of the will. Love seeks the true welfare of the beloved; hatred, on the contrary, seeks to hinder, obstruct, injure, and even destroy the one who is hated. So long as one is master of his antagonisms and refrains from doing any shadow of injury to those who arouse his antipathies, and when opportunity arises tries to help them and forward whatever is for their true welfare, one does not hate, no matter how intense may be his dislike.

The plane of our emotions may be conceived of as balanced and pivoted at its center so that it may tilt in any direction. In normal human life the emotional plane is ever in motion, tilting now to joy and back again to sadness, now to excitement and back again to depression, now to fondness and then to antagonism, and so on throughout the whole gamut of the emotions. The balanced person is the one who exercises a certain amount of control over the tilting of the emotional plane and particularly of the reactions that are likely to be set off whenever the plane dips too far in one direction.

When one feels very sad and one's feelings are hurt, one may have a tendency to give up and quit, resign a position on which his livelihood depends, go off to some distant place and be lost forever to all whom one has ever known.

When one feels intense dislike, all sorts of acts of revenge may be set off, murder itself lies in their midst, but most individuals have sufficient control over the tilting of the emotional plane to limit their reactions so that murder at least makes no real appearance no matter how often it may be thought about. Patterson points out to us that while the threats of children to kill those who interfere with their wishes are often taken lightly, nevertheless certain neurotic adolescents carry out their threats with disastrous effects.[1] We must look upon actual murder as a possibility that looms on the horizon whenever hatred becomes intense.

How is it that the balanced personality is enabled to control, if not the tilting of the emotional plane, at least the reactions which are likely to be set off whenever the plane dips too far in a given direction? Largely by developing *attitudes* of *mind, ideals, and principles.*

Brown gives the following definition of an attitude of mind: *A state of readiness for response, organized through experience, which exerts a directive influence on the individual's behavior toward all the objects and situations to which it is related.*[2] Instead of a "state of readiness for response" we would like to say a habitual manner of thought. The "attitude of mind"

[1] R. M. Patterson, "Psychiatric Study of Juveniles Involved in Homicide," *Am. J. Orthopsychiat.* **13**: 125–30, 1943.

[2] J. F. Brown, *Jews in a Gentile World: The Problem of Anti-Semitism* (ed. by Isacque Graeber and Steuart Henderson Britt), New York: Macmillan, 1942, p. 125.

is the "intellectual habit" of scholastic philosophy. No one
is free from intellectual habits or attitudes of mind and it is a
matter of vast mental hygiene importance that each and every
individual should take great care about allowing attitudes of
mind to develop within himself. It requires a bit of private
personal philosophizing, but without this rational consideration
of the edifice that is being constructed within the mind, one's
whole life may collapse upon him and he will be buried in the
ruins.

What should be the dominant attitude of mind in one's relations to the individuals with whom he comes in contact? Evidently one of friendliness, embodying a sincere desire to be
helpful if it is in any way possible. Practical proof that such an
attitude is the true one is given if we think for a moment about
what would result in society, if all over the world each one took
this attitude towards everyone else. Human society would
at once become a paradise on earth. On the contrary, if very
often or in general each one took towards everyone else an
antagonistic, unfriendly attitude, the state of the world would
be even worse than it now is. The partial reign of charity
prevents the collapse of the social order.

And what *ideal* will enable us to balance the personality in
its interpersonal relations? The ideal is intimately related to
the friendly attitude of mind, but refers rather to the character
of the individual himself. Before our minds should hover the
concept of one who has a natural warm affection as well as a
volitional helpful love towards all with whom he comes in
contact. I must have the idea of making myself just such a
personality and school myself in attaining it in every actual
contact with any other human being, no matter what his race,
his color, his nationality, his religion or political affiliation.
Any such thing as a difference of opinion should be eliminated
from my mind as a cause of personal antagonism. Antagonism
itself should not be allowed to arouse antagonism. It may not
be possible to keep one's feelings from being hurt but one can
refuse to render evil for evil and railing for railing.

And what should be the *principle* that preserves the balance of the personality in all interpersonal relations? The principle which lies at the basis of the American Declaration of Independence: "All men are created equal" and "are endowed by their Creator with certain unalienable rights" to "life, liberty, and the pursuit of happiness." The principle should not be taken as affirming the absolute equality of intellectual powers any more than of stature. But it does mean that there is no individual under the sun who has by nature more or less right to life, liberty, and the pursuit of happiness than any other individual; and therefore I must do all in my power to refrain from restricting or limiting in any way the fundamental rights of any human being.

The fundamental principle of ethics is to do good and avoid evil. Kant termed this the categorical imperative. He gave it several formulations, one of which ran thus: Regard a human person ever as an end, never as a means. The term "human person" is general and without restriction—everyone with whom I come in contact. I can use no one merely for my own ends. Each one has an end and I must help him to attain it. That means I must love in the true sense of the word and be truly helpful. But when I try to help I cannot possibly hate. And so our principle might be formulated: Do good and avoid evil, that is to say, help each one to attain his end and avoid all selfishness in your dealing with other human beings.

These are the main balancing forces in the organization of our conduct in relation to other individuals. They deal with the problem in the conscious sphere and it is in this region that personal effort amounts to most. When we ask how it is that prejudices arise, the answer is that there are two sources of our antagonisms:

1. Conscious friction with an individual who blocks our activity, speaks against us, writes against us, or seriously opposes us in any way.
2. Blind prejudice for which we can give no adequate explanation.

Prejudice and antagonism are of course psychological facts on the conscious plane. Nevertheless it sometimes happens that a person says: "I am not the least bit prejudiced against So-and-so," while as a matter of fact he is most bitterly antagonistic. Were he to be cross-questioned, it would probably come out that he is aware of a bitter feeling against "So-and-so"; however, he does not want to admit it and calls it by another name, perhaps by some such euphemism as righteous indignation. In this way the prejudice takes on a kind of subconscious character.

Again, a person is violently prejudiced against Catholics, Jews, or Negroes and looks upon it as perfectly natural, justifiable, and reasonable. If however, he should be cross-questioned, he would be able to give no good account of his prejudice. If anyone is aware of a prejudice in his own mind, it would be well for him to make a psychological study of himself.

A condition which commonly gives rise to prejudice is lack of any kind of close personal contact. When two groups come into some kind of external contact, but seldom or never intermingle, there often arise animosities and conflicts between them. Thus the rich and the poor, the Negro and the white, the Jew and the Gentile, develop interclass antagonisms due in part to the mere lack of social contact. This antagonism is often deepened by parents who, more or less embittered themselves, tell children from infancy on all manner of stories about the iniquity and cruelty of the class they despise. Parents would do well to keep the law of charity and never instil hatred and antagonism towards any individual or any class— not even towards our enemies in the present war.

When a minority group has definite racial characteristics by which its members are easily discerned by the majority group, this tends to arouse dislike, particularly in the uneducated or in those who live within a narrow circle of friends and seldom travel. If now along with racial characteristics there is a certain clannishness and seclusiveness, the factor of isolation is added to that of being different and the minority race easily becomes disliked by the ignorant and thoughtless.

A majority group may threaten the rights or even the existence of a minority group. The minority group reacts not merely by taking cold, logical steps to prevent any restriction of its liberties, but also by a storm of protest and invective which the majority group looks upon as a piece of insolent impudence, and it so expresses itself. No matter what the final issue, it takes a long time for the hatred and prejudice thus aroused to die down and perhaps it will never completely disappear.

And then there is the natural competition in business and politics, often associated with injustice and calumny. This is a frequent source not only of rivalry, but also of hatred. Honesty and square dealing in both business and politics would do a great deal to lessen the sum total of hatred and antagonism in the world. If political issues were freely and calmly discussed on their merits, when the judgment of the people has been passed no antagonism should remain.

Then there is the common human fallacy of attributing to all what was done by one. A priest or nun speaks sharply or scolds; therefore, the one scolded nourishes an abiding antipathy to all priests or all nuns for the future. One is cheated by an Italian or a Jew or a Jap or "what not"; therefore all Italians, or Jews, or Japs, or "what nots" are liars and thieves forever afterwards.

One has really himself to blame for his failure, but who wants to blame himself? So one thinks the Jews have conspired against him or gets angry at his wife for lack of interest in his work, or kicks his dog or vents his spleen on whoever first comes his way.

And so in various ways antagonisms arise, but it is probably very seldom that the one who becomes antagonistic is justified in attributing to the one or to the group he hates the downfall he rues or the restriction of his liberties of which he complains. Much is merely what psychiatrists term "ideas of reference," that is, connecting in thought with oneself what really has no such connection.   But let us suppose that the piece of persecution was really legally demonstrated without any flaw in the evidence: would not the mind be more at peace if one would put it down to profit and loss, forgive and forget, regret what one must, but hate no one and set about repairing as best one may the damage that has been inflicted?

On the other hand individuals in the race or group that is hated by the majority group become oversensitive.   They see antagonism at times where none exists and may exaggerate their accounts of what is done to them and see history in a false light in virtue of this selfsame mechanism of ideas of reference.   However, at times the facts need no exaggeration.[3] And yet one might make a false generalization.   Thus from the fact that Negroes have been lynched in the South it would be wrong to conclude that all Southerners hate Negroes.   As a matter of fact the Negro is loved and respected by none as he is by certain Southerners.

When one's hatreds and antagonisms are due to ideas of reference or to association of present percepts to past emotionally toned episodes, psychiatric help may be enlisted to discover the complex and get rid of one's unreasonable emotional reactions.   But it is in general the case that the one who hates wants to keep on hating and has no desire to seek psychiatric aid in overcoming this type of emotional difficulty. Here he differs profoundly from the patient afflicted by an abnormal anxiety.   The anxious person wants to be relieved of his phobia, the one who hates wants to nourish the hatred. It is for this reason that hatred from the point of view of mental health is the most dangerous of emotions as it is also the most wicked of vices.   Hatred also tends to widen its sphere.   You

---

[3] For an account of the atrocities inflicted on Jews, cf. "Anti-Semitism," *Universal Jewish Encyclopedia*, New York, 1939, vol. 1.

hate one person, therefore you will have nothing to do with him or any of his friends. You refuse to associate with him or his friends. If they are going to be present, you feel that you must be absent, and so you have lost a sphere of reality. But you have learned to hate and nurse your hatred. Someone else crosses your path and so you hate him and his friends and work against him and his enterprises and you have lost another sphere of reality. Pretty soon you commence to need friends, but their number has dwindled. There are few or none to whom you may turn. You feel persecuted. You are sore and discontented. You think the world has turned against you. You *project*, as psychiatrists say, the hatred of your own mind into the minds of others. You think they hate you when as a matter of fact they have no reason to think about you. They neither hate you nor do they even think of you. You are deluded. You have become a paranoiac.

By their fruits you shall know them. Hatred leads to paranoia, charity to peace and friendliness with all the world. No one can make you or persuade you to let go the bulldog grip of hatred. But you can do so yourself and it is for you to choose between hatred and charity, antagonism towards all or malice towards none, and kindly, happy personal relations with all with whom you come in contact.

2. The Balanced Personality and the Balanced Nation

Let us now consider for a moment in the light of all we have said the concept of a balanced personality. In the balanced personality there is seldom if ever a violent emotional storm. The emotional plane tilts but it does not get off balance and fall heavily to one side and there remain. Furthermore, the undesirable reactions which so often appear when the emotional plane tilts are subject in the balanced personality to intellectual control. It is mainly this intellectual control which brings about the balancing of the personality. This control is dependent on the acquisition of attitudes of mind, ideals, and principles. When they are established, there results a relative peace in emotional life and reason controls conduct.

Let us now apply the concept of the balanced personality to the state and see what may be meant by a balanced nation.

The legal system of a nation constitutes the essence of its balancing power. The law of the nation corresponds to the intellect and will of the individual. A nation is balanced when its legal system does not single out any class for special favor or for definite limitation of privileges. Theoretically the thirteen colonies were a balanced nation when in 1776 they signed the Declaration of Independence. Practically, the United States did not become a well balanced nation until December 18, 1865, when Article XIII abolishing slavery was declared to have been ratified by the requisite number of states. England may be looked upon at the present day as a balanced nation, but during the reign of Henry the Eighth, and on down to the emancipation of Catholics, England was not a balanced nation. It is only when the courts give to all citizens equal justice under law that a country can be classed among the balanced nationalities.

If a nation can be in some sense a "balanced personality" as an individual can, we must look upon the medieval state as the expression of a balanced corporate personality. It is hard for us to realize that there was such a thing as a medieval state constituting an organic unity in spite of national differences. It was due to the union of church and state in one organic living whole. The Eternal Law, God Himself, was conceived of as the soul of this living organism. Now God is charity and hates none of the creatures of His hand. Therefore equal justice under law must be meted out to Jew and Gentile alike.

Guido Kisch, an eminent Jewish lawyer, gives the following picture of Jewish rights in the medieval state: "The Jews of Europe very early received from various rulers guarantees for the protection of their persons and property, for life, honor and possessions, for their religious practices and necessary buildings, protection for their economic activities, freedom of trade, exemption from tolls and duties, permission to apply Jewish law, the recognition of Jewish tribunals for internal Jewish affairs and permission to employ Christian servants. . . .Within the framework of these privileges the life of the Jews developed favorably. They could unfold their commercial activity freely, they could care for their property and they were on the best of terms with the Christian population."[4]

The concept of all men having fundamental rights guaranteed to them by God was the basis of medieval law. Anyone who denied a human being his fundamental rights was answerable before God. And the medieval judge seems to have taken seriously his accountability to God.

The judge in the Middle Ages according to Kisch looked upon himself as acting in God's place: "Equality of all men before God leads to equality of all men before the law. Hence disputes affecting Jews are decided in the same manner and according to the same principles as those of Christian parties. In the many legal decisions of the twelfth to the fifteenth centuries in the Magdeburg courts, which represented a sort of supreme court in medieval Germany and the judicial decisions of which were highly respected throughout Europe, we never find that a judge would let himself be carried away by his prejudice against the person of the Jew to the point of twisting the law."[5]

This does not signify by any means that no Jew was unjustly treated by bitter and unreasonable men, but "for centuries legal doctrines and judicial decisions did not allow such anti-

[4] Guido Kisch, "The Jews in Medieval Law," *Essays on Antisemitism* (ed. by Koppel S. Pinson), Jewish Social Studies Publications, no. 2, New York: Conference on Jewish Relations, 1942, pp. 60–61. Kisch tells us that the source material and literature on which this essay is based will appear in a more detailed study, "Jewry Law, Past, Present and Future."

[5] Kisch, *op. cit.*, pp. 62–63.

Jewish tendencies any access into the realm of the law. They also granted the Jews law and justice. That will remain forever a glorious act of justice, hitherto hardly known in the 'dark middle ages.' "[6]

In every country where laws are wisely made by enlightened rulers the lives of individuals lag behind the ideal that lies in the legal enactments. This was true in the Middle Ages and it remains true today in our own United States of America. But it is for us as individual citizens to rise to the ideal of our nation and do away with all manner of hatred, invective, unjust and unkind treatment of anyone, no matter what his race or creed or previous condition of servitude.

In our United States the ideal of universal charity has dictated the law of the land, which found its first expression among us when the Declaration of Independence declared that governments are instituted among men to secure their fundamental rights to life, liberty, and the pursuit of happiness. This we see was the fundamental principle of medieval law. But between the papal enactment, the decisions of councils and the writings of theologians in the Middle Ages, and the Declaration of Independence, there is a big gap filled in not only by individual hatred and criminal acts but also by legal enactments depriving men of their fundamental rights.

It is indeed something of a mystery how the broad principles of universal rights to life, liberty, and the pursuit of happiness were embodied in the Declaration of Independence and the American Constitution. In the last analysis it must be attributed to Divine Providence by Whom all things are directed to their final end. Attempting to trace things to secondary causes, we note that a number of the American colonies were formed by groups of men seeking freedom to profess the religion of their choice without interference by those who held the reins of civil power. But this led in general to no broad concept of religious tolerance. Thus the Puritans in New England aimed

Ibid., p. 66.

in the first place at establishing and preserving their own religious system and church membership was looked upon "as a prerequisite for the suffrage privilege."[7] But this led many to a bitter resentment against being discriminated against and so to a demand for religious freedom which was voiced in many quarters.

And then a little later the Puritans themselves were disturbed by attempts to establish the Church of England and in 1684 they lost their charter, and one of their meeting houses was confiscated in 1686 for use by the Anglican Church, and so the Puritans commenced to clamor anew for religious freedom.[8]

When Lord Baltimore founded the Maryland colony he laid it down as a fundamental principle that "no person or persons whatsoever within this Province . . . professing to believe in Jesus Christ, shall from henceforth be anyways troubled, molested or discountenanced for in respect to his or her religion."[9] And the door was opened to Puritans, Presbyterians, Lutherans, and all other sects to enter and practice their religion unmolested. But before long things had so changed and come to such a pass that Catholics were molested in the practice of their religion and even had to pay a double tax. And so there was naturally a reaction and a demand for religious freedom.

The Declaration of Independence calls attention to a whole series of arbitrary actions on the part of the British government which in the sphere of civil and political rights led to a violent reaction on the part of the colonists and a demand for a voice in the disposition of their own affairs. It was only natural that one would hear all over the colonies the cry that govern-

[7] Cf. Florence A. Pooke, *Fountain Sources of American Political Theory*, New York: Copeland, 1930, p. 93.

[8] Menen Chamberlin, *John Adams, the Statesman of the American Revolution*, Cambridge, Mass.: Houghton, 1898, pp. 27 ff.

[9] Ellen Hart Smith, *Charles Carroll of Carrollton*, Cambridge, Mass.: Harvard Univ. Press, 1942, p. 6, citing *Archives of Maryland*, "Proceedings and Acts of the General Assembly, 1637-38" (Sept., 1664), pp. 245-46.

ments are instituted among men to guarantee their rights to life, liberty, and the pursuit of happiness, and when any form of government instead of protecting destroys these fundamental rights, it becomes lawful for the citizens to alter or to abolish it.

And so when Thomas Jefferson was called upon to draft the Declaration of Independence he gave expression not so much to his own personal view as to that of a voice and a spirit that were finding expression all over the colonies. The ideas and some of the expressions of the Declaration of Independence had been repeated over and over again in the Continental Congress for some two years previously[10]; and several county or town conventions before 1776 had declared the colonies a free and independent people.[11]

And so in drafting the Declaration Jefferson was not creating and giving expression to a philosophy of his own. He expressed the mind of a country rising up against intolerance of all kinds which was voiced in the Continental Congress, whose spirit for the time being became Jefferson's own mind.

No one can assert the principle that all men are created equal, with inalienable rights to life, liberty, and the pursuit of happiness, and countenance slavery. And so Jefferson introduced a passage in the Declaration accusing the king of Great Britain of maintaining a market where men could be bought and sold and of "suppressing every legislative attempt to prohibit or to restrain this execrable commerce."[12] The Congress deleted the passage. But in writing it Jefferson was false to his own line

[10] "Adams tells us that the ideas of the Declaration had become 'hackneyed' in Congressional debates for many months before the drafting of the Declaration was ordered": "Sources of the Declaration of Independence," address by Albert J. Beveridge before Historical Society of Pennsylvania, June 2, 1926, quoting Edmund Code Burnett, *Letters of Members of the Continental Congress*, Carnegie Institute of Washington Publications, 1: 516, 1921 (no. 299); John Adams, *Works*, vol. 2, p. 512.

[11] Charles G. Washburn, "Who was the Author of the Declaration of Independence?" (reprint), *Proc. Am. Antiquarian Soc.*, April, 1928.

[12] Cf. Carl Lotus Becker, *The Declaration of Independence*, New York: Peter Smith, 1933, p. 212.

of conduct, if not to his principles. There seems to have been a conflict here between principle and practice all his life. He thought emancipation would only make a bad situation worse. "He steadfastly refused to allow his name to be connected in any way with any movement designed to affect the institution of slavery. He went even further; he refused to accept membership in a society for the suppression of the slave trade even though the previous year he had written to Edward Rutledge, who was endeavoring to stop the importation of slaves into South Carolina, that 'this abomination must have an end, and there is a superior bench reserved in heaven for those who hasten it.' "[13]

The Declaration of Independence was not the expression of the private views and practices of those who signed it, but the final voicing of principles that had forced themselves on the minds of men who envisioned political and religious freedom and, whether through their own fault or the blind selfishness of those in power, had sought it but found it not. One could easily study the lives and writings of the signers of the Declaration and find many examples of bigotry and intolerance. Jefferson himself was antireligious.[14] In the draft of the Declaration he submitted to the Congress the name of God was not mentioned.[15] And John Adams seems to have shared Jefferson's anti-Christian spirit.[16]

The man whose life and thought were the embodiment of the principles of the Declaration of Independence was George Washington. A careful study of his character reveals him too as a well-balanced personality of great power and strength.

It was due mainly to the vigor of Washington's personality that the Revolutionary War was carried to a successful end. He had to put up with intolerable conditions which led weaker

[13] Kenneth Umbreit, *Founding Fathers*, New York: Harper, 1941, pp. 29–30.
[14] *Op. cit.*, pp. 82–85.
[15] Cf. the text with deletions and additions in Becker, *op. cit.*, pp. 174–84.
[16] Cf. Umbreit, *op. cit.*, p. 158.

personalities to resign their commissions. The army was composed of detachments sent by the various states. Men enlisted for a definite period at the end of which they were free to return home. The states did not send their quotas. Washington complained to his nephew: "Great bodies of militia in pay that never were in camp: . . . immense quantities of provisions drawn by men that never rendered . . . one hour's service . . . every kind of military [discipline] destroyed by them. . . . They [the militia] come without any conveniences and soon return."[17]

In the same letter he gives expression to his own internal conflict: "In confidence I tell you that I never was in such an unhappy divided state since I was born. To lose all comfort and happiness on the one hand, whilst I am fully persuaded that under such a system of management as has been adopted, I cannot have the least chance for reputation, nor those allowances made which the nature of the case requires; and to be told on the other that if I leave the service all will be lost, is, at the same time that I am bereft of every peaceful moment, distressing to a degree."

In such conflicts the weak personality draws into itself and quits. But Washington sees his duty and determines to follow it and a little further on writes: "If the men will stand by me (which by the by I despair of) I am resolved not to be forced from this ground while I have life."[18]

Weaker minds acted differently: "General Sullivan determined to quit the service because of abuse and ill treatment. For the same reason Schuyler proposed to resign."[19] Washington was a balanced personality and so in spite of the drive to quit he hung on and did his best.

[17] Quoted from A. J. Beveridge, *The Life of John Marshall*, vol. 1, p. 84, citing George Washington's letter to his nephew, Lund, Sept. 30, 1776, in Ford, vol. 4, pp. 457–59; also in John C. Fitzpatrick (ed.), *The Writings of George Washington*, Washington, D. C.: Gov't Print. Off., 1932, vol. 6, p. 137.

[18] Fitzpatrick, *op. cit.*, vol. 6, p. 138.

[19] Beveridge, *op. cit.*, vol. 4, p. 86.

Because he was a balanced personality he was free from prejudice and hatred.

In spite of the fact that he was a slaveholder he regarded the Negro as having fundamental rights to life, liberty, and the pursuit of happiness and therefore slavery should be abolished and the Negro freed—but by slow degrees, that the economic life in America might not be disrupted.

"Some petitions for the abolition of slavery had been presented to the Virginia legislature but they scarcely obtained a reading, and Washington felt that to set the matter afloat at that time would be productive of mischief. 'But, by degrees it certainly might, and assuredly ought to be affected,' was the way he expressed it a month later to Lafayette. He summed it up to John Francis Mercer in September: 'I never mean (unless some particular circumstances should compel me) to possess another slave by purchase; it being among my first wishes to see some plan adopted by which slavery in this country may be abolished by slow, sure and imperceptible degrees.' "[20]

He did what he could to keep Catholics from being irritated and offended by what he termed "that ridiculous and childish custom of burning an effigy of the pope."[21]

Colonel Benedict Arnold was sent with a thousand men to march into Canada and Washington gave him instructions to avoid showing any contempt for the Catholic religion when he was in that region, saying: "While we are contending for our own liberty, we should be very cautious of violating the rights of conscience in others, ever considering that God alone is the judge of the hearts of men, and to Him only in this case they are answerable."[22]

And writing to the Hebrew Congregation of Savannah he

[20] J. C. Fitzpatrick, *George Washington Himself: A Common Sense Biography Written from His Manuscripts*, Indianapolis: Bobbs-Merill, 1933, p. 458.

[21] *Op. cit.*, p. 183.

[22] *Op. cit.*, p. 182.

manifested a profound respect for the Jews, welcoming them to the freedom of the United States: "May the same wonder-working Deity who long since delivered the Hebrews from their Egyptian oppressors, and planted them in the promised land, whose providential agency has lately been conspicuous in establishing these United States as an independent nation, still continue to water them with the dews of heaven, and to make the inhabitants of every denomination participate in the temporal and spiritual blessings of that people whose God is Jehovah."[23]

It is a remarkable fact indeed that out of the violent prejudices of the eighteenth century and the attempts in many quarters to conquer and rule without regard to the inalienable rights of man, and with civil authority demanding that subjects conform in their beliefs and practices to what the state established by law, the Declaration of Independence was proclaimed and the American Constitution was adopted.

The fundamental principles that emerge from these documents are:

1. The right to life, liberty, and the pursuit of happiness is an inalienable right given by God to each and every human being. In this respect all men are equal. One cannot think that the framers of the Declaration meant to say that all men have equal intellectual, artistic, and muscular ability. And yet this assumption lies back of slurs which are thoughtlessly aimed at its fundamental principle.

2. The function of government is to secure these rights for its citizens.

3. The immediate source of all civil power is the will of the governed. This does not deny that ultimately all power is from God.

[23] Washington to the Hebrew Congregation of Savannah, cited by Albert Bushnell Hart, *Washington as a Religious Man*, Honor to George Washington series, no. 5, Washington, D. C.: George Washington Bicentennial Commission, 1931, p. 33.

4. The people can alter or abolish a government which deprives them of their fundamental rights to life, liberty, and the pursuit of happiness.

There has been much discussion as to the philosophic source of the principles enunciated. Hunt[24] finds that the concepts were made popular by Algernon Sidney, who was executed in England for maintaining similar principles, on December 7, 1683. Thomas Jefferson possessed a copy of his *Discourses on Government*, in which he defends the philosophy of St. Robert Bellarmine against Sir Robert Filmer. St. Robert Bellarmine maintains as a matter of fact that the authority of all rulers, though ultimately from God, is bestowed by the people and they may, for lawful cause, change a kingdom into an aristocracy or a democracy:

"It depends on the consent of the people to decide whether Kings or consuls or other magistrates are to be established in authority over them; and, if there be legitimate cause, the people can change a kingdom into an aristocracy, or an aristocracy into a democracy, and vice versa, as we read was done in Rome."[25]

5. The government will not interfere in any way with the free exercise of religion nor demand any religious test as a qualification for office.[26]

On the basis of these principles our country for years has been the refuge of the oppressed of all nations. And our policy towards all mankind has been one of friendliness and cooperation. If there have been wars they have but clouded for a time

[24] Gaillard Hunt, "The Virginia Declaration of Rights and Cardinal Bellarmine," *Cath. Hist. Rev.* **3**: 276–89, 1917.

[25] Robert Bellarmine, *De laicis* or *Treatise on Civil Government* (transl. by Kathleen E. Murphy), New York: Fordham Univ. Press, 1928, p. 27.

[26] In the original Constitution it says: "No religious test shall ever be required as a qualification to any office or public trust under the United States" (Art. 6, sec. 3) and the First Amendment, adopted Sept. 25, 1789, reads: "Congress shall make no law respecting an establishment of religion or prohibiting the free exercise thereof." (Cf. James Brown Scott [ed.], *The Declaration of Independence* . . . , New York: Oxford, 1917, p. 43.)

the spirit of American friendliness. In the Declaration of Independence we said to England: "We must, therefore, acquiesce in the necessity, which denounces our separation, and hold them as we hold the rest of mankind, enemies in war, in peace friends." This thought has dominated our foreign relations ever since. Fundamentally and essentially it is the law of charity. It is charity that develops the well-balanced personality; and it is hatred that unbalances the nation and the mind of the individual as well.

The law of the land is the balancing factor in the nation. To a very great extent the fundamental moral philosophy of our country has been that which gave the Jew in the Middle Ages his rights and privileges as maintained by the medieval courts. Unfortunately in those ages, in our own day, and in our own country unbalanced personalities have set themselves against the law of God and the law of the land. They have spoken and acted in a manner that Washington would have termed "childish and unreasonable," they have committed outrages,[27] and murders still occur in the name of lynch law; but if the law of the land remains what it is and the courts will be guided in the future by the natural law and the principles of the Constitution, all these irrational elements will eventually come under control and all men will be free and equal not only by law but also in the minds and hearts of the people.

3. The Unbalanced Nation

But the first half of this century has seen the growth of another concept of the rights of man and the functions of the state. This movement grew from a small group of forty men who met in a Munich *Bierhaus* in 1918 till it took control of the German nation and attempted to supplant the law of charity by the law of hate and dominate the world by force. The

[27] For an account of the disabilities of the Jews in our country, cf. Bruno Lasker, "Jewish Experiences in America," *Inquiry*, 1930, and Maurice Joseph Karpf, *Jewish Community Organization in the United States*, New York: Bloch, 1938.

Declaration of Independence, the Constitution of the United States, and the personality of George Washington present a remarkable contrast to the tenets of national socialism and the ideals of Adolf Hitler.

The first expression of the principles of national socialism may be taken as the formulation of the twenty-five points on February 24, 1920. In that formulation it is maintained that the good of the state comes before the good of the individual.[28] But in the Declaration of Independence it is maintained that governments are instituted among men to secure their rights and that all men are equal in respect to having rights to life, liberty, and the pursuit of happiness, and therefore no government can lawfully attack the fundamental rights of a class living within its borders, but on the contrary has a duty to protect all classes. Furthermore, that all men are created equal is a principle applying to all tribes and nations, so that no nation has a right to crush another nation without regard to the fundamental rights of human beings.

Very different from the concept that all men are created equal, that they are endowed by their Creator with certain unalienable rights, that among these are life, liberty, and the pursuit of happiness, is the Hitlerian concept that there is one superior race that has a right to use inferior races for its needs just as man has used such animals as the horse. Hitler says that "the first culture of mankind certainly depended less on the tamed animal, but rather on the use of inferior people."[29] And the suggestion is made that just as man now no longer needs the horse, so the superior race will soon no longer need the inferior and so by various techniques these inferior races are to be eliminated.

The concept of the inequality of other races as against the

[28] Cf. Konrad Heiden, *A History of National Socialism*, New York: Knopf, 1935, p. 17.

[29] Adolf Hitler, *Mein Kampf* (ed. by John Chamberlain *et al.*), New York: Reynal, 1939, p. 405.

State Teachers College Library
Willimantic, Conn.

Aryan, as the highest product of civilization, was not created by Hitler, but derived from current German literature. The source from which a number of writings on this matter flowed was a work by Joseph Arthur, Compte de Gobineau, entitled, *Essai sur l'inégalité des races humaines.*[30] It was soon translated into German and as late as 1920 Paul Kleinecke gave a digest of it in his little work entitled *Gobineau's Rassenlehre*[31] and long before the days of Hitler it was much read, talked, and written about in Germany. Perhaps Hitler owed more to the work of his friend Housten Stewart Chamberlain, *Die Grundlagen des neunzehnten Jahrhunderts,*[32] who Konrad Heiden says was the first member of the Nazi party to enjoy worldwide fame.[33]

At all events Gobineau rather than Hitler introduced the Germans to the ideas that the only way in which a race degenerates is by mixing its blood with that of another race and that at the present time the German races have attained the height of culture and all other races are inferior. But Gobineau looked upon the Prussian as on the outer edge rather than at the very center of Germanic culture.[34]

It is not in place to enter into the biological justification for Gobineau's concept. It is certainly very doubtful from the scientific point of view. Actual measurements of the intelligence levels of sample groups of various nationalities indicate that the differences found can be largely accounted for by the errors of sampling and inequalities of training.[35] That some human races approach the ape in their intelligence level is not the case. The highest level of performance of the chimpanzee

[30] Ed. 6, Paris: Firmin-Didot, 1933; ed. 1, Paris, 1854. There is an English translation of the first book: (Joseph) Arthur de Gobineau, *The Inequality of Human Races* (transl. by Adrian Collins), New York: Putnam, 1931.

[31] Stuttgart: Frommann, 1920.

[32] Ed. 6, Munich: Bruckmann, 1906; ed. 1, 1899.

[33] Heiden, *op. cit.*, p. 74.

[34] *Essai sur l'inégalité des races humaines* (ed. 6), vol. 2, p. 491.

[35] Otto Klineberg, "Mental Testing of Racial and National Groups," in H. S. Jennings *et al.*, *Scientific Aspects of the Race Problem*, New York: Longmans, 1941, pp. 251-94.

approaches the 3-year-old human level.[36] The intelligence level
of no human race can be placed as low as that. Vast differences in racial levels in natural endowment intelligence
do not exist. But were the differences much greater than
they are, there would be no justification for Hitler's concept
that the more intelligent races have a right to use the less
intelligent as long as they find it profitable, just as they have
used domestic animals, and then eliminate them when they so
desire.

But Hitler took the matter very seriously. He looked upon
the blending of races as the sole cause of racial degeneration.
Hence foreign races living in Germany must be eliminated.
First of all therefore the Jews must be destroyed. Then all
nations below the Aryan must be conquered and in their turn
eliminated from the world: "All that is not race in this world
is trash."[37]

And so the German National Socialist Workers' Party
set about its task of destruction. It is readily seen that given
the concept of charity as willing and working for the welfare
of others and hatred as willing and working for their downfall,
it was a movement in which the attempt was made to banish
charity and establish hatred. And whenever hatred appears
murder lurks in the background.

First Hitler established himself as the sole authority in his
party. Then he organized the SA (*Sturmabteilung*), whose
function it was to destroy freedom of speech and break up
every meeting in which views were expressed contrary to the
philosophy of national socialism, and to make trouble for the
Jews, who, living in the midst of Germans, threatened the purity
of German blood. Somewhat later he organized his own personal bodyguard (the SS or *Schutzstaffel*), which he termed the
Storm Troop Hitler, and then commenced the reign of terror.

When finally Hitler forced himself on Hindenburg as chan-

[36] Cf. T. V. Moore, "Animal Intelligence," in *Scientific Aspects of the Race
Problem*.[35]

[37] Hitler, *op. cit.*, p. 406.

cellor he made full use of his powers to prevent any free expression of opinion or discussion of political problems, in meetings or in the press, by calling on the president to sign an emergency decree by which political meetings could be prevented if it seemed that views contrary to the principles of the Nazi party would be expressed. Newspapers also were to be suppressed in case they incited to "civil disobedience."[38] Some 50,000 special policemen recruited from the SA and SS were armed and sent forth to crush all opposition by murder, violence, and terror.[39]

The concept of a universal right, even of all Germans living in Germany, to life, liberty, and the pursuit of happiness disappeared. All rights were reserved for a class of Germans. Those who could not give up their honest convictions were murdered or sent to concentration camps, where they suffered unbelievable persecution, or perhaps managed to escape persecution by silence and hiding or stealing out of the country. Every effort was made to destroy Christianity. Though in July, 1933, Hitler signed a concordat with the Holy See giving independence to Catholic schools, he at once proceeded to legislate Catholic schools out of existence and lay down conditions that demanded that the young be absorbed in the Hitler Youth, and arranged meetings so that it would be impossible to be a member of the Hitler Youth and at the same time to go to church. When Catholics and Protestants both protested Hitler said: "There are some old fools with whom it is too late to do anything. But we take the children away from them! We educate them to be new German people. When the little rascals are ten years old, we take them and form them into a community. When they are eighteen, we still do not leave them alone."[40] Soon religious instruction degenerated into an

[38] Heiden, *op. cit.*, p. 235.
[39] *Ibid.*, p. 238.
[40] Hitler, *op. cit.*, p. 643 n.

inculcation of hatred of the Jews, the apotheosis of Hitler and the virtues of the Aryan soul.[41]

In the meantime a vigorous campaign was organized against the Jews. The whole race was ostracized. The universities were closed to the Jewish student. Jewish property was destroyed. Many Jews were forced into concentration camps where they died of the hardships they had to suffer. The plan was to reduce them in time to an ignorant mass who might be used as beasts of burden, should they survive the conditions imposed upon them.

And preparations were made for the war that would conquer the world. Hitler envisaged this in 1924 when he wrote *Mein Kampf* while serving his term in the prison of the fortress at Landsberg on the Lech. He looked forward to a future peace "supported not by the palm branches of tearful pacifist professional female mourners, but founded by the victorious sword of a people of overlords, which puts the world into the service of a higher culture."[42] He spoke of the coming "fight for our new conception" and the apparent hopelessness of subjection of the world to the German overlords; but the battle cry will scare away the small minds and become "the signal for the assembling of real fighting characters. . . . Just in the seeming hopelessness of our enormous struggle lies the greatness of our task and also the possibility of success."[43]

And so Hitler entered upon the task of dominating the world first by gaining what he could by treaty and then taking what he promised to leave untouched and finally, in spite of the 1934 pact of friendship and nonaggression with Poland, he declared war on and conquered that unhappy land. One nation after another succumbed to the German armies and the German Gestapo followed and the inhabitants became the slaves of the

[41] *Ibid.*, p. 644.
[42] *Ibid.*, p. 599.
[43] *Ibid.*, p. 603.

German overlords according to the plan conceived by Hitler fifteen years previously in the prison of the fortress in 1924. That many of the inhabitants were put to death in measures of reprisal or starved or died of illness brought on by hardship was all in the plan. They constituted an inferior race and must ultimately die out or be destroyed, for, according to Hitler's philosophy, should the Germans blend with the lower conquered peoples, it meant the degeneration and ultimate destruction of the pure German race. That innocent people suffered untold agony amounted to nothing. "All that is not race in this world is trash." Human beings have no inalienable rights to life, liberty, and the pursuit of happiness. There exists an "obligation in accordance with the Eternal Will that dominates this universe to promote the victory of the better and the stronger, and to demand the submission of the worse and the weaker."[44]

The truth of a philosophy is made manifest when it is put to the test of reality. Hitler's philosophy has been tried and found wanting. His attempt to impose upon mankind his philosophy of hate has clearly and evidently brought about the present condition of Europe. The good and the true work together in harmony for the welfare of mankind. But human welfare can never result from hatred and race prejudice. Logically the philosophy of hate has no basis, but the present condition of the world is a clear demonstration that Hitler's concepts cannot be lived out in reality.

The choice between the Declaration of Independence and the philosophy of hatred is not a matter of picking an ideology that is more or less suited to one's temperament. There is a moral duty to respect the dignity and rights of every human being. There is an obligation on all minds to recognize the existence of the universal social order in which God the Supreme Intelligence lives in communion with the world of intelligent beings. An insult, an unkindness to any intelligence, is an

[44] *Op. cit.*, p. 580.

offense against this universal order which is permeated by charity to the utter exclusion of all hatred. As intelligent beings we must get rid of our antipathies and let conduct be dominated by charity—and so work towards the day when the law of nations will be identical with that charity which rules the interpersonal relations of individuals. As one individual should help another, so one nation should be of assistance to another nation. And let us hope that the supranational society will come into existence in the not very distant future and that its constitution will be the expression of the law of charity. Nor should the nations with whom we are now at war be long excluded from membership. This is not the American way which was expressed so aptly in the Declaration of Independence: we are "enemies in war, in peace friends."

CHAPTER VII

DEFECT OF GUIDANCE AND CONTROL IN EMOTIONAL LIFE

THERE is a class of patients whose condition is known to psychiatrists by the term "constitutional psychopathic inferiority." The name would imply that certain patients have an organic constitutional defect in virtue of which their conduct is more or less definitely abnormal, that is to say, psychopathic in character. In spite of the implication in the name, it is quite within the sphere of possibilities that these patients are not suffering entirely from an organic and perhaps hereditary defect, but to a significant degree from defect of training and lack of consistent and persistent effort to develop a stable control over the emotional tendencies of their lives. At all events we have good grounds for hoping that almost anyone, even though he may be inferior owing to a true constitutional defect, is capable of overcoming his inferiority by careful training and persistent personal effort.

Here, as is generally the case, character change is scarcely to be brought about by being externally imposed. It occurs as a rule only by personal internal effort. When a patient really becomes interested in changing his temperament and overcoming his defect of character, half the battle is already won. To do this intelligently we must become sensitive to our character defects. We can be aided in understanding ourselves by observing the behavior of others and studying the mistakes of historic personalities.

Oliver Goldsmith is a historic personality well worth study from the mental hygiene point of view. Could a modern psychiatric clinic have been born out of due time and the young Oliver have been brought before the chief psychiatrist, his diagnosis would certainly have been recorded as that of constitutional psychopathic inferiority.

Let us first look at what might be termed the misfortunes of Goldsmith, with the idea of discovering to what extent they depended upon faults of character, the overcoming of which would have given a much brighter coloring to his life.

We may merely touch upon the fact that he was a rather homely youth and various taunts in childhood developed an inferiority complex about his personal appearance. His later peculiarly bad taste for dressing in flashing colors was perhaps an overcompensation for his ideas about his personal appearance. It is said that when at the urgent requests of his friends, Oliver Goldsmith appeared before the bishop as a candidate for orders, he was rejected for "having presented himself before his right reverence in scarlet breeches."[1]

A leaf from an old ledger gives us an idea of how he dressed as a medical student in Edinburgh. It tells of his tailor bill with its charges for rich sky-blue satin, his superfine silver-laced small hat, his rich black Genoa velvet, and his best superfine high claret-colored cloth.[2] And all the time that he was spending money on such finery he often went hungry and just before he left Edinburgh for London he was arrested by bailiffs for security given to a fellow student.[3]

After having received his medical degree he practiced for a while as a poor physician among the poor. An old school acquintance one day saw him "in a suit of green and gold, miserably tarnished."[4]

When Johnson pronounced Goldsmith's *Traveller* "a poem to which it would not be easy to find anything equal since the death of Pope"[5] and all the world commenced to talk about him, "out came Goldsmith . . . in purple silk small-clothes, a handsome scarlet roquelaure buttoned close under the chin,

---

[1] John Forster, *The Life and Times of Oliver Goldsmith*, London, 1854, vol. 1, p. 43.

[2] *Op. cit.*, pp. 53–54.

[3] *Op. cit.*, p. 55.

[4] *Op. cit.*, p. 79.

[5] *Op. cit.*, p. 391.

and with all the additional importance derivable from a full dress professional wig, a sword, and a gold-headed cane."[6]

Leaving aside such amusing trivialities, Goldsmith's life as a whole was one series of calamities and the most of them were his own fault.

His schoolmates "described his temper as ultra-sensitive, but added that though quick to take offense, he was more feverishly ready to forgive."[7]

This sensitiveness and quickness to take offense stood in his way in the course of his life and blocked opportunities which were the stepping stones to better things.

Besides being emotionally sensitive, Goldsmith was peculiarly unable to hold before his mind the definite purpose of his present work and the immediate future. He lacked a sense of values and a feeling of responsibility for his present conduct, though his cheerful good fellowship at times helped where reason had failed, as the following incident shows.

"At the close of his last holidays, then a lad of nearly seventeen, he left home for Edgeworthstown, mounted on a borrowed hack which a friend was to restore to Lissoy, and with store of unaccustomed wealth, a guinea, in his pocket. The delicious taste of independence beguiled him to a loitering, lingering, pleasant enjoyment of the journey; and instead of finding himself under Mr. Hughes' roof at nightfall, night fell upon him some two or three miles out of the direct road, in the middle of the streets of Ardagh. But nothing could disconcert the owner of the guinea, who, with a lofty, confident air, inquired of a person passing the way to the town's best house of entertainment. The man addressed was the wag of Ardagh, a humorous fencingmaster, Mr. Cornelius Kelly, and the schoolboy swagger was an irresistible provocation to a jest. Submissively he turned back with horse and rider till they came within a pace or two of the great Squire Featherston's, to which

[6] *Op. cit.*, p. 422.
[7] Forster *op. cit.*, 20.

he respectfully pointed as the 'best house' of Ardagh. Oliver rang at the gate, gave his beast in charge with authoritative rigour, and was shown, as a supposed expected guest, into the comfortable parlour of the squire. Those were the days when Irish innkeepers and Irish squires more nearly approximated than now; and Mr. Featherston, unlike the excellent but explosive Mr. Hardcastle, is said to have seen the mistake and humored it. Oliver had a supper which gave him so much satisfaction, that he ordered a bottle of wine to follow; and the attentive landlord was not only forced to drink with him, but, with a familiar condescension, the wife and pretty daughter were invited to the supper room. Going to bed, he stopped to give special instructions for a hot cake to breakfast; and it was not till he had dispatched this latter meal, and was looking at his guinea with pathetic aspect of farewell, that the truth was told him by the good-natured squire."[8]

Forster's description of how on this trip Oliver Goldsmith allowed himself to be beguiled into a loitering, lingering, pleasant enjoyment of the journey aptly describes how many a constitutional psychopath ambles through life, accomplishes nothing, and fails to attain his destiny at the journey's end.

Poor and unfortunate himself, Goldsmith was always keenly sensitive to the misfortunes of others. He could not bear to see anyone suffering without doing whatever he could to relieve it, no matter what the personal sacrifice. Human prudence and even the consideration of obligations he owed in justice to others never prevented him from relieving the misfortune of anyone who happened to call upon him for aid, if he could find any physical possibility of giving the necessary relief.

He had to work his way through college, and during this period of his young life lived in squalid poverty. "He would write street ballads to save himself from actual starving; sell them to the Rein-Deer repository in Mountrath-court for five shillings apiece; and steal out of the college at night to hear

[8] Forster, *op. cit.*, pp. 21–22.

them sung. . . . It is said to have been a rare occurrence when the five shillings of the Rein-deer repository reached home with him. He was the most likely, when he was at the utmost need, to stop with some beggar on the road who might seem to him even more destitute than himself. Nor this only. The money gone, often, for the naked shivering wretch, had he slipped off a portion of the scanty clothes he wore, to patch a misery he could not otherwise relieve. To one starving creature with five crying children, he gave at one time the blankets off his bed, and crept himself into the ticking for shelter from the cold."[9]

Later on when starving in London he presented "himself at Surgeons Hall for examination as a hospital mate: an appointment sufficiently undesirable, to be found always of tolerably easy attainment by the duly qualified."[10] To present himself for this examination, it had been necessary to get a new suit of clothes, for the one suit he had, at the time he resolved to take his examination, was fit for service only after nightfall. For his promise to write some book reviews, the editor of the *Monthly Review* undertook to become security with a tailor for a new suit of clothes, which were either to be returned, or the debt for them discharged, within a given time.[11]

Goldsmith got his clothes, presented himself for the examination, and failed. All hope was then gone that he would ever be able to pay for the clothes. Only four days elapsed during which Oliver had time to meditate on the promised return of the clothes and his future destitution. Then there came an urgent appeal to his charity. The man who kept the wretched lodging where he lived had been dragged by bailiffs from his home on the previous night and his wife came sobbing to the destitute Oliver, begging for help. And so the new suit of clothes was carried to the pawnbroker's and the money realized

[9] Forster, *op. cit.*, pp. 29–30.
[10] *Op. cit.*, p. 165.
[11] *Op. cit.*, p. 165.

given to his landlady to help her in her distress. Here, as always, Goldsmith allowed himself to be dominated by the emotional appeal of the moment. Naturally he had no right to give away what did not belong to him. But such intellectual considerations appear to have had but little influence on his conduct. He seems to have had a consciousness of the noble and the reprehensible elements in his conduct, if we may take the following lines from the *Deserted Village* as giving expression to his own perplexities.

> Careless their merits or their faults to scan,
> His pity gave ere charity began.
> Thus to relieve the wretched was his pride,
> And e'en his failings leaned to Virtue's side;
> But in his duty prompt at every call,
> He watched and wept, he prayed and felt for all.

Oliver never ceased to give to those who needed help. And as his means increased so also did his charities. On hearing of his death a lady wrote, "I am sincerely glad to hear he has no family, so his loss will not be felt in domestic life." His biographer replies to this remark: "The respectable and learned old lady could not possibly know in what other *un*domestic ways it might be felt. The staircase of Brick-court is said to have been filled with mourners, the reverse of domestic; women without a home, without domesticity of any kind, with no friend but him they had come to weep for; outcasts of that great, solitary, wicked city, to whom he had never forgotten to be kind and charitable."[12]

It is always an important thing in the study of any author to find the author himself in his works. "The gentleman dressed in black" in the letters of *The Citizen of the World* is an amusing caricature that Oliver Goldsmith drew of his own self as he reflected upon the penury to which his unreasonable generosity brought him. Not only does he show us that he could see through one of the weak points in his own character,

---

[12] Forster, *op. cit.*, vol. 2, p. 467.

but in one passage he also gives an insight into how he came to acquire this unbalanced spirit of giving which kept him impoverished:

"My father, the younger son of a good family, was possessed of a small living in the church. His education was above his fortune, and his generosity greater than his education. . . .

"As his fortune was but small, he lived up to the very extent of it; he had no intentions of leaving his children money, for that was dross; he was resolved they should have learning; for learning, he used to observe, was better than silver or gold. For this purpose he undertook to instruct us himself; and took as much pains to form our morals as to improve our understanding. We were told that universal benevolence was what first cemented society; we were taught to consider all the wants of mankind as our own; to regard the *human face divine* with affection and esteem; he wound us up to be mere machines of pity, and rendered us incapable of withstanding the slightest impulse made either by real or fictitious distress; in a word, we were perfectly instructed in the art of *giving away* thousands, before we were taught the more necessary qualifications of *getting* a farthing."[13]

"The gentleman in black" gives us in a flash of wit the story of Oliver Goldsmith's life: "If you are fond," says he, "of hearing of *hair-breadth escapes*, my history must certainly please: for I have been for twenty years upon the very verge of starving, without ever having starved."[14]

Nor was he happy when he died.

"Is your mind at ease?" asked his attending physician.

"No, it is not," was Goldsmith's melancholy answer, and these were the last words he uttered in this world.

We find that, in spite of a few years of relative prosperity, Oliver Goldsmith died as he lived, burdened with debts, but remembered and mourned by the poor to whom he had been

[13] *Citizen of the World*, Letter 26, in J. W. M. Gibbs (ed.), *Works of Oliver Goldsmith*, London: Routledge, 1885.
[14] *Op. cit.*

kind. "Everything he possessed, with such small fragments of property as he had left at the Edgeware cottage, was of course in due time sold by public auction, including his 'large valuable, and well-chosen library of curious and scarce books,' his 'household furniture and other effects': but Bott, Griffin and others, still remained with unsatisfied claims; and his brother Maurice, who had come over to London in the month preceding the sale for the purpose of 'administering' to what had been left, soon saw how hopeless it was to expect that his brother's debts would not absorb everything, and, even before the sale took place, therefore, went back empty-handed as he came."[15]

Let us now consider some of the definite faults of character which Goldsmith manifested and which were responsible for the misfortunes of his life. They are quite characteristic of what we find in the constitutional psychopath.

1. Emotional Display without Regard to Consequences

When Goldsmith left college he remained idle for some time, but through the influence of his uncle Contarine he found employment as a tutor in a private family. This gave him a place to live and a respectable income. With a little prudence the income could have been allowed to accumulate and this fairly comfortable beginning in life made the stepping stone to better things.

But during a game of cards Goldsmith became angered at what he thought to be unfair play and accused one of the members of the family of cheating. And so he lost his position by this unreasonable outburst of emotion and returned to his life of idleness.[16]

Later on, when a medical student in Edinburgh, he gained admission in some capacity to the household of the Duke of Hamilton. With a little management he could have developed

---

[15] Forster, *op. cit.*, vol. 2, p. 468.
[16] Forster, *op. cit.*, vol. 1, p. 44.

friendships valuable for life, but his sensitive nature was offended in some way by the attitude which he though he perceived in the Duke's family and he wrote to his uncle: "I have spent more than a fortnight every second day at the Duke of Hamilton's; but it seems they like me more as a jester than a companion; so I disdained so servile an appointment."[17]

One should learn to consider the incidents, the opportunities, and the troubles of life in the light of reason rather than follow emotional drives. It may seem to us that we are not treated by others with the consideration to which we feel entitled. But we should learn to bear humbly with the unpleasant elements in any situation, that we may make rational use of the opportunities it affords. This was a lesson that Goldsmith never learned; and he lost an opportunity in his contact with the Duke of Hamilton which might have opened the way to better things.

Though very sensitive, Goldsmith could under circumstances keep from manifesting it and maintain a calm exterior. This is illustrated by the following incident:

"Mr. Piazzi has told the following story of Goldsmith's demeanor after the first performance of this his first play (The Good Natured Man). 'Returning home one day from dining at the chaplain's table, he (Dr. Johnson) told me, that Dr. Goldsmith had given a very comical and unnecessarily exact recital there of his own feelings when his play was hissed,[18] telling the company how he went indeed to the Literary Club at night and chatted gaily among his friends as if nothing had happened amiss; that to impress them the more forcibly with an idea of his magnanimity, he even sang his favorite song about *an old woman tossed in a blanket seventeen times as high as the moon*; but "all this while I was suffering horrid tortures," said he, "and verily believe that if I had put a bit into my mouth it would have strangled me on the spot, I was so excessively ill; but I made more noise than usual to cover all that; and so they

[17] Forster, *op. cit.*, p. 51.
[18] The Bailiff's Scene in the third act.

never perceived my not eating . . . but when they were all gone
except Johnson here, I burst out a-crying, and even swore by
. . . that I would never write again." ' "[19]

In the *Vicar of Wakefield* Goldsmith constructed a situation
in which emotional display without regard to consequences
finds complete justification. The answer of the vicar of
Wakefield to Mr. Thornhill expresses the spirit that dominated
Oliver Goldsmith's conduct in circumstances that lacked more
or less completely the ideal justification of his dreams.

" 'Mr. Thornhill,' replied I, 'hear me once for all: as to your
marriage with any but my daughter, that I never will consent
to; and though your friendship could raise me to a throne, or
your resentment sink me to the grave, yet would I despise
both.' "[20]

Such a spirit is certainly justified when morality is at stake.
But what too often happens is that one develops a fictitious
sense of moral responsibility when one is merely unwilling to
suffer an affront to vanity.

2. Lack of Preparation for Critical Moments

If reason is going to dominate conduct we must look forward
to the critical moments in our lives and prepare to meet them
with all the energy and insight in our power. This was a
lesson that Oliver Goldsmith never learned.

It appears that when Goldsmith's friends persuaded him to
put an end to his after-college idleness by applying to the bishop
as a candidate for orders, he neglected the preliminary professional studies and perhaps, as we have mentioned, even
appeared before the lord bishop in a pair of scarlet breeches.[21]

Furthermore, even in college, instead of studying and attending lectures he wasted his time and was lowest in the list of
graduates who passed their examinations.[22] Like Samuel

[19] Gibbs, *op. cit.*, vol. 2, pp. 214–15.
[20] *Vicar of Wakefield*, chap. 24.
[21] Forster, *op. cit.*, p. 43.
[22] *Op. cit.*, p. 36.

Johnson at Oxford he avoided lectures when he could, and was a "lounger at the college gate."[23]

He went to Leyden to study medicine and spent nearly a year without an effort to get a degree, and then begged a friend for a little money in order that he might leave the city.[24]

3. Tendency to React to Impractical Dreams

Adler has pointed out that there are likely to be in every individual two plans of life, one by which it is practically possible to earn one's daily bread and another which is possible of realization only in dreams and which usually lands the dreamer in a quagmire of difficulties and troubles if he is ever foolhardy enough to carry it out.

Before the mind of Goldsmith there hovered continually a floating vision of America. Several times he attempted, but without any practical preparations, to attain to this Mecca of his dreams,[25] but in vain. This love of foreign lands finally enticed him to leave Edinburgh for Leyden under the pretence of continuing his medical studies, which, however, were not continued.

The vicar of Wakefield is Goldsmith's father and his wandering son George is no other than Oliver himself. In George's account of his travels there are many items of true autobiography. We see in these travels no sign of a rational preparation for a future life work but a mere living out of the same wandering impulse which takes many of our present day constitutional psychopaths of the United States to Florida, Canada, and California.

Quite characteristic of this tendency to react to impractical dreams is an incident related by Dr. Farr, one of his fellow students at Oxford.

"In this visit I remember him relating a strange Quixotic

[23] Forster, *op. cit.*, p. 77.
[24] Forster, *op. cit.*, p. 58.
[25] *Op. cit.*, pp. 44–45.

scheme he had in contemplation of going to decipher the inscriptions of the *written monuments*, though he was altogether ignorant of Arabic, or the language in which they might be supposed to be written."[26]

And just as characteristic is George's account in the *Vicar of Wakefield* of how he hoped to support himself on arriving in Amsterdam—so characteristic indeed that we may well suppose that behind the external coloring there is some kind of *fundamentum in re*.

"As I was going out with that resolution I was met at the door by the captain of a ship, with whom I had formerly some little acquaintance, and he agreed to be my companion over a bowl of punch. As I never chose to make a secret of my circumstances, he assured me that I was upon the very point of ruin in listening to the office-keeper's promises; for that he only designed to sell me to the plantations. But, continued he, I fancy you might by a much shorter voyage be very easily put into a genteel way of bread. Take my advice. My ship sails tomorrow for Amsterdam. What if you go in her as a passenger? The moment you land, all you have to do is to teach the Dutchmen English, and I'll warrant you'll get pupils and money enough. I suppose you understand English, added he, by this time, or the deuce is in it. I confidently assured him of that; but expressed a doubt whether the Dutch would be willing to learn English. He affirmed with an oath that they were fond of it to distraction; and upon that affirmation I agreed with his proposal, and embarked the next day to teach the Dutch English in Holland. The wind was fair, our voyage short, and after having paid my passage with half my movables, I found myself as fallen from the skies a stranger in one of the principal streets of Amsterdam. In this situation I was unwilling to let any time pass unemployed in teaching. I addressed myself therefore to two or three of those I met, whose appearance seemed most promising; but it was impossible to

[26] Forster, *op. cit.*, p. 81, quoting Percy, *Memoir*, pp. 39-40.

make ourselves mutually understood. It was not until this very moment I recollected, that in order to teach Dutchmen English, it was necessary that they should first teach me Dutch. How I came to overlook so obvious an objection is to me amazing; but certain it is I overlooked it."[27]

4. Lack of Appreciation of Personal Responsibility

Intimately associated with the desire to live out impractical dreams is the lack of due appreciation of personal responsibility.

This is well exemplified in an incident which terminated in the closing of one of the several excellent opportunities which as a young man had been offered to him to establish himself in the world.

"His Uncle Contarine gave him the sum of fifty pounds to travel to Dublin and London and commence the study of law, but a Roscommon friend laid hold of him in Dublin, seduced him to play, and the fifty pounds he would have raised to a hundred, he reduced to fifty pence. In bitter shame, after great physical suffering, he wrote to his uncle, confessed, and was forgiven."[28]

Oliver Goldsmith was no moron. His writings show that he was at least a man of average intellectual ability. But in some way he never learned the lesson: Pause and consider before important actions. He showed more than once in his life that he was particularly lacking in the realization of his personal financial responsibility. All this is quite characteristic of what is termed the constitutional psychopath; but there is reason to believe that the peculiar state of these psychopaths is not entirely hereditary but to a large degree dependent on certain habits and ideals that develop, and others that fail to develop, in childhood.

Had it not been for this same lack of realizing the consequences of his actions, Oliver Goldsmith might perhaps have been

---

[27] *Vicar of Wakefield*, chap. 20.
[28] Forster, *op. cit.*, p. 47.

numbered among American poets and authors. He had actually paid for his passage to America, but the ship could not sail on account of unfavorable weather. So Oliver went wandering in the country region about the seaport. While he was gone there came a favorable wind and the captain set sail without him. So Oliver was left in Cork and finally returned home with no money in his pocket, riding a thin and bony horse to which he had given the appropriate name of Fiddleback.[29]

With all this there were two redeeming traits, an optimistic attitude that nothing could conquer, and unremitting practice at the art of writing. The first is well exemplified in the words he put in the mouth of George, the wandering son of the vicar of Wakefield.

"The first misfortune of my life, which you all know, was great, but though it distressed, it could not sink me. No person ever had a better knack at hoping than I. The less kind I found Fortune one time, the more I expected from her another, and being now at the bottom of her wheel, every new revolution might lift, but could not depress me."[30]

This optimism was probably derived from instruction and examples received in childhood from his father. The vicar of Wakefield probably mirrors with fair correctness the character of his father. When the simple-hearted vicar had lost his money and been put out of his comfortable home he remarked of his new quarters: "Though the same room served us for parlour and kitchen that only made it the warmer.[31]. . . In this manner we began to find that every situation in life may bring its own peculiar pleasures: every morning waked us to a repetition of toil; but the evening repaid it with vacant hilarity."[32]

His unremitting toil at the art of writing made possible the turn of the tide of fortune in his favor. The year 1764, when

[29] Forster, *op. cit.*, pp. 44–45.
[30] *Vicar of Wakefield*, chap. 20.
[31] *Ibid.*, chap. 4.
[32] *Ibid.*, chap. 5.

Goldsmith was 36 years old, seems to have been the darkest of his life. Along with various other troubles he was unable to pay his rent and his landlady had him arrested for debt. From his prison he sent an urgent message to Johnson, who visited him, talked the situation over with him, and found out that he had just completed a novel. Johnson looked over the manuscript, took it to a printer, sold it for sixty pounds, and gave the money to Goldsmith. This novel was the *Vicar of Wakefield*. In the latter part of the same year he published his poem *The Traveller*. Largely owing to Johnson, this poem was an immediate success. The publication of the *Vicar of Wakefield*, which soon followed, at once made Dr. Goldsmith famous and secured him a permanent place in the history of English literature.

The closing words of the *Good-Natured Man* are perhaps Goldsmith's criticism of his own self. "Yes, Sir, I now too plainly perceive my errors: my vanity, in attempting to please all by fearing to offend any: my meanness in approving folly, lest fools should disapprove. Henceforth, therefore, it shall be my study to reserve my pity for real distress; my friendship for true merit; and my love for her who first taught me what it is to be happy."[33]

The unhappy days of Oliver Goldsmith are an example of results that flow from a lack of guidance and control in emotional life. He need never have suffered for so many years the pinch of extreme poverty. His life might have flowed on in peace and comfort and his help to the poor and unfortunate have become vastly greater than many times the sum total of all the many acts of generosity that were unguided and unchecked by the dictates of reason.

No life can develop normally except under the guidance of reason. No power of reason and understanding can guide and direct without a goal. But this goal will never be attained, even though it may have been clearly seen, unless emotional drives are submitted to rational control.

[33] Gibbs, *op. cit.*, vol. 2, p. 213.

Oliver Goldsmith entered life without a goal.   For some reason he failed to acquire a power of emotional control that would have rendered possible the utilization of various opportunities that opened to him the door of progress and success.

Let those who have to do with the training of the young develop in them a rational view of life.   Let them help to outline an object and a purpose in living which will make life worth while when finally it has been lived out.   Let them teach by precept and example the nobility and the fruitfulness of a life in which the emotions are in all things subject to reason, and reason to the law of God.

Chapter VIII

THE PLAY OF INTELLECT AND EMOTION IN THE PROBLEMS OF LIFE[1]

IN ORDER to have an insight into the relation which exists between emotion and intellect we must naturally understand in a rough sort of way at least the two terms of the relationship, namely, intellect and emotion.

In order to do this in as concrete a manner as possible, I am going to mention an incident of my own experience which was accompanied by considerable emotional resonance. When I was on the transport on my way to France in September, 1918, the influenza broke out on board ship and the ship's bay being crowded with sick, the officers were put to bed on deck. We were approaching Brest. On the day I went to bed with the influenza the officers were warned that we were nearing the danger zone, and a vessel had only recently been torpedoed in the region we were about to traverse. I remember asking a fellow officer to inquire for me whether or not in case of accident the sick were supposed to go to their formerly assigned boat stations, or whether special provision would be made for them in boats. For, since there were from three to four thousand men on board, it was impossible for all to get in boats, and the provision that had been made was that we were to go to our assigned places when the signal called us to our stations; and here ropes were provided and we were expected to go down these hand over fist and drop into the sea, and then, sustained by our life preservers, swim to large floating rings, euphemistically termed rafts, and hold on to rope loops until, in case events should take a favorable turn, we might be picked up by some friendly craft. My friend did not return and I concluded that no special provision could be made for the sick, and

---

[1] This study was first published in *The Healthy Mind* (ed. by Henry Byron Elkind) New York: Greenberg, 1929, pp. 105–41.

that, strong or weak, one would have to climb down those dangling ropes and treat his fever by a prolonged course of hydrotherapy in the chilly waters of the Atlantic Ocean. I remember feeling that it would be utterly impossible to attempt the climb, and making vain efforts to sleep in spite of the many peculiar sensations that accompany the onset of the "grippe." It was a cold foggy night, broken now and then by moments of bright moonlight. At half past twelve the "Finland," the boat on which we were making our way to France, blew her fog horn—a long piercing blast. Such a thing had never happened at night time before. For we steamed on as silently as possible and even the interior of the ship was kept in almost complete darkness. I sat up in bed. In a moment there was another piercing blast, and in the next instant an awful and terrible crash. Immediately the gong was sounded that called all to their boat stations. Never did anything in my life go through me like that crashing sound. With it came the flashing realization, "The Germans have got us"—accompanied by a turmoil of memories of all I had read of torpedoed and sinking ships, and beneath it all a certain sense of dismay that the many things I would like to do in life might now be left undone. In a moment I was on my feet and threw my life preserver about me. All weakness and sense of illness were gone. Scrambling down those ropes seemed the merest child's play. I could have climbed down the Washington monument. Fortunately I did not have to scramble. We had not been torpedoed, but had collided with another ship in the convoy, and though the iron plates in our bow were bent in, the front water compartments held, and after rolling about in the sea for thirty-five minutes, we began slowly to move ahead and then picked up full steam and caught up with the rest of the convoy.

The purpose in recounting this incident is to point out the intellectual element in emotional experience. In humans, emotion involves mental activity. Animals possibly have a general sensory appreciation of a situation. An emotion is a reaction to our insight into the meaning of a situation. It cannot be explained by a mere appeal to the senses. A luscious strawberry covered with powdered sugar will not only give one a sensation of deliciously flavored sweetness, but also an affective experience of satisfaction. A sensory stimulus followed by an affective reaction seems entirely adequate to explain simple experiences of this nature. But this simple affective reaction to a sensory stimulus is not what is meant by an emotion. Could the experience of those on board the "Finland" on that September night in 1918 be adequately explained as a reaction to a very loud sound? It was not the sound alone that conditioned our behavior, but an intellectual appreciation of the whole situation— our knowledge that we were crossing the ocean on an army transport in time of war, our memory of the warning only just given that we were entering the danger zone, crowded recollections of the many accounts we had read of torpedoed ships and collisions at sea, the sense of impending death that has no sensory stimulus, our hopes for the future and images of the past. The emotion was the reaction to the total experience, which was initiated, indeed, by a sensory stimulus, but which broadened out into vistas of insight to which our senses, as such, are blind and which intellect alone can appreciate. It is interesting to note that Beulah Morrison in the University of California Studies in Psychology[2] has pointed out that in the feebleminded, the emotions become more and more shallow the deeper the degree of mental defect. This is only what we should expect if emotions are reactions to intellectual insights, for the weaker the power of mental vision, the less the effect it has on emotional life.

Having glanced for a moment at the emotional experience and perceived that it involves an intellectual element, let us turn now to the process of reasoning which we shall find in its turn profoundly affected, sometimes at least, by emotional

[2] Beulah May Morrison, "A Study of the Major Emotions in Persons of Defective Intelligence," Univ. California Pub. Psychol. **3**: 3 (Dec. 30), 1924.

factors. To bring out the nature of the reasoning process, consider for a moment the following problem.

Stoffer attacked Webb on the street with the intent to murder him with a knife. But Webb's friends came upon the scene and Stoffer fled, followed by Webb and his friends throwing stones and crying, "Kill him!" Stoffer took refuge in the house of a stranger and locked the door. Webb and his friends forced the door and assaulted Stoffer. In the conflict which immediately ensued, Webb was killed by Stoffer. Is Stoffer guilty of murder?[3]

When asked to solve this problem some people will say Stoffer is not guilty of murder. When asked why, they will say, "He killed Webb in self defense." But the two propositions—He killed Webb in self defense and he is not guilty of murder—do not make a complete argument. Something else is implied but not expressed, viz., the major premise: If anyone kills a person in self defense, he is not guilty of murder. It was found by Miriam Dunn in her study of the psychology of reasoning that the principle which determines the whole process, the major premise, is subconscious in 25 per cent of the cases.[4] Reasoning about a problem is possible because there is stored in the mind a considerable stock of principles which govern the cases and problems ordinarily met with in an individual's experience. These principles even in normal reasoning frequently remain below the level of focal consciousness. Individuals vary in their ability to crystallize and formulate the principles that govern their conclusions; but they often conclude with perfect correctness, even though they can only say that their conclusion is valid "because," and then can delve no further into the logical depths of the mind.

But there is a pathological type of reasoning which is profoundly influenced by emotional life, and it is this with which

[3] Miriam Frances Dunn, *The Psychology of Reasoning*, Stud. Psychol. & Psychiat. 1: 62, 1926.

[4] *Op. cit.*, p. 132.

we are particularly concerned at the present. Reasoning and conduct that flows from it is pathological because

1) The mind harbors a number of false principles. Granting the principles, the conclusions flow with absolute necessity, and the patient cannot be made to see that there is any error in his thinking;

2) The principles are fixed in the mind because of their emotional resonance and the fact that they are essential to the system of desires that has been woven into the very fabric of mental life;

3) The principles are suppressed into the unconscious because, if viewed by focal consciousness, they would reveal the unworthiness of one's conduct; and no one is naturally desirous of seeing himself and his conduct in a true light if the details that are revealed are not compatible with a high estimation of himself.

Personal convictions and conduct are, therefore, profoundly influenced by subconscious principles and this is possible because in normal reasoning it is not necessary to formulate the major clearly in consciousness and express it in clear-cut and definite words.

An actual case will exemplify my meaning more than further analysis of the problem in general terms. I shall start with the emotion of and craving for sympathy.

The capacity for sympathy is one of the most important elements in our emotional nature. According to Adam Smith, sympathy is the foundation of morality. Experimental research shows[5] that it is closely correlated with will and if so, though we might not agree with Adam Smith, we could at least admit that the power of feeling sympathy is an important psychological factor in the development of good moral conduct. If the power to sympathize with others is so important a factor in the higher mental life, it is not surprising that it should be,

[5] Sister Rosa McDonough, *The Empirical Analysis of Character*, Stud. Psychol. & Psychiat., vol. 2, nos. 3 and 4, 1929.

on many occasions, the dominating factor in human behavior. I might give many examples of how this craving for sympathy leads to various types of abnormal behavior.[6] But for the present we are only interested in the association of this emotional factor with our intellectual operations. We shall therefore try to see how the craving to have others feel with us and take our part is at times the dominating factor in certain pathological types of behavior.

Even in a pathology of the intellect the mind operates in syllogisms, or at all events, its procedure is capable of syllogistic analysis. Here, even as in normal reasoning, the premise that comes to the focus point of consciousness is the minor.

In these cases the minor is, as always, the mere expression of a fact which is in itself usually harmless.

Let us take for instance this situation: A middle-aged gentleman and his wife had in charity given a temporary home to a woman of their acquaintance who had presumed upon their kindness and hospitality and decided to make their abode her permanent home. The gentleman and his wife were of the kindly, gentle, retiring type, who abhor quarrels and would yield their rights and put up with all manner of discomfort rather than to have to fight for them with noisy words and drastic actions. Repeated suggestions to their parasitic acquaintance were apparently not understood. Finally the gentleman had a quiet talk with her and made matters quite clear, only to be told that she could not possibly go elsewhere, and her tears and talk about being put out of her "home" and made to sleep in the gutters sent him from her room in utter confusion. As the situation became more and more intolerable, the wife commenced to be more and more insistent with her husband that it was his duty as a man to protect her, and rid their home of the undesirable visitor. But every interview resulted only in tears and talk, and he retired from the encounter with mingled feelings of indignation and confusion.

[6] Moore, *Dynamic Psychology*, pp. 238 ff.

There was no hope but to call the police, but that seemed altogether too horrid even to be considered by a gentleman of his high culture. As the outlook became more and more gloomy and hopeless the wife developed fainting spells and convulsive seizures that the family physician was unable to control. At this period the case came under my notice, and having learned the details, it seemed to me quite clear that the convulsive seizures were psychogenic and of a hysterical rather than of an epileptic nature. They were appeals for sympathy and said to her husband more vigorously and insistently than the most unbridled and uncouth language could say, "See what you have gone and done to me, you and this unreasonable woman, whom you brought into my home. You have ruined my life and undermined my health. It is you and your unmanly conduct that have thrown me into this condition, which makes me again and again fall unconscious at your feet."

A simple suggestion in this case sufficed to cure the seizures and spare the poor man the effort of a final open and decisive conflict with his unwelcome guest, for which he had been unable to muster the necessary courage. The lease on their house was expiring. So one fine morning they went to a hotel and sent a storage company to move the furniture from the home and store it for the summer. The wife had no more fainting spells nor convulsive seizures during the summer, nor did these return when in the autumn they moved back into another house and started housekeeping, undisturbed by the presence of their unwelcome guest.

Let us now investigate the logical process which lies at the basis of this conduct.

The minor in this case is the evident fact: I am unjustly treated. But a minor premise is inactive and leads to no conclusion, no course of action, unless it is subsumed under a major premise. The major premise and its argument in this case can be formulated in this wise: If I am unjustly treated my husband must be made to realize it.

But I am unjustly treated. Therefore, my husband must be made to realize it so that he will really feel for me in my unhappy plight.

The conclusion is clear; on the other hand, how is the "must" to be changed from a mere logical to an ontological necessity? Talking had not brought about the desired result and there was no hope for any alleviation in this way in the future. There was no dignified, reasonable mode of action left to the wife but to take matters into her own hands, expel the woman herself. But this was just as impossible to her as it had been to her husband. The tendency in such a dilemma is to give a *demonstratio ad oculos* of the minor: See how unjustly I am treated, behold what you have gone and done to me. The particular form that this demonstration is going to take depends on the make-up of the individual. The hysterical temperament is likely to develop convulsive seizures. And this is what happened in the present case. That they were conditioned by the circumstances and not by some obscure organic disorder is rendered likely but not absolutely demonstrated by the fact that removal from the impossible situation caused a sudden and permanent cessation of the seizures.

Sometimes the craving for the sympathy and attention of others concerns itself not with a particular person, for example the husband, as in this instance, but is perfectly general, the particular form of display being manifested before anybody and everybody.

I remember a soldier who was under my care when I was stationed at Plattsburg during the war. He had convulsive seizures that I witnessed several times. I felt sure they could not be of an epileptic nature. Thus when I approached him when he was having one of these seizures on the floor, his fists clenched and several well-directed blows which I had considerable difficulty in dodging were aimed at my toes. He would sometimes wander towards the summer school at Cliff Haven and on seeing a group of young ladies would fall in a convulsive seizure. I understood that on one occasion they gathered about him and one was heard to exclaim: "The poor shell-shocked soldier!" This whetted his appetite and his seizures multiplied. One day he was having a convulsion on the hospital porch and quite a crowd of soldiers had gathered about him. I happened to pass and told them to go along and leave that man alone. As I entered the building just a little behind him I stopped a moment and looked back. He sat up, looked about. Seeing no one, he got up and quietly walked away as if nothing had happened.

The logical background of this behavior can be expressed in the following manner:

All the world must know and sympathize when I am persecuted.

But this action is a piece of persecution.

Therefore all the world must know and sympathize.

If the world must know, I must reveal it or it will remain unknown.

But the world must know.

Therefore I must reveal it.

In this little sorites the part present focally in consciousness is the proposition in italics: *This action is a piece of persecution.* It is this that the patient is continually turning over in his mind. The rest is experienced but does not come to the focus point of consciousness. It is deducible, however, from the behavior of the patient.

Leaving the pathology of sympathy, let us turn next to the logical mechanism in other forms of affective disorder.

Among the affective elements most commonly subject to pathological manifestations is the feeling of self-complacency. Adults are often as sensitive to the least injury to their feelings as a spoiled child to the most trivial bodily pain. This is carried to such an extent that the consciousness of personal irreproachable goodness becomes a blind conviction. As a consequence blame is never accepted, no matter how patent may be one's own folly and neglect, but the burden of responsibility is always shifted to the shoulders of someone else. In the more advanced states of mental disorder no alternative is too bizarre or even too impossible to be readily adopted in preference to the more evident possibility that the patient himself may have made a mistake or that his conduct is not absolutely irreproachable. Thus a patient feels sexual excitement, and attributes it to the malign influence of a hypnotizer in the next room, for he feels that such a thing would be incompatible with his own purity of mind; or, when auditory images of obscene and profane words arise, the patient feels perfectly sure that these could not originate in his own mind, but must be due to malevolent individuals putting bad words into his head. "It is really surprising," he tells you, "what these people will do with your mind. In fact, that fellow upstairs is using my brain so much that I don't have any chance to make use of it myself."

The logical mechanism that underlies this defense of the feeling of self-complacency may be expressed as follows:

If I am good, anything wicked in me must be due to something else besides myself.

But I am good.

Therefore what appears in me to be wicked must be due to something else besides myself.

"The king can do no wrong, and I am the king," expresses succinctly the attitude of many people.

Don't think that this is a rare disease; it is one of the most common of failings. Have you ever deep down in your heart blamed anything on someone else when you yourself were responsible? Have you ever said to yourself, "If it had not been for X and Y and Z my undertaking would have been successful?"

In the long run it will pay us to shoulder responsibility and take the blame for our own actions and say willingly, "It's really my fault; blame me." This is after all good mental hygiene, for if we develop the habit of surrounding our sense of self-complacency with a system of defense reactions that make it impossible for our vanity ever to receive a wound, our egoism will swell beyond limits till finally like a cancerous growth it will eat into and destroy reason and common sense. This is precisely what happens and leads not only to the explaining away of all our personal deficiencies but also to building castles in the air and eventually holding with absolute assurance to the objective validity of our dreams.

Once I was conducting the mental examination of a young fellow by the name of Edwardson.[7] After revealing to me various delusions and hallucinations he became more confidential and told me that he had learned to understand the language of the birds.

"Well," said I, "what is it the birds are saying?"

"Why, they are giving me an important message."

"Would you mind letting me know the nature of the message?"

After a moment's hesitation he said, "They inform me that I am the true and lawful heir to the throne of England."

"But how can you be the true and lawful heir to the throne of England?"

"Well, it is just this way. Some time ago, I don't know at just what period of English history, there was a king whose name was Edward. And my name is 'Edward's son.' I am therefore the son of the king of England and the lawful heir to the throne."

"But there are other people in this world called Edwardson—how is it that among all the Edwardsons you are at this day the lawful heir to the throne of England?"

"The matter is perfectly clear," he replied, "It is an absolutely fixed law of inheritance that it is always transmitted to the eldest son of the family. My father was the eldest son of the family and I am his heir."

[7] For a further discussion of the disorders of reasoning see T. V. Moore, *Cognitive Psychology*, Philadelphia: Lippincott, 1939, pp. 389 ff.

Though he was able to see through various less evident fallacies, as I found by actual experiment, this most glaringly fallacious argument fettered the patient's mind. Why? Because it had an emotional value to his personality. It was connected with certain daydreams of childhood; it developed with his ever growing egoism until it became essential to his self ideal and could no longer be dissipated by an appeal to common sense. Beware, therefore, how you indulge in daydreams and vain imaginings, and shrink from seeing yourself as others see you, or some fine day you may discover that you have learned to understand what the birds are saying.

Let us now pass to a type of pathological reasoning that is so close to normal that it does not seem to be a disease process at all. I refer to what might be termed "praiseworthy excuses." A few examples will make clear the mechanism to which I refer.

A young man agreed with a firm to give his services for a short period with the understanding that in view of the training he had received he would remain indefinitely when the stipulated period was over. When it came to the point of making the contract for the longer period he pointed out certain possibilities which might arise in the future. He was assured that these things were unlikely to happen; but he replied that he felt it a high moral duty not to make a contract which later on he might find difficult or impossible to fulfil. This, however, was only a "praiseworthy excuse." As a matter of fact other possibilities had opened out before him that had very strong attractions and he wanted to be free from all obligation to the firm that had made it possible for him to take the new opportunity.

An example of a "praiseworthy excuse" is to be found in the conduct of Judas. Judas complained of the waste of precious ointment, saying: "Why was not this ointment sold for three hundred pence, and given to the poor? Now he said this, not because he cared for the poor, but because he was a thief, and

having the purse, carried the things that were put therein"
(cf. St. John 12:5–6.)

You have only to look into your own experience perhaps to
find occasions when in little things you also have manifested
the Judas reaction, for it is a very common human failing.   A
young nurse in training makes up her mind at the beginning of
Lent to give up candy.   During the second week she is presented with a box of her favorite bonbons, which is carefully
locked up on account of her good resolution.   But before long
she commences to realize that the weather is cold and raw.
Her throat feels inflamed.   Surely she must do something to
prevent tonsillitis.   A demulcent would surely be helpful and
what better demulcent could there be than one of those delicious bonbons that are only getting stale while they are stored
away in her locker.   The matter seems perfectly clear to her
mind and she feels justified in reconsidering matters and at once
proceeds to make an exception to her resolution.

By the same mechanism the toper quotes St. Paul, and
in spite of promises that he has sworn most faithfully to keep,
proceeds to take a little wine for his stomach's sake.

See how innocent the Judas reaction appears in its little
beginnings.   But it can become malignant and open the way
to the most flagrant violation of sacred duties, while all along
the violator feels that his conscience is not tainted by any crime
and that he is actuated by the most praiseworthy motives of
conduct.

The logical mechanism of the Judas reaction may be expressed as follows:

If anything I want to do is based on noble motives, I not
only can but should do it.

But the course of action I am now considering is based on
noble motives of action.

Therefore I not only can but should do it.

The major of this conditional syllogism is derived from
moral and religious education.   As a general principle it is

unimpeachable. It is in the demonstration of the minor to one's own personal satisfaction that the fallacy slips in. Here one's emotional and affective life makes it possible for one to see only what harmonizes with one's established system of desires and contrariwise inhibits the appearance of considerations that would reveal the true nature of the proceeding, namely, an attempt to make conduct that is more or less seriously immoral appear in the light of conscientious fidelity to the highest spiritual principles.

So far I have written more of the pathology of emotion and intellect than of the positive normal value of the affective states in cognitive experience. But it must not be supposed that emotions are always detrimental factors in human behavior, or at most negligible quantities as far as actual accomplishment is concerned.

It is to our emotions that we owe the joy of living that is ever overflowing into the enthusiasm of accomplishment. Without ideals that are not only understood but also loved, it would scarcely be possible to overcome the obstacles that ordinarily stand in the way of success, or to bear the burdens that life must necessarily impose.

Consequently, though emotions may have a pathological influence on our intellectual life in various ways, the lack of emotional resonance is itself a disease of the mind. It is unfortunately a rather common malady among those who commence life as pure amusement and pleasure seekers. Such persons pass through a period of intense enjoyment of life's exciting pleasures at a time when hard labor should be laying the foundations of a future wholesome activity that would not only be productive of works beneficial to society, but also bring to the toiler stable mental peace and perennial happiness. When a human being fails to develop high ideals of his function in life or when he reacts to his own disregard of the principles of conduct by yielding to depression, by the avoidance of responsibility, by doubt and disbelief in the meaning of life, and by ceasing all serious effort, his sense of values is deadened and nothing makes any appeal. Projects and plans which once aroused vistas of numerous possibilities no longer awaken even a passing interest. And unless something is done to arouse new interests and stir the individual to visualize a new goal he is likely to sink into the emotional indifference of the schizophrenic.

Shelley has described with vivid expressiveness the first stage of this malady, when all things commence to lose their interest and joy departs while only grief remains.

> O world! O life! O time!
> On whose last steps I climb,
> Trembling at that where I had stood before;
> When will return the glory of your prime?
> No more—O, never more!
>
> Out of the day and night
> A joy has taken flight;
> Fresh spring and summer, and winter hoar,
> Move my faint heart with grief, but with delight
> No more—O, never more!

In a poem written about a year earlier he expresses the same idea but seems to be describing a step further along the path to emotional indifference.

> First our pleasures die—and then
> Our hopes, and then our fears—and when
> These are dead, the debt is due,
> Dust claims dust—and we die too.
>
> All things that we love and cherish
> Like ourselves must fade and perish,
> Such is our rude mortal lot,
> Love itself would, did they not.

Now all of this is good poetry and an excellent description of a pathological state but if it is maintained that emotional death is the normal terminus of human existence, it is misleading in the extreme and very bad psychology.

Intellectual labor and the joy of accomplishment can remain to the very end, if life is not wasted in the bewitching of trifling but consecrated by toil and hardship to the realization of eternal ideals.

Cuthbert's letter on the death of the Venerable Bede gives us precisely such a picture of labor to the very end, with the delights of pure emotion neither faded nor perished even as the eyes were closing in the sleep of death.

It seems that the Venerable Bede suffered a heart attack about two weeks before Easter, 735. (*Gravatus quidem est infirmitate maxima creberrimi anhelitus, sine dolore tamen.*) Nevertheless, joyful and happy, he continued to be present at the canonical hours and kept up his daily work in the classroom until the vigil of the Ascension. On the feast of the Ascension he was busily engaged dictating to a scribe his translation of St. John into the Saxon language of the people. The ancient letter of his disciple Cuthbert calls particular attention to the joy with which he worked in spite of his shortness of breath and the dropsy which was creeping over him. Before the hour of None the boy, who was writing for him, said to him, "Dearest Master, one chapter is still wanting, does it worry you too much for me to question you further?"

But Bede answered, "It is easy, take your pen and set to work and write quickly."

The work must have been done at intervals for at the time of Vespers the boy said to him, "There is still one sentence, dear Master, which is not finished."

And he answered, "Write quickly."

After a moment the boy said, "Now the sentence is finished."

And Bede replied, "Well hast thou said that it is finished. Lift my head with your hands, for it is a great delight for me to be opposite to my little oratory in which I was wont to pray, so that sitting I may call upon my Father."

And so lying upon the floor of his cell he sang the "Glory to the Father and to the Son and to the Holy Ghost"; and when he pronounced the name of the Holy Spirit he breathed the last breath from his body and so passed to the heavenly kingdom.[8]

Many cases might be cited of productive effort throughout the space of a normal human life or on up to ripe old age, accompanied by undiminished joy in living and an inexhaustible enthusiasm of accomplishment. Emotional death is a disease, not the necessary terminus of mental life. Loss of interest, mental exhaustion, intellectual torpor, the sense of hopelessless in all forms of activity, abiding discontent, cynicism, hatred, disdainful contempt for the feeble productions of others, sadness, and despair of ever being successful, are all pathological symptoms. They should arouse us to the seriousness of our mental state and stimulate effort to bring about a cure just as much as a hemorrhage from the lungs would make a tubercular patient realize that it is high time for him to do something about his physical condition.

Let us now cast a glance back on the type of mental mechanism we have examined, in which the intellectual and affective life are inextricably interwoven.

There seems to be a common factor involved in all. Why does the mind cling to the pathological major that all the world must know and sympathize when it is persecuted? Why, unless the ego sets a wholly unbalanced and biased value upon the self, exaggerating the importance of self and seeking to place the self in a center of interest and esteem for all?

Why does the mind build up the conviction of personal excellence to such an extent that truth and justice are blinded and it can no longer see its own defects and be conscious of its own guilt? Why, unless the ego persists in cherishing an ideal of personal excellence to such a degree that it cannot allow self estimation to be lowered by admitting the presence of guilt or defect of any kind whatsoever?

Why does the mind take such excessive pains to demonstrate to its own personal satisfaction that the questionable line of conduct that it seeks to pursue proceeds from the very noblest

[8] Migne, *Patrologia latina*, vol. 90, cols. 39–41.

motives of action? Why, unless it cherishes with the most scrupulous care an ideal of personal excellence that it cannot relinquish, even when it is determined to seek the satisfaction of desires with which that ideal is essentially incompatible?

Why, finally, does the mind after battling vainly to maintain the self ideal walled up from the approach of self criticism and the honest judgment of plain common sense, finally give way to anxiety, chagrin, anger, disappointment, discontent, disdain, and hatred and sink into the emotional death of intellectual torpor and hopeless indifference? Why, unless the ego has been made the supreme end of life in a conflict that has been carried on by a neurotic drive to "seem" rather than the rational mode of warfare that aims at accomplishment by labor, honest self criticism, and personal sacrifice?

This egoism which is the source of so many ills has its origin in infantile life and is bound to develop in everyone unless early training, friction with reality, and personal endeavor finally eradicate it. We might say that the natural tendency of the untrained or poorly trained personality is to ultimate mental disaster. Fortunately in one way or another the training comes to us. The pedestal that the ego is ever building is broken or we are persuaded to step down and take up a humble task before the structure is raised so high that a fall means irreparable ruin.

In this process of training it is a great help to become aware of the part that the self ideal plays in rooting out of our minds a number of pathological premises that govern thought and conduct from the unconscious, while we remain blissfully ignorant of the true motives of our actions. We can know ourselves if we will, but it means a real sacrifice to attain to an honest evaluation of our own personalities, with their schemes of desires and motives of conduct.

We must learn that nothing real finds its ultimate end in ourselves. Our life must be conceived of as a contribution. The harder we work the more we will contribute.

But to what is this contribution made? To think that we

have added to the possibilities of happiness even in a few lives is helpful. But the sum total of human beings, considered as such, has no real existence. It exists, if at all, only in the individuals who compose it, and of these the ego is one. But there is no absolute reason why one mortal being should be sacrificed for another or for two or three or as many as you will if all are mortal and all sacrifice ends in death beyond which there is nothing more. But if beyond all temporal rewards there are eternal values, if society has a final end, unseen indeed but towards which it is ever advancing through war and pestilence and social conflict, and if this end will not pass with the passing of time, but by that very passing attain its eternal expression, then whatever the individual does in furthering the work of the social order has absolute and eternal value. To realize this even as a possibility brings a new glimmer of hope into the disordered mind. To know it with the assurance of faith plants in the mind principles that dominate conduct and eliminate from the personality the malignant growth of egoism.

The very vastness of this end makes us see our own tiny contribution in the proper light. One grain of sand is bigger than another, but what difference does that make in comparison with the vastness of the continental coast? One should not be grieved, therefore, because he has done only a little, or that others have done so much more, but rather consoled that he has done something and that the little good he has done is a contribution to a work that will never die.

But we shall have nothing to give until we have attained; and we shall never attain until we come down from the pedestal of our vanity and do the humble work that lies before us.

Chapter IX

BALANCED AND UNBALANCED PERSONALITIES AND THEIR SENSE OF VALUES

IT IS sometimes thought that emotional maladjustment is far more common in our own day than it has ever been before, and that owing to this emotional imbalance of individuals the world itself is unbalanced and tottering to its fall.

But it appears, if you interrogate history, that in every age some have been firmly convinced that the world is in a very bad state and that formerly it was in a much better state. The ancient phrase *laudator temporis acti* was often applied to grumbling old men in days of old, and bears witness to the fact that even in the age of ancient Rome there were those who thought that their days were evil, that before them there was a time when the world was really better because men were truly virtuous and the wickedness of the present was unknown.

Boethius in his prison recalled the tradition of the golden age:

> Most happy, indeed, were the days of old
> When men were content with the yield of the faithful fields
> When none were corrupted by idle luxury
> And men satisfied their hunger with what nature herself
>   provided in abundance.

And then he expressed the yearning

> Would that our age would return to the morals of the past.

Was the age of Boethius really worse than the ages that had gone before? Was there ever a golden age of virtue free from the evils to which human nature is prone? And, if so, has man been ever deteriorating in the centuries that have elapsed since Boethius wrote on the consolations of philosophy?

Or have there been great cycles of degeneration and regeneration, and, if so, is society lower now in the moral scale than in the days of our grandparents?

117

No matter what may be the answer to these questions, one thing is certain, and that is this: if the world is balanced or unbalanced, it is one or the other only because the mental life of the individuals who constitute it is normal or abnormal. There is no mental life apart from the minds of individuals.

When, therefore, we wish to discuss the problem of balancing the mental life of an unbalanced world, the direct approach is through the mind of the individual. What constitutes mental imbalance and how is normal mental equilibrium to be maintained? This, after all, is a very practical problem. We may rightfully regard the problem of balancing an unbalanced world as far beyond any one of us. But how can each of us balance his own mind? That is the great problem.

Let us commence with the presentation of a case that modern psychiatry would probably designate by the term psychopathic personality. The term psychopathic personality is so very broad and vague in its connotation that no one may look upon it as essentially an insult should he hear some fine day that it had been applied to himself. In fact, should anyone be conscious of the fact that he often has disagreements with others and find that he has more or less difficulty in getting along with other people, he can conclude that some psychiatrist could easily be found who would diagnose him as a psychopathic personality. To proceed now with the presentation of our case. There enters a gentleman somewhat beyond middle life, but perfectly healthy and of rather robust physique. On looking more closely we see that he is not what Kretschmer would select as a perfect type of the pycnotic constitution. The fingers for instance are not stubby, but taper markedly, and the whole physique resembles what those familiar with physical build would term the hypopituitary rather than the pycnotic type.

Some time ago I had a long conversation with this gentleman, who was leading a rather solitary life. Various things made me suspect that he was a person with a paranoid trend.

Though usually sour and silent he became rather talkative on this occasion and told me about his career as a musician.

When a young boy he wanted to learn to play the pipe organ but instead was forced by his parents to take up the violin. "I did so," he said, "because, as you know, I can be obedient. But I made up my mind then, that as soon as I was free I would put that violin aside and never touch it again." He had talent and learned to play. From time to time he would, however, do a little practicing on the pipe organ. He became very proficient and was the first violinist in an orchestra that had sixty violins. "I," he said with a tone of boastfulness, "I was the leader of them all." Finally circumstances changed, he did not tell me how, and he was free to do as he chose. So he gave up his musical career. A great friend of his asked him as a special favor to play once more for him. He consented with the proviso that a suitable accompanist be found. An accompanist was secured and for an hour he entertained his friend with pieces that only the most skilled would be able to execute. "I then laid aside my violin, a genuine Stradivarius, which I eventually gave away. I remembered the resolution I made when they would not let me learn the organ and for twenty-six years I have never touched a violin."

This throwing away of a valuable acquisition that took years to develop, out of a sense which seems to have an element of spite, and in order to be consistent with a childish resolution that unduly persisted in memory, reveals to us traits that are often found in the paranoid character.

It exaggerates minor ills. The child or young man thought himself injured because he was not allowed to have his own way and choose his own instrument.

It nurses the memory of past injuries and never allows them, however trivial they may be, to fade into oblivion. After a brilliant career as a successful musician this man kept his spite and resentfulness still glowing so that it finally dominated his conduct.

The paranoid character is not appealed to by a sense of values but seeks to satisfy the drive to say "I won't" and carry this resolution into effect after it has been blocked for years. This man lays the wonderful Stradivarius in its box and allows the habits developed by years of practice slowly to disintegrate so that now he no longer possesses the wonderful instrument or the ability to play it, but chuckles vaingloriously to himself as he tells how he finally said "I won't"; and for twenty-six years no one had ever been able to persuade him to yield and say "I will." Such a triumph is no evidence of noble strength of will but merely an example of the subjection of a human being to the blind and unreasonable instinct of stubbornness.

A few other points in his behavior may enable you to get a more complete picture of his mental make-up. He is very precise in his habits, winds his watch every day at exactly 6:15 a.m. Certain doors must be opened and closed in his house at certain times. Everything on his desk is in perfect order and seems to have a special definitely limited space in which it is placed. He seems to be selfish in that the comfort of others is a trivial matter compared to the sanctity of his regimen. He is not a lover of animals. He went to get his gun to shoot a dog that was barking, but desisted when he found he had left his "shells" in the garage.

He seems to be very prompt in what he has to do, appearing for his appointments exactly on time. He is essentially "old-timey" and decries such modern things as automobiles and radios.

Let us now try to discover the fundamental difficulty in our violinist's condition and deduce from it whatever principles of mental hygiene we may.

The pathological element that at once attracts our attention is the ease with which an accomplishment of great value was thrown away. And when we ask why, we see that the difficulty is essentially one of impulsive life—a blind, unreasonable drive to have one's own way in spite of all. It is essentially egoism and selfishness. There is no marked emotional upset, no evidence of the presence of delusions, but a strong drive to seek his own way without regard to consequences.

Besides laying aside his violin, he surrounded himself by a ritual and regimen which enabled him to live as he wanted without any disturbance from outside influences.

Let us not be surprised at the extreme to which the old musician has gone. We differ from him only in degree. There is no human being who does not want his own way and few who do not scruple to make other people unhappy in order to have things done the way they want.

What are we going to do about it? How are we going to prevent the development of these psychopathic personalities? Naturally the place to start is with the child. Most psychopathic persons were once undisciplined children. But most of us are no longer children. How are we going to deal with adults so as to prevent them from continuing on paths that are bound to terminate in a hopeless psychopathic condition?

Of this we can be sure: we can scarcely hope to reason with, or in any way improve, a case such as I have presented unless the patient is his own therapist and deeply interested in effecting a cure before the malady progresses to its final stages. Adults cannot be helped by others unless they want to be, and even then it is a difficult task.

If now we wish to prevent psychopathic conditions similar to the one we have depicted from arising in ourselves, we must in the first place become sensitive to our own selfishness and the inconvenience it causes others when we insist on having things our way. There are often several ways of attaining the same end. Suppose it occurs to one member in the family that one of these ways would be desirable. No one should be surprised if he insists upon his way and some one else insists upon another way. But if *you* are insisting, try to realize that you do so at your mental peril, to say nothing of the danger to the happiness of the family. Try to realize that the matter of dispute is not so important after all, that what seems to you to be plain common sense is merely a mask for your own selfishness. And it is a very important thing for you to be conscious of your selfishness and the way it affects others.

After having become conscious of your selfishness you must seek opportunities of yielding your way to that of someone else and develop the habit of being mindful of the sensibilities of others and of being helpful to them in accomplishing what they reasonably desire. If you do this you will at first feel cramped and thwarted, but you will soon realize how in the past you have made much ado about nothing, and now at the price of trifles you are gaining peace and mental stability.

Some time ago there came to the clinic with her husband a lady from the South. She gave a history of mental abnormality that had seemed definitely noticeable for the four months previous to this visit and more or less vaguely evident in the past year. The presenting symptoms were delusions (a) that she had syphilis, (b) that she was pregnant, (c) that all her friends and neighbors knew that she was diseased and had been false to her husband. Examinations by several eminent specialists gave no evidence of pregnancy nor of syphilis and the account of the supposed infidelity to her husband bore all the earmarks of an evident delusion. The fundamental factors in the analysis of her case were that the patient thought she came from a very highly respectable family of excellent lineage, that she was far superior to the ordinary run of girls, and that if any scandal did get out about her it would cause a vast amount of comment. She had never submitted to marriage duties from the day of marriage on throughout the several years of her married life and from early years had an uncontrollable fear of dying in childbirth. Though fairly well-to-do she never took part in any social, charitable, or religious work, living quietly by herself an easy, comfortable existence.

Let us now ask ourselves what was the essential pathology

in the case of the lady in question, that from her difficulty also we may develop some rules of mental hygiene.

We find that the presenting symptom in this case was a number of delusions. It will be most important to understand if possible the mechanism of these delusions, for delusions do characterize a goodly percentage of psychopathic conditions. Though the explanation of some delusions will not clear up the problem of the origin of all delusions, it will nevertheless be a helpful step and lead to the formulation of a few principles of mental hygiene which will be based, as all good hygiene should be based, on a clear insight into etiology.

From our analysis of this case it becomes clear that the delusions of the patient were not fabrications of the conscious mind. I feel that this is demonstrated by the fact that no amount of logical common sense nor of sound reasoning nor appeal to the senses could in any way rid her of her belief in her impossible ideas. Some ground must be sought for her conviction other that what ordinarily leads the conscious mind to draw a conclusion.

We are at once led to suspect the unconscious. Can the unconscious fabricate convictions in the human mind? If this is so, it is of prime importance for us to know it and find out what precautions must be taken to prevent the develop ment of those pathological convictions which psychiatrv recognizes as delusions. Let us first ask ourselves: Can the unconscious fabricate anything? Let us turn for a moment to dream life. Do dreams have a symbolic meaning which is not understood by the conscious, waking mind? If so, then it seems only likely that they are fabricated by the unconscious. For if the conscious mind wove the story of the dream in symbolic language it should understand its own symbolism. But dreams do have a meaning and the conscious mind does not understand the symbolism. But something produces the dream and if it is not the conscious we have a right to refer it to something, whatever it may be, that we term the unconscious. The following dream illustrates more than the mere fact that dreams have a meaning.

"I wàs dreaming that a man was relating to a boy of about 13 how it was demonstrated for the first time that lifeboats could save lives. A lifeboat was launched from a vessel in which were five mariners and passengers making a total of forty-two. He asked the boy whether he thought the boat was crowded; and I was surprised at the stupidity of the boy, who did not answer promptly that it was. At this time another lifeboat appeared in the dream and the man went on to tell the boy that a mariner attempted to tie the bow of the second boat to the stern of the first and then—at this point I thought the mariner was going to be told that this must not be done, when to my surprise the man went on to relate that in attempting to do so the mariner fell overboard and was drowned. I was rather surprised at this conclusion of the story, for I thought that the mariner should have been able to swim, and I thought that the conclusion was going to be that he would be told not to tie the two boats together. I also wondered why the word mariner was used instead of sailor. I wondered also, if it was rough enough to drown the mariner who fell overboard, how it was possible for the boats with so many people in them to weather the storm."

Leaving aside the interpretation of this dream let us note:
1. The ego consciousness listening to the tale.
2. The ego consciousness is not constructing the tale, for
   a) it does not turn out as the ego consciousness expected;
   b) it has various other elements of surprise.
3. The tale must therefore be fabricated by a type of consciousness of which the ego consciousness during the dream is not aware.

If in the normal mechanism of our conscious—though sleeping—life, we have a type of consciousness capable of fabricating a story, what is to prohibit this subconscious mechanism from fabricating suspicions and various concepts that have a peculiar appeal to the ego consciousness?

Consider the case of the lady already referred to. We can point to an unsettled state of mind, preceding by several months the development of her delusion. The delusion of pregnancy is associated with a certain event but did not develop for some weeks after it, and has no foundation in memory or actual present symptoms and could not be shaken by the assurances of physicians. Were it a fabrication of the ego consciousness it could not resist the appeal to logic and common sense. Were it an idea developed by the unconscious but without appeal to the ego consciousness it would soon fade into oblivion. But it had a distinct value to the ego consciousness. It was an element in the formation of a system of defense reactions that justified the patient in refusing marriage relations, so preventing the real pregnancy which she feared. This association with the fundamental complex of her life gave it an unreasonable persistence.

We are trying to get an insight into the mechanism of the formation of delusions, that we may see how to proceed rationally in preventing their development in the human mind. It is fairly certain that in some delusions the dominating factor is some form of unworthy motivation. One is tempted to say that this is true of many cases and then with true Freudian generalization to say in all cases. It is probably true of many cases, but one would hesitate to make the generalization and say in *all* cases.

If now we are going to attack a delusion or to prevent its formation, we can see that logical reasoning with the ego consciousness is not going to be of any great value. We must attack the process of motivation which has centered the individual in himself and walled off all approaches that might allow entrance for the dethronement of his egoism. To attempt this in trying to cure an adult mind, in which this condition has been progressing for years, usually from early childhood to middle age or beyond, is as vain as a frontal attack on the Rock of Gibraltar with a tack hammer.

Prevention, not cure, is our only hope. And here we must commence with the training and development of the child mind. It is vain or at least almost certainly vain to attempt to cure a well-established paranoia by any treatment whatsoever. But the condition often makes itself apparent in middle life. And when we speak of mental hygiene we are giving principles for individuals to apply to themselves. How can I keep paranoid ideas from developing in myself? I have already pointed out one source of them. It is that of unworthy motivation proceeding from selfishness and disregard for my duties to other people. If I do not conquer this, the unconscious may build the air castle of my delusions and my selfishness will wall it in so that reason can never attack it on the ground of reality.

If I do not humble myself before truth and reality I shall conceive that I possess abilities that exist only in my imagination. I shall explain failure by accusing others of what they have done to thwart me and upset my plans. The greater my actual failure, the higher will I elevate my concept of myself and so compensate by vain imaginings for my defects of judgment and good will. It is so much easier to dream than it is to work.

If I do not give up my own way I shall be the prey of the blind drive to show that my will is indomitable and waste my life in the vain display of stubbornness.

If I do not learn to suffer willingly all that duty entails, I shall block the way to peace and prosperity by defense reactions that will make it impossible to rid my mind of delusional concepts or a delusional system fabricated by the unconscious.

Such are some of the principles of mental hygiene suggested by a study of the etiology of the intellectual mental disorders.

Let us think now of another case, this time dominantly emotional. Let me ask you to consider a young physician of about

30. Several years ago his wife brought him to me because he was subject to unreasonable crying spells. A change had come over him. Formerly he enjoyed society, moving pictures, card games, dances, and now he sat moping at home, at times bursting into tears, now moaning that there was no longer any use in anything and now threatening to retire from practice and end his life in poverty. The young physician himself attributed his condition to some obscure disorder of metabolism. He had had himself examined for foci of infection, but everything was negative. He was nevertheless anxious about his condition and felt that he was losing mental and physical vigor. There was a history of a previous attack in which he spent some time in an asylum.

Essentially the condition is one of an inexplicable unmotivated depression associated with a certain amount of unjustifiable anxiety.

The following dream gave the cue to the situation:

"I dreamed of a footbridge leading to water. Ducks and swans were swimming. I walked down this bridge and stood on the end watching these creatures swimming and ducking. I saw one in particular, a great white swan, that appeared of mammoth size. I was alone and I appeared to look around to see if anyone watched so that I could go into the water to disappear."

The path leading down to the water called up a situation which had arisen some time before between the patient and a girl who was working for him in his office. He had fallen in love with her. His wife, partly because of a slow wasting illness from which she was suffering, had lost her attraction for him. He and the girl frequently talked of going off together on a sea voyage. The second part of the dream called up his little children and his wife playing beside a pond whither from time to time they were in the habit of going for an afternoon's rest. The dream evidently was the expression of his conflict. He thought the matter had been ended. He had made up his mind, on the basis of religion and moral grounds, that he could not desert his wife and children, and told the nurse to get another position, which she did. Some time after she left, his mental trouble developed, but he had no idea that it was connected with the former conflict.

I pointed out to him that he had done the wise thing in maintaining the integrity of his family life, but that it was evident that so far his adjustment to life had been on the rather low plane of pure animal enjoyment, that a young man of his ability should be able to make headway in his profession, which presented so many fields of investigation and possibilities for intellectual work; he had a good background for happiness in his mental life, a wife whom he really loved in spite of her illness and who loved him in return, and a happy family of children. The result was that he threw himself into the work of his profession and commenced to effect an adjustment on a higher plane and so was able for a time to cope with his depression.

Various other complicating factors, however, entered into the situation and for some years afterwards, while not suffering a complete mental break, he would cause trouble periodically by unreasonable whining and crying.

The essential elements in this case are:

1) A conflict between desire and religious and moral principles resolved in favor of religion and morality.

2) A resultant depression.

3) Amelioration by analysis of the cause and opening a path for sublimation.

What principles of mental hygiene are involved?

To begin with, someone may say that religion and morality were responsible for the whole difficulty. If it had not been for religious and moral principles there would have been no conflict and no resultant depression. Just what the result would have been had the young man deserted his wife and children, it is hard to say. That he would have escaped mental trouble is very unlikely.   I feel quite sure that mental trouble would certainly have followed and would probably have been more serious than the difficulty he did experience.   Furthermore, his wife and children would have been involved in the calamity, so that religious and moral principles in this man's mental life and in that of his family were potent factors in mental hygiene.   Once the difficulty developed, amelioration was possible because the patient had an education which enabled him to develop an adjustment to life on a higher plane than that on which he had lived in the past.

And now let us leave for a moment the region of the abnormal and see how a normal human being reacted to a physical handicap in such a manner that his reaction became a service to humanity.

Sir Walter Scott, when he was at the age of about 18 months, suffered an attack of infantile paralysis—though he himself speaks of the illness as "the fever which often accompanies the cutting of large teeth."[1]   His subsequent lameness became not only a handicap but also a source of a feeling of inferiority for which he tried to make good.   He tells us how he was actually conscious of compensating by story telling for his inability to gain popularity by muscular activity on the playground.

"Among my companions, my good nature and a flow of ready imagination made me very popular.   Boys are uncommonly just in their feelings, and at least equally generous.   My lameness and the efforts which I made to supply that disadvantage, by making up in address what I wanted in activity, engaged the latter principle in my favour; and in the winter play hours, when hard exercise was impossible, my tales used to assemble an admiring audience round Lucky Brown's fireside, and happy was he that could sit next to the inexhaustible narrator. I was also, though often negligent of my own task, always ready to assist my friends; and hence I had a little party of

---

[1] Lockhart, J. G., *Life of Sir Walter Scott*, chap. 1, "Memoir of Sir Walter Scott's Early Years Written by Himself," p. 10.

staunch partisans and adherents, stout of hand and heart, though somewhat dull of head—the very tools for raising a hero to eminence. So on the whole, I made a brighter figure in the *yards* than in the *class*."[2]

Sir Walter Scott's lameness thus became the determining factor in his career. It withdrew him from active sports in childhood and threw him back upon books for his enjoyment of life. His excellent verbal memory supplied important aid and so he became the prince of story tellers.

"My lameness and my solitary habits had made me a tolerable reader, and my hours of leisure were usually spent in reading aloud to my mother Pope's translation of Homer, which, excepting a few traditionary ballads, and the songs in Allan Ramsay's *Evergreen,* was the first poetry which I perused. My mother had good natural taste and great feeling: she used to make me pause upon those passages which expressed generous and worthy sentiments, and if she could not divert me from those which were descriptive of battle and tumult, she contrived at least to divide my attention between them. My own enthusiasm, however, was chiefly awakened by the wonderful and terrible—the common taste of children, but in which I have remained a child even unto this day. I got by heart, not as a task, but almost without intending it, the passages with which I was most pleased, and used to recite them aloud, both alone and to others—more willingly, however, in my hours of solitude, for I had observed some auditors smile, and I dreaded ridicule at that time of my life more than I have ever done since."[3]

His reading soon extended beyond Pope's translation of Homer. "My appetite for books," he writes, "was as ample and indiscriminating as it was indefatigable."[4] But it was not to lead him to a life shut up in the dreams of literature. At school it enabled him to compensate for his lameness and

[2] Lockhart, *op. cit.*, p. 20.
[3] Lockhart, *op. cit.*, p. 18.
[4] *Ibid.*, p. 26.

gain the admiration of his schoolfellows by his unrivaled ability as a story teller.

Even when studying law in his father's office he continued to read literature. Perhaps his love for tales of the wonderful deeds of knights of old was a compensation for his own lameness. At all events, he lived out in the dreams of literature what he himself could never experience.

"Everything which touched on Knight-errantry was particularly acceptable to me, and I soon attempted to imitate what I so greatly admired. My efforts, however, were in the manner of the tale-teller, not of the bard."[5]

And so he became, by a process of reacting to his own disabilities, the most admired, the much beloved, the unsurpassed story teller of his day; and the tales he told were in his day and still remain a genuine service by which a paralytic made his life of value to humanity.

But what of those who never obtained or who threw away the opportunities of an education, who have no foundation for fruitful activity when the days draw nigh that please us not? Moving pictures, automobiles, dancing, sex pleasures, will not satisfy a normal mind for the entire space of the average life. These people present a doleful picture. They come to every clinic from time to time. But where is the clinician who can help them? Let me quote a case from my *Dynamic Psychology*.

"I recall a German, past the prime of life, who came to the clinic for help. He had accomplished nothing in life and had nothing to which he could look forward. He had arteriosclerosis and various accompanying symptoms of a premature onset of old age. My attempts to get him to adjust himself to his present situation did not satisfy him at all. He wished to be rejuvenated, as it were, by miracle. One day he broke out into tears and commenced to cry: 'Meine Jugend! Meine Jugend! Meine verlorene Jugend!' Had Mephistopheles an-

[5] *Ibid.*, p. 30.

swered as he did Doctor Faust he would have found a ready subject in this old German."[6]

Here we are confronted with the hopelessness of all psychology. Religion alone can here open the way to a sublimation that will transcend all the difficulties of life and the final failure of death. If mankind is to establish in society a stable mental peace it must come about by the realization that all nations and peoples constitute one single social order, that in this social order God is the Infinite Intelligence in a universe of intelligent beings, that every finite intelligence owes obedience and service to the Infinite Mind that presides over all, that the happiness of the finite mind lies not in the dominance of its ego but in its subjection to the Supreme Being, that nothing exists without a purpose or an end in human society, that every human being has a work to do in the world and when it is done he will attain to the knowledge of Truth, that the human mind never dies but is dest'ned to live forever in the eternal social order over which God reigns supreme.

[6] Moore, *Dynamic Psychology*, pp. 154–55.

CHAPTER X

THE MENTAL HYGIENE OF THE HOME

1. THE CONCEPT OF THE FAMILY

THE GUIDING principles in the mental hygiene of the home must flow of necessity from the psychological nature of the family. These principles are based on the fact that man is what he is; and we will run into all sorts of mental hygiene difficulties if we attempt to conceive of him as he is not and direct his conduct according to our fancy.

What is the family? In the strict sense it is a social group consisting ordinarily of a father, a mother, and one or more children. In a wider sense it is conceived of as all those living together under the same roof with the parents and children.

A ceremony of marriage is the normal origin of the family in our own day and has been since the grey dawn of antiquity. Taking the word "ceremony" in a broad sense as a rite or act setting apart two individuals to live together and bring forth children, this principle will find general confirmation in the anthropological studies of our day.

It was natural when the interest in evolution was acute that some should conceive of the original condition of mankind as that of a horde of animals living together in sexual promiscuity.[1] But a careful study of the available data gives no evidence of any such condition of promiscuity among primitive races of the present day. After examining the data Lowie concludes: "Sexual communism as a condition taking the place of the individual family exists nowhere at the present time; and the arguments for its former existence must be

---

[1] This concept was put forward by Johann Jacob Bachofen, *Das Mutterrecht*, Stuttgart: Krause & Hoffman, 1861; also by J. F. McLennan, *Studies in Ancient History: Primitive Marriage*, Macmillan, 1881.

rejected as unsatisfactory. This conclusion will find confirmation in the phenomena of primitive family life."[2]

Furthermore, when we consider the necessity of years of care for the human infant, it is unlikely that a gregarious horde could ever have represented the original condition of the human race.

The long period of human infancy and the necessity of protection and care of the mother and a number of children by some one leads to the conclusion that the father must have assumed the role of protector and provider, under ordinary circumstances, from the very beginning of the human race.

2. MORALS AND MORES

It is not necessary, however, to wander through the interesting regions of anthropology to find out what man is at the present day and how his very nature determines the structure of the family and its principles of mental hygiene, though some who deal with the fundamental moral problems of the family treat morals as "mores," customs, that exist at present and may be exemplified in the accounts of the past. And some seem to look upon long-established customs as having a moral sanction by their antiquity and others deny the existence of any stable moral principles because of the existence of all manner of conflicting customs. What is right in one tribe is supposed to be right because it is the custom in that tribe; but where different customs prevail there is a contradictory moral code. And so the idea of morality disappears because it is confused with the concept of etiquette.

But morality needs no customs for the source of its prin-

[2] Robert H. Lowie, *Primitive Society*, New York: Boni & Liveright, 1920, p. 62. Cf. also Edward Westermarck, *History of Human Marriage*, London: Macmillan, 1921, vol. 1, p. 124: "Not a single statement can be said to be authoritative or even to make the existence of promiscuity at all probable in any case. That no known savage people nowadays is, or recently has been living in such a state, is quite obvious, and this greatly discredits the supposition that promiscuity prevailed among any of the peoples mentioned by classical or mediaeval writers in their summary and ambiguous accounts."

ciples. Were all history destroyed, the fundamental relations of man to man in the existing social order would supply the material from which reason sitting in judgment on conduct would derive the necessary natural principles of the moral order. And action in accordance with these principles would constitute the essence of sound mental hygiene.

So let us look at marriage and the mental hygiene of the home from this point of view.

3. The Essential Nature of Marriage

What leads to marriage at the present day is the strong attraction that a man and woman feel for each other. It is this that urges them to enter into a matrimonial contract and bind themselves to one another by a marriage ceremony.

If we would trust the psychiatric literature of the present day, we would see in this mutual attraction dominantly if not exclusively the conscious experience of a purely sexual charm.

Whereas it is quite true that the motive force back of some marriages is pure sexual charm, it is also true that a genuine, perfect friendship is something independent of sexual attraction. This derives from the fact that the human mind not only perceives what the senses present, but also interprets the data of sense and draws conclusions and establishes principles and delineates ideals. It not only senses but also understands; and so the mind is not only attracted by that which has sensory charm, but it also determines to seek that which transcends the data of sense and is intellectually worth while. The whole realm of science, philosophy, and religion is intellectually worth while; but there is very little in these regions which lies on a purely sensory plane and could be appreciated without the play of intellectual activity.

Similarly, in a human individual, what the eye can see may possess a more or less sensory charm; but the personality that lies behind, with ideals of life and high resolutions and volitional strivings, has a nobility and a value that the eye alone can never see and the sensory powers of apprehension can never appreciate.

True friendship is based on a mutual understanding and a deep appreciation of one human being for another. What is given by pure sensory perception does not lie at the basis of perfect human friendship. It is the intellect alone that can understand and appreciate a human personality.

When now we come to an attempt to understand the nature of marriage we arrive at its first fundamental principle. Marriage is not a union of two individuals initiated and maintained by the experience of sexual charm but in its formal nature it is a pact of perfect friendship.

"The essential nature of marriage consists in a certain indivisible union of minds by which each one of the consorts is bound to keep inviolably his faith with the other."[3]

Marriage, therefore, by its very nature, is initiated and maintained by true friendship and not merely by sexual attraction. Many unhappy marriages might have been prevented if each consort had paused to think and ask himself: Is it the true nobility of the personality that attracts me or am I merely bewitched for the moment by a sexual charm which may disappear completely in the daylight of experience?

There is a psychological fallacy here that it might be well to point out. By a psychological fallacy I mean one in which the fallacious principle is assumed in virtue of an emotional drive to have our wishes come true.

As an exercise in a course in experimental psychology, I had the boys rate the photographs of a class of girls for intellectual ability and genuine moral worth. The class grades were available as a check on the intellectual gradings. There was a rather low correlation between class gradings and the judgments of intellectual ability; but there was a high correlation between the ratings for intellectual ability and those for

[3] St. Thomas, *Summa theologica* III, Q 29, Art. ii, Corp.

genuine moral worth. The students were then asked to arrange the photographs according to a scale of good looks. It was thereupon found that there was a high correlation between good looks and estimated intellectual ability and genuine moral worth. In other words, my boys thought that the good-looking girls had high intellectual ability and were fine moral characters. The reverse experiment was made with girls and it turned out that the girls in their turn thought that the fine-looking boys were highly intelligent young men with sterling moral characters.

And so there is a tendency for sexual charm to lead the human mind to a belief in the value of the personality that exerts the charm. Hence the danger of precipitous marriages based on love at first sight. Mental hygiene points to the importance of a deep knowledge of the personality before marriage is seriously contemplated. For marriage is a union of minds that know and understand each other and have formed a pact of perfect friendship flowing from mutual knowledge, love, and admiration of the personalities. Love and admiration of a personality does not imply that one has before him a flawless character; for in this life perfect characters without stain or defect are not to be found. But true love does mean the knowledge of something genuinely worth while in the object of love.

Marriage therefore by its formal and essential character is a pact of perfect friendship. It is the human personality that loves and is loved. The human personality transcends the brute animal by its understanding of the better things and a high determination to attain and realize in the self what is truly worth while. And because all this is so, we cannot make marriage anything else than it is: a pact of perfect friendship between man and woman. The laws of matrimony are not arbitrary but fixed by the law of nature. We cannot make the family anything we please by an agreement between prospective parents or even by the enactment of civil laws and hope to have it permeated by a sound mental hygiene, unless what we will or legislate is in accordance with the natural laws of family life.

4. THE STABILITY OF MARRIAGE

By the very nature of man as a social being, the family is a stable social unit. Its stability derives from the nature of marriage as a pact of perfect friendship between man and woman, which is entered into not only that two friends may live together, but also that they may bear children and so fulfil the important duty of continuing the human race and handing down to posterity the religious, moral, intellectual, and aesthetic culture of previous ages.

The family, therefore, must possess a certain stability:

In the first place because true friendship is eternal.

Second, because the long period of human infancy and childhood demands the stability of the home for the mere physical needs of a family of children.

Third, because the parents must prepare the child to receive the culture of previous ages and equip the child to create a new family that in its turn will transmit the religious, moral, and aesthetic values that it received.

The concept, therefore, of the permanence of the marriage tie and the generous resolution to take each other "for better or worse, till death do us part" is an element of fundamental importance in the mental hygiene of the home. When husband and wife realize that marriage is no mere trial of compatibility, but a lifelong partnership of true and perfect friendship, each is much more likely to attempt to overcome the defects of his own personality and to bear patiently with the temperamental defects of the consort, than when divorce is regarded as the natural solution of more or less serious marital difficulties.

Lorine Pruette for example expresses the advantage of divorce by saying that it is better for the child to have "peace with one parent than strife with two."[4] But this is one of

---

[4] *The Parent and the Happy Child*, New York: Holt, 1932, p. 11.

those euphemisms that cloud the issue by singling out one favorable aspect while many tragic possibilities lurk in the background.

Divorce is always a tragedy. It is the dissolution of a friendship, the marring of the lives of at least two individuals and a profound disturbance in the emotional life of the child. Seldom does the child find emotional peace with one parent. Often he lives now with one, and now with the other, and while he loves both his father and his mother, each parent is competing for his love and trying to persuade him of the cruelty and iniquity of the other.

To prevent any such calamity to the child, the parents are bound to endure strain and bitterness and make all possible effort to soften it, and try their best not to let it appear before the child, and settle their difficulties by quietly talking over their problems when the children are not around.

Parents should realize that children are often deeply grieved when hearing them in dispute about even minor matters. I remember being in one house when the father and mother were arguing some trivial point and were really not angry with each other, but were speaking rather loudly. The little 10-year-old boy was nevertheless very deeply concerned and was doing all he could to make peace between them, running first to one and then to the other to bestow an appealing hug and a kiss.

5. Age of Marriage and Period of Courtship

Though legal in many states[5] and by canon law,[6] it is seldom that the marriage of a girl much under 18 years is permanent

[5] The minimum marriageable age for girls is 12 in 14 states, namely, Kentucky, Louisiana, Virginia, Florida, Maine, Pennsylvania, Rhode Island, Tennessee, Colorado, Idaho, Maryland, Mississippi, New Jersey, and New York; it is 14 in 9 states, Alabama, Arkansas, District of Columbia, Georgia, Iowa, North Carolina, South Carolina, Texas, and Utah; it is 15 in 8 states, Missouri, Minnesota, North Dakota, Oklahoma, Oregon, South Dakota, Washington and Wisconsin; and it is 16 in 17 states, Arizona, California, Connecticut, Delaware, Illinois, Indiana, Kansas, Massachusetts, Michigan, Montana, Nebraska, Nevada, New Mexico, Ohio, Vermont, West Virginia, and Wyoming.

and happy. Naturally much depends on individual and racial characteristics, and these perhaps in their turn depend on climatic conditions.[7] But in the United States child marriages are often very unhappy and soon terminate in separation and divorce. Thus Richmond and Hall studied 250 cases of children who married: 16 never established homes and lived together; 11 lived together only a few days, 7 only a few weeks, 8 only a few months. Out of 90 cases whose whereabouts were still known at the time of the investigation, only 16 married pairs were still living together.

There is a crying need for reformation of the present processes of granting marriage licenses and of celebration of the marriage before a justice of the peace or a minister who makes no investigation before he functions in the ceremony.

The very nature of normal marriage as a contract entered upon by a man and a woman who undertake to establish a home and rear children points out the necessity of the woman's having sufficient maturity not only to bear children but also to manage a home, and of the man's being able to provide at least with meager frugality the food, clothing, and shelter for those who live in his household. Ordinarily a girl much under 18 is not able to manage a home and a boy must be somewhat over 18 before he can provide for a household.

Seeing that marriage is a compact of perfect friendship

Data given by Mary Ellen Richmond and Fred S. Hall in *Child Marriages*, New York: Russell Sage Foundation, 1925, pp. 20-45.

[6] Codex of 1067, 1. The male partner must have completed the sixteenth year and the female partner the fourteenth year. But according to the second paragraph of this Canon, though a marriage contracted after these ages would be valid, the pastor in charge of souls should do what he can to prevent young people from marrying before the age in which according to the accepted customs of the region in which they live marriage is wont to be contracted.

[7] Richmond and Hall present an interesting table which on its face value indicates that a larger percentage of girls marry between 15 and 19 in the warmer climatic zones in the United States than in the colder: *op. cit.*, p. 31. Furthermore, while 14 per cent of foreign-born white girls marry between 15 and 19, only 6.3 per cent of native white girls of foreign-born parentage marry between those ages (*op. cit.*, p. 30).

that is to endure for life, it should not be entered on until each party knows thoroughly by adequate experience the personality of the consort. One has but to observe the deep chagrin of the adolescent girl when her boy friend quits calling (or vice versa, *mutatis mutandis*) and then how in a few days this hopeless despair passes off and new interests are in the making, to realize that a friendship should be tried and found true before a marriage ceremony is enacted. The fact that marriages after an acquaintanceship of 5 years and over give a definitely better mental adjustment than those after 2 to 4 years, and those after 2 to 4 years better than those after 6 to 23 months, and these better than those after less than 6 months, indicates that the marriage partner should be thoroughly known and investigated for some time before the marriage. Similar figures for the period of *courtship* indicate that courtship should last not less than a year. And those who were *engaged* 24 months or longer have the largest percentage of good adjustments in marriage.[8]

6. Theory and Practice in the Problems of the Home

We have attempted to derive a concept of marriage and its formal essence from the very nature of man and have concluded that it is essentially a pact of perfect friendship which by its very nature is permanent and lasting. This, however, is not the concept current in psychiatric discussions and in the actual practice of many who live in the world today. Let us now pass from the theoretical point of view to the practical point of view and ask ourselves whether or not the concept of marriage as a trial procedure or as a living together which does not involve any obligation of mutual fidelity even while living together, would be compatible with the happiness of the partners in such a life and conducive to sound mental hygiene.

[8] Ernest W. Burgess and Leonard S. Cottrell, *Predicting Success or Failure in Marriage*, New York: Prentice Hall, 1939, pp. 164-68.

There are many in our day who assume that marriage is a trial procedure and that husband and wife are not bound to keep an inviolable faith and be true to each other and never seek sexual satisfaction from another partner. Subterranean currents of thought eventually find a champion in some kind of a popular philosopher; and this is what has happened to the nihilistic concept of marriage in the writings of Bertrand Russell.[9] His concepts may be taken as typical of a considerable class.

Russell does not believe in the stability of marriage, largely because he is convinced that most marriages turn out unhappily. "Among civilized people in the modern world," he writes, "none of these conditions for what is called happiness exist, and accordingly one finds that very few marriages after the first few years are happy."[10] He is inclined to think, however, "that when a marriage is fruitful and both parties to it are reasonable and decent the expectation ought to be that it will be life long; but not that it will exclude other sex relations."[11]

Let us view this concept of the family for a moment from the point of view of mental hygiene. There is a necessary harmony between that which is objectively true and that which is good. The true works out in practice. Miscalculate your stresses when you build a bridge and it won't bear the burdens it is expected to carry. Make marriage what you think you would like to have it, but mistake the true nature

[9] For a general critique of Bertrand Russell and his school of thought, cf. George Ernest Newsom, *The New Morality*, New York: Scribner, 1933, p. 319; also Jacques Leclercq, *Marriage and the Family* (transl. by Thomas R. Hanley, O.S.B.), New York: Pustet, 1942.

[10] Bertrand Russell, *Marriage and Morals*, Garden City, N. Y.: Sun Dial Press, 1938, p. 137. The conditions he mentions are:
1. The more civilized people become the less likely they seem of life-long happiness with one partner" (p. 135).
2. "Paucity of unowned women and absence of social occasions when husbands meet other women" (p. 130).
3. Recognition that the bonds of marriage are irrevocable.

[11] *Op. cit.*, p. 142.

of man with his ideals and strivings, and it will not give the peace and happiness that are expected to reign in the home.

One might react to his complexes and demand for either party in a marriage the right to seek satisfaction, when desired, from a third party. But such a concept of marriage does not work in theory because it is inherently incompatible with the concept of perfect friendship which is the real basis of marriage. That it does not work in practice is borne out by scientific investigation. G. V. Hamilton made a study of a number of elements in the marriage relationship by personally interviewing a group of 100 married men and an equal number of married women living in New York City. He did not evaluate his findings statistically. This task was undertaken by Ferguson, who attempted to find out which of his conclusions were and which were not statistically reliable.[12]

Two of his conclusions indicate that extramarital love affairs, the right to which Bertrand Russell demands for either spouse, are very definitely associated with unhappiness in the home.

According to Ferguson's calculations, a higher percentage of both happy men and happy women than of unhappy men and unhappy women have not had extramarital love affairs.[13] Higher percentages of both happy men and happy women than of unhappy men and unhappy women have never committed adultery.[14]

To realize that statistics here tell the truth we have but to think of the acute misery of a husband or wife when a third party steps in and shares or absorbs the love of one who has sworn to keep an inviolable faith and be true even to death.

[12] Gilbert van Tassell Hamilton, *A Research in Marriage*, New York: Boni, 1929.

[13] Leonard W. Ferguson, "Correlates of Marital Happiness," *J. Psychol.* **6**: 285–94, 1938.

The critical ratio of the difference was 3.2, which means that the difference would not occur as a chance event more than once in a thousand times.

[14] The critical ratio of the difference was 3.5, which means that the difference would occur as a chance event less than once in a thousand times.

And when we consider human nature as it is, it is not likely that a happy home would develop out of an attempted marriage in which mutual fidelity was not contemplated in the first place and the living together was regarded merely as a trial to be terminated at will when either party was dissatisfied. All such concepts of marriage fail to take cognizance of the higher nature of man, who, being an intellectual and moral being, craves for a perfect friendship with another intellectual and moral being to whom he is attached and whom he admires because of the beauty of the personality he has grown to love and reverence. Such a friendship results in a complete consecration of one human being to another which is so full and exclusive that a third party is not tolerated and a termination of the friendship is not contemplated. The partner in a marriage is not primarily and essentially a mere object and means of sex satisfaction. Only those who regard sex satisfaction as the primary and essential thing in marriage can look upon it as temporary or as admitting of extramarital sex contacts.

To what condition of the human race does the Bertrand Russell concept of marriage lead? He pictures the state as taking over more and more the support of the children— the father eventually ceasing to serve any obvious purpose whatsoever. "With regard to the mother, there are two possibilities. She may continue her ordinary work and have her children cared for in institutions, or she may if the law so decides, be paid by the state to care for her children while they are young."[15]

Such a condition would be the outcome of a general adoption of Bertrand Russell's theories of marriage and morals, but what would be its mental hygiene value? Mental hygiene endeavors to provide the best conditions for a healthy and therefore happy state of the mind. Would any woman's life be happy if she had to choose between the two alternatives given her by Bertrand Russell? Would any father be truly

[15] Russell, *op. cit.*, p. 307.

happy were he condemned to a nomad existence, serving no obvious purpose whatsoever, even though he might be relieved by the state of the burden of supporting his own children? Would he not be deprived rather of a source of peace and satisfaction, for does not the healthy-minded father seek merely the opportunity of providing for his wife and children and does he not take a real and justifiable pleasure in feeling that he has contributed to their happiness?

Let us now ask the questions:

Are most marriages unhappy?

Is the family actually disintegrating and being supplanted by a Bertrand Russell type of cohabitation?

7. The Actual Happiness of Family Life

In 1921, Dr. Katherine B. Davis, general secretary of the Bureau of Social Hygiene, New York City, published a preliminary report on a questionnaire sent to a thousand young married women.[16] The questionnaire was first sent to "married women of respectable standing in the community, of sufficient intelligence and education to understand and answer in writing a rather exhaustive set of questions as to sex experience." To this appeal 436 replies were received. A second group was then chosen "from the alumnae of our colleges and universities and from published lists of members of women's clubs." The population was drawn largely from the better and more educated classes. Out of this group 49 expressed themselves as very happy, 822 as happy, 28 as fairly happy, 37 as intermittently happy, or happy in general. Only 44 said they were unhappy. (No response was received on this point from 12 and 8 were cited as special cases.)

We may say that fully 90 per cent of this group were happy and only from 4 to 5 per cent definitely unhappy.

Lewis M. Terman in his valuable study *Psychological Factors*

[16] "A Study of the Sex Life of the Normal Married Woman," *Social Hyg. Bull.* 8: 9–11 (June), 1921.

in Marital Happiness[17] worked out an objective scale for measuring marital happiness. The scale gave quantitative values from 0 to 87. He says of the application of this scale: "For both husbands and wives, particularly in the case of the latter, the scores are heavily bunched at the happy end of the scale."[18] The average of the scale was 68.40 for men and 69.25 for women.

He also had the members of his population rate the happiness of their marriages, much as was done by the New York Bureau of Social Hygiene, and compared the ratings of a group obtained by fieldworkers attending meetings of men and women in professional, business, trade union, and other social groups and asking those present to check but not sign cards presenting a rough scale of marital happiness.

The accompanying table gives the result.

Subjective Ratings of Marital Happiness by an Unselected Population, Compared with Those by the Experimental Group of Married Couples

RATING OF HAPPINESS	UNSELECTED POPULATION		EXPERIMENTAL GROUP	
	Men (N = 902)	Women (N = 644)	Husbands (N = 792)	Wives (N = 792)
	%	%	%	%
1. Extraordinarily happy	25.5	27.2	29.5	34.6
2. Decidedly more happy than average	29.4	28.0	36.8	35.9
3. Somewhat more happy than average	13.1	10.1	16.3	14.7
4. About average	18.2	16.3	12.9	9.2
5. Somewhat less happy than average	6.6	7.3	2.9	3.0
6. Decidedly less happy than average	3.2	4.0	1.6	1.8
7. Extremely unhappy	4.0	7.1	0.1	0.8
Total	100.0	100.0	100.0	100.0

From Lewis M. Terman, *Psychological Factors in Marital Happiness*, New York: McGraw-Hill, 1938, p. 78.

It will be seen that there is an essential agreement with the results of Katherine Davis. Happy and very happy mar-

[17] Lewis M. Terman, *Psychological Factors in Marital Happiness*, New York: McGraw-Hill, 1938.
[18] *Op. cit.*, p. 62.

riages are common, and marriages less happy than average are relatively rare.

We may now ask what type of individual is likely to be happily married. Let us first look at the happy wife as pictured by the statistics of this investigation.

"Happily married women, as a group, are characterized by kindly attitudes towards others and by the expectation of kindly attitudes in return. They do not easily take offense and are not unduly concerned about the impressions they make upon others. They do not look upon social relationships as rivalry situations. They are cooperative, do not object to subordinate roles, and are not annoyed by advice from others. Missionary and ministering attitudes are frequently evidenced in their responses. They enjoy activities that bring educational or pleasurable opportunities to others and like to do things for the dependent and underprivileged. They are methodical and painstaking in their work, attentive to detail, and careful in regard to money. In religion, morals and politics they tend to be conservative and conventional. Their expressed attitudes imply a quiet self-assurance and a decidedly optimistic outlook upon life."[19]

It might be well to point out specifically that similar results have been found by Burgess and Cottrell. "A group of background items constituting what may be called the social factor in marital adjustment is found to be significantly related to success in marriage. Among these items are: higher level of education; objective evidence of religious activity, such as duration and frequency of attendance at Sunday school and church; the number and sex of friends; participation in social organization; and residence in neighborhood of single-family dwellings."[20]

The fact that marriage in a church is associated with a higher proportion of happy marriages is probably one more indica-

[19] *Op. cit.*, pp. 145–46.
[20] Burgess and Cottrell, *op. cit.*, pp. 345–46.

tion that religious ideals tend to develop and preserve the happiness of married life. "Of those married by civil officials only 19.6 per cent fall in the class with 'good' adjustment while 54.9 per cent are in the class with 'poor' adjustment. In cases in which the wedding was solemnized by a religious ceremony, 46.0 per cent are in the category of 'good,' and 25.7 per cent in the classes with 'poor' adjustment."[21]

Let us now turn specifically to the happily married man. "Happily married men show evidence of an even, stable emotional tone. Their most characteristic reaction to others is that of cooperation. This is reflected in their attitudes toward business superiors with whom they work; in their attitude towards women, which reflects equalitarian ideals; and in their benevolent attitudes toward inferiors and underprivileged. In a gathering of people they tend to be unself-conscious and somewhat extroverted. As compared with U (unhappy) husbands, they show superior initiative, a greater tendency to take responsibility, and greater willingness to give close attention to detail in their daily work. They like methodical procedures and methodical people. In money matters they are saving and cautious. Conservative attitudes are strongly characteristic of them. They usually have a favorable attitude toward religion and strongly uphold the sex mores and other social conventions."[22]

And now let us take a look at the unhappy husband and wife. "It is especially characteristic of unhappy subjects to be touchy or grouchy; to lose their tempers easily; to fight to get their own way; to be critical of others; to be careless of others' feelings; to chafe under discipline or to rebel against orders; to show any dislike that they may happen to feel; to be easily affected by praise or blame; to lack self-confidence; to be dominating in their relations with the opposite sex;

---

[21] *Op. cit.*, p. 126. The critical ratios of these differences are given as 4.02 and 4.39 respectively.

[22] Terman, *op. cit.*, p. 155.

to be little interested in old people, children, teaching, charity or uplift activities; to be unconventional in their attitudes toward religion, drinking, and sexual ethics; to be bothered by useless thoughts; to be often in a state of excitement; and to alternate between happiness and sadness without apparent cause."[23]

It is rather interesting to note that the average happiness scores of both wives and husbands are at a maximum in the first two years of married life. The high degree of happiness falls slowly till the marriages have lasted six to eight years and thereafter there is a general trend to rise slightly till the marriages have lasted twenty-seven years or longer.[24]

The presence or absence of children is not essentially related to the happiness of the marriage. The mean scores of childless and nonchildless wives are almost identical. "Childless husbands average 1.6 points above the non-childless, but so small a difference may be due to chance."[25] Of the 797 couples, 32.3 per cent were childless. Of 562 couples who had been married five years or longer, 80 were childless.

There is however, a definite tendency for childless marriages to terminate in divorce, as the following table from Cohen indicates:[26]

Percentage of Distribution of Divorces According to Size of Family

No children	63.0
One child	20.5
Two children	9.5
Three children	3.9
Four children	1.7
Five or more	1.4
Total	100.0

[23] *Ibid.*, p. 369.
[24] *Ibid.*, p. 127.
[25] *Ibid.*, p. 171.
[26] Alfred Cohen, *Statistical Analysis of American Divorce*, dissertation, Columbia University, 1932, p. 112.

Poverty and wealth contribute little or nothing to the prediction of happiness in marriage. "In so far as a good savings bank account has anything to do with success in marriage, it is in all probability entirely indirectly and by way of indicating the psychological stability of the depositor."[27]

8. The Disintegration of Family Life

It has been said that "perhaps the characteristic of the twentieth century family that most sharply challenges the attention of the student of family history is its instability."[28] In various quarters we hear that the old order passeth and giveth place to the new and so marriage and family life are vanishing and will be replaced by a new type of social institution that will preside over the propagation of the human race.

That there are various influences at work to undermine society itself as well as the family there can be no doubt. That these forces have been to some extent successful is evident to anyone who looks at the facts. Let us glance for a moment at the influences that have been gnawing away at the foundations of the family.

The stability of the family in the Middle Ages rested to a large extent (1) on the law of charity governing the relations between parents and children, (2) on the Catholic doctrine of the indissolubility of the marriage tie, and (3) on the general concepts of duties and obligations existing between all members of the social order.

With the advent of the Reformation, there extended into all spheres of life a tendency to deny the existence of authority and throw aside the ancient regard for all obligations and so assert the supremacy of the individual and his right to satisfy his personal desires. After ecclesiastical authority had been called in question, it was only natural that the existence of civil authority should be denied. And if there is no such

---

[27] Cf. Burgess and Cottrell, *op. cit.*, p. 134.
[28] Willistyne Goodsell, *A History of Marriage and the Family*, New York: Macmillan, 1934, p. 481.

thing as church or state authority, parental authority is easily disregarded.

With the change in the fundamental concepts of moral philosophy there rose a sensationalistic philosophy which found no place for the existence of any principles, moral or metaphysical, and so the higher values commenced to disappear from the minds of men. When this took place it was only natural that the satisfaction of the personal desires of the individual should loom large on the horizon and so marriage commenced to be regarded as a mere opportunity for sex indulgence. It was thus natural to draw the conclusion that, if husband and wife come together mainly for sex satisfaction, then, if conditions arise in which that is no longer possible, they can and should separate.

Literature followed naturally the trend in religion and philosophy and perhaps all the more easily because all who took part in the general revolt followed the natural drive of the human mind to rationalize and justify what is in itself unholy and unjustifiable. Thus Shelley cast aspersions on the sacred character of matrimony. After deserting his pregnant wife and going off with Mary Godwin and contemplating the desertion of Mary for still another love[29] he wrote in his *Epipsychidion* of those who are faithful to their marriage ties as traveling along the beaten road

> Which those poor slaves with weary footsteps tread
> Who travel to their home among the dead
> By the broad highway of the world, and so
> With one chained friend, or perhaps a jealous foe,
> The dreariest and the longest journey go.

Men commenced to think that it was possible to make the laws of marriage and the home whatever personal desire might dictate; and the sexual took on a false importance in the organization of the individual's life and personal aims.

[29] T. V. Moore, *Percy Bysshe Shelly: An Introduction to the Study of Character*, Psychol. Monog., vol. 31, no. 2, p. 34.

And so Grete Meisel-Hess could write: "The truth is that the sexual life is the focal point of every healthy being whose instincts have not undergone partial or complete atrophy; that upon the full satisfaction of sexual needs depends the attainment of a true equilibrium of the mental no less than the physical personality."[30]

But by its very nature the sexual function is a means by which the race is propagated and it must therefore be subordinate to the ultimate end of the social order. The focus point of any human being's existence should be to attain the end of his existence and make his due contribution to the social order. As Plato pointed out, the end of any type of being must be something specific to its very nature and to use it for another purpose is to degrade it. The end of a beautiful Stradivarius, for instance, is to give its peculiar note when it is played either solo or in the orchestra. The violin is made of wood and so it could be burned to make a fire or it might be used as a bludgeon, but to use it for such purposes would be to degrade it. Furthermore, as Aristotle said, the end of anything is specific and cannot be attained by any other type of creature. Now what is it that he says differentiates man from all other types of animal life? It is his power of intellect. Man's end therefore must be to know, and that too the highest of all truths, the idea of the Good, that is to say, the Divine Being, God Himself.[31] Man lives to know, not to make sexual pleasure the focal point of his existence. The focusing of the mind more or less exclusively upon the enjoyment of sex pleasures is not a normal but a pathological condition. Owing to the fact that in many quarters, from the feminists of the street to the psychiatrist in his office, the demand is again and again reiterated that we should "make it socially possible for everyone to satisfy this desire as may best commend itself to the individual judgment,"[32] many

[30] Grete Meisel-Hess, *The Sexual Crisis*, New York: Critic and Guide Co., 1917, p. 117.

[31] *Nichomachean Ethics* I. vii. 11–16; i. 4–7.

[32] Meisel-Hess, *op. cit.*

slip into the pathological condition of mind in which the pursuit of the sexual is the dominant driving force of existence.

When such individuals marry, or attempt marriage, it becomes a trial arrangement to be continued as long as there is mutual sex satisfaction and terminated when greater sex satisfaction is found elsewhere. There is no idea of utilizing and enjoying the exercise of the sex function for its purpose of establishing a home and bringing children into the world and developing a family bound together by ties of affection, in which there is a sense of security and a holy happiness because the children spontaneously feel that they were wanted in the beginning and are loved for their own sakes at the present. In such a trial marriage children are naturally regarded as unfortunate accidents and so the married partners become very much interested in the techniques of birth control. To what extent have these concepts infiltrated into the minds of the youth of our day and tended to prevent the establishment of wholesome family units consisting of father, mother, and a number of children?

A very illuminating table in the Sixteenth Census of the United States (1940) gives comparisons of the differential fertility of married couples in 1910 and 1940 (p. 154).

It is seen that 20.3 per cent of women who were or had been married at the time the 1940 census was taken, were childless, as compared with 13.6 per cent in the 1910 census. At the same time the percentage of the married population had increased somewhat in the intervening period; 59.0 per cent of the female population 15 years and over were married in 1910 and 61.1 per cent of the population were married in 1940.[33] Again, in 1940 there were 2532 children born per 1000 women ever married; in 1910 there were 3626.[34] It has been calculated that to keep the population from decreasing there must

---

[33] Sixteenth Census of the United States, 1940, *Population*, "Nativity and Parentage of the White Population: General Characteristics," p. 109, Table 15.
[34] *Ibid.*, "Differential Fertility," Tables 3, 4, pp. 3, 4.

NUMBER OF CHILDREN EVER BORN	1940		1910	
	Number of women ever married	Per cent	Number of women ever married	Per cent
Total, 15 to 74 years...........	35,108,480	100.0	20,476,625	100.0
Reporting on children........	30,648,780	87.3	18,911,838	92.4
Not reporting...............	4,459,700	12.7	1,564,787	7.6
Reporting on children.........	30,648,780	100.0	18,911,838	100.0
No children..................	6,223,960	20.3	2,570,074	13.6
1 child......................	6,606,120	21.6	3,187,739	16.9
2 children...................	5,990,700	19.5	2,964,832	15.7
3 children...................	3,943,240	12.9	2,338,236	12.4
4 children...................	2,586,240	8.4	1,857,260	9.8
5 children...................	1,707,040	5.6	1,451,787	7.7
6 children...................	1,164,140	3.8	1,173,150	6.2
7 children...................	779,000	2.5	913,581	4.8
8 children...................	580,120	1.9	744,884	3.9
9 children...................	384,860	1.3	558,800	3.0
10 or more...................	683,360	2.2	1,151,495	6.1
10 children.................	(1)		440,991	2.3
11 children.................	(1)		267,960	1.4
12 children.................	(1)		201,377	1.1
13 or 14 children...........	(1)		171,416	0.9
15 or more..................	(1)		69,751	0.4

From Sixteenth Census of the United States, 1940, *Population*, "Differential Fertility, 1940 and 1910," Table 1, p. 2.

(1) Statistics for 1940 not available.

be 2632 children to every 1000 married women.[35] Dublin and Lotka, basing their calculations on the constitution of the population in 1920 and the current mortality rates, calculated that there should be 3150 children to every 1000 *fertile* married females to maintain a stable population in the United States.[36] It is worth noting that in the 1940 census there were reported 3177 children ever born per 1000 mothers. These facts indi-

[35] L. I. Dublin and A. J. Lotka, "On the True Rate of Natural Increase as Exemplified by the Population of the United States, 1920," *J. Am. Statist. Assoc.* **20**: 305–39, 1925, cited by Raymond Pearl, *Natural History of Population*, New York: Oxford, 1939, p. 141.

[36] *Op. cit.*

cate that we must expect in the very near future a falling
population for the United States unless our predicament is
relieved by immigration or an upward trend in our vital
statistics.

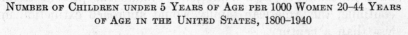

NUMBER OF CHILDREN UNDER 5 YEARS OF AGE PER 1000 WOMEN 20–44 YEARS
OF AGE IN THE UNITED STATES, 1800–1940

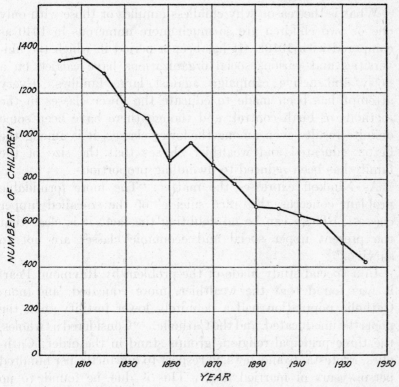

From P. K. Whelpton, "Recent Fertility Trends," *Human Fertility*
6: 162, 1941.

Raymond Pearl points out that "it seems a fair postulate
that if, in a given year, a woman produces her *fourth living
child*, she may be regarded as having adequately reproduced."[37]

[37] Pearl, *op. cit.*

Consider the accompanying curve, which shows how the size of the American family has dwindled since 1810. Nor does the shape of the curve indicate that it is nearing an asymptote, that is to say, a minimum size of family below which we need expect no further reduction. Should the present trend continue, the American family would approach extinction in less than a century.

What is the reason why childless families or those with only one or two children are so much more numerous in 1940 as compared with 1910? It has been a period in which the universities and various social organizations have carried on a noisy and active campaign against large families. Every attempt has been made to educate the lower classes in the methods of birth control; and though there have been some definite results even among the lower classes, it is among the better educated and wealthier classes that the size of the family has been reduced to dwindling proportions.

As Nimkoff expresses the matter: "The more formidable problem concerns the 'race suicide' of the so-called 'upper classes.' There can be no doubting the fact: it is clear that the present upper social and economic classes are not to survive."[38]

In a special study made of the problem by Raymond Pearl it was found that the wealthier, more educated, and non-Catholic population had a definitely lower fertility than the poor, the uneducated, and the Catholic. "Considered as wholes, the three principal religious groups stand in the order: Catholics, Protestants and Jews, in respect to live births per hundred person-years of married life." This is due, he found, to no biological difference in fertility but to a differential tendency to postpone marriage and practice contraception and abortion. "From the somewhat tedious statistical analysis to which the

[38] Meyer Francis Nimkoff, *The Family*, Boston: Houghton, 1944, p. 273. Cf. also data in Frank Lorimer and Frederick Osborn, *Dynamics of Population*, New York: Macmillan, 1934, pp. 317 ff.

Distributions of Native White Wives or Ever Married White Women 40–44 by Number of Live Births, Indianapolis Household Survey of 1941. Indianapolis Sample from 1910 Census and 1940 Census Data

NUMBER OF CHILDREN EVER BORN	INDIANAPOLIS HOUSEHOLD SURVEY, 1941 (WIVES AGED 40–44)*				INDIANAPOLIS CENSUS SAMPLE, 1910 (WIVES 40–44)†	TOTAL U.S., 1940 (EVER MARRIED WHITE WOMEN 40–44)‡
	Religion of both husband and wife					
	All religions	Both Protestant	Both Catholic	Prot.-Cath.		
Total................	100.0	100.1	100.0	100.1	100.1	100.0
0	18.8	18.8	14.8	25.6	13.8	15.2
1	23.2	24.0	16.6	22.4	18.9	18.7
2	23.6	24.2	20.6	20.5	19.4	21.9
3	14.7	14.4	19.3	13.0	16.2	15.3
4	8.1	7.7	11.6	7.5	12.6	10.1
5	4.5	4.3	6.8	3.6	5.6	6.4
6	2.6	2.4	4.0	3.2	4.6	4.2
7	1.6	1.5	2.7	1.0	3.4	2.9
8	1.0	1.0	1.1	1.0	2.4	2.0
9	.8	.8	.6	1.0	1.3	1.3
10 or more	1.1	1.0	1.9	1.3	1.9	2.0
Number of wives.......	6,551	5,283	784	308	593	3,126,880

* In unbroken first marriages of native white couples.

† In unbroken first marriages of white couples of native parentage. Special tabulations of punch cards from 1910 census fertility sample.

‡ The number of ever married white women 40–44 "reporting" on number of live births (3,126,880), as well as the distribution, is based on the experience observed in the 5 per cent random sample of the 1940 census. See *Population*, "Differential Fertility, 1940 and 1910," Washington, D.C.: Gov't Print. Off., p.7.

Table from Clyde V. Kiser and P. K. Whelpton, *Social and Psychological Factors Affecting Fertility*, "II. Variations in the Size of Completed Families of 6,551 Native-White Couples in Indianapolis," *Milbank Memor. Fund Quart.* **22**: 72–105 (Jan.), 1944.

From *Social and Psychological Factors Affecting Fertility*, "I. Differential Fertility Among 41,498 Native-White Couples in Indianapolis," *Milbank Memor. Fund Quart.*, **21**: 221–80 (July), 1943, Table 15.

data have been subjected one consistent broad result may fairly be said to have emerged. *It is that if it were not for the effect of contraceptive efforts and the practice of criminal abortion, together with correlated habits as to postponement of marriage, there would apparently be little or no differential fertility as between economic, educational or religious classes of urban American married couples.*"[39]

Essentially the same results are found in a survey conducted by the Committee on Social and Psychological Factors Affecting Fertility sponsored by the Milbank Memorial Fund with grants from the Carnegie Corporation of New York.[40] The accompanying table is based on data obtained from 6551 native white couples in Indianapolis, in which the wives were from 40 to 44 years of age. Such families in general have attained their maximum size.

If we study fertility in relation to economic status, we find that minimum fertility occurs in families who pay rents ranging from $50 to $59 a month, and a maximum fertility occurs in families who pay less than $10 a month.[41] Such at least is the indication from a survey made in the summer of 1941 in Indianapolis, which may be looked upon as a fairly representative American city.[42]

If we look at fertility from the point of view of the education of the parents we find that the main source of replacement of American population is among those who have had only a grammar school education.

Protestant couples and consorts in mixed marriages who have been to high school or college do not have nearly enough children to replace themselves in the population. Catholic couples of high school and college education fall a little below their replacement quota. Yet "in the 'both grammar school' group, the births to Protestant couples approximate the maintenance figure, but births to Protestant-Catholic couples are

[39] Pearl, *op. cit.*, p. 244.   (Italics in original.)
[40] P. K. Whelpton and Clyde V. Kiser, "Social and Psychological Factors Affecting Fertility" (reprint), *Milbank Memor. Fund. Quart.* **21:** 221–28, 1943; **22:** 72–105, 1944.
[41] *Ibid.*, reprint p. 25, Table 9.
[42] *Ibid.*

Total Number of Children Ever Born per 100 Wives, by Age of Wife and by Broad Educational Attainment and Religion of the Couple, Indianapolis Household Survey, 1941

RELIGION OF THE COUPLE AND AGE OF WIFE	CHILDREN BORN PER 100 WIVES			NUMBER OF WIVES		
	Both college	Both high school	Both grammar school	Both college	Both high school	Both grammar school
All religions						
Total 15–44*	101	127	223	3,669	17,811	6,497
15–19		39	71	18	1,110	170
20–24	27	77	131	460	4,644	568
25–29	72	113	185	856	4,626	779
30–34	119	137	255	975	3,372	1,221
35–39	147	164	287	765	2,318	1,818
40–44	168	171	308	595	1,741	1,941
Both Protestant						
Total 15–44*	99	123	224	3,126	14,085	5,290
15–19		39	76	17	942	139
20–24	29	78	127	396	3,729	471
25–29	68	113	192	704	3,633	643
30–34	119	130	262	816	2,619	990
35–39	145	157	286	675	1,789	1,478
40–44	166	164	305	518	1,373	1,569
Both Catholic						
Total 15–44*	134†	154	230	247	2,130	639
15–19		38†			73	4
20–24		79	153†	22	428	32
25–29	100†	120	147†	68	579	53
30–34	142†	180	241	71	458	128
35–39	214†	209	319	49	339	193
40–44	232†	224	351	37	253	229
Protestant-Catholic mixed marriages						
Total 15–44*	80†	117	181	154	1,094	326
15–19		39†			66	8
20–24	21†	72	127†	28	345	26
25–29	73†	106	177†	40	295	43
30–34	120†	136	167†	46	191	61
35–39	80†	141	245†	25	120	86
40–44		153†	243	15	77	102

* Rates for totals are standardized for age.

† Standardized rate based on 100–209 wives, or age-specific rate based on 25–99 wives. Respective types of rates based on fewer cases are not shown.

well below it, and births to Catholic couples are well above it."[43]

The accompanying table illustrates the general trend.

Taking all these facts together it is evident that the city populations of our country are being largely recruited from those who pay less than $10 a month for rent and whose education did not extend beyond the grammar grades. A consideration of agricultural districts might brighten the picture somewhat, but we must awaken to the fact that the race of "old Americans" is passing away. And those who constituted the cream of that race, who gave us our statesmen, our generals, our university professors, our physicians, lawyers, and financiers, are rapidly ceasing to be. Biologically it is quite possible that the lower classes of the present day can give rise to a generation intellectually adequate to the needs of the future, but there will be a profound change in social traditions and unless something is done to counteract the forces that are bringing the American family to the vanishing point, our land will be taken over by a more virile and powerful nation.

Strange to say, some view our declining birth rate with a sense of satisfaction. Thus Goodsell points out that the United States will soon "join France, Great Britain, Sweden and other countries which have practically stabilized populations. . . . Is this to be regretted?" He continues: "In the opinion of many thoughtful students of population problems a stable population is a boon, not a curse."[44]

A thoughtful student of population problems unaffected by the emotional excitement that now clouds the discussion of birth control might well ask: When the birth rate drops till it equals the death rate, by what means can it be held at this

[43] *Ibid.*, p. 44. The Milbank Fund data refer to Indianapolis as a typical city. That the size of the family decreases with the years of schooling is, however, a general phenomenon. Cf. Metropolitan Life Insurance Company, *Statist. Bull.* **25:** 8–9 (June), 1944.

[44] Goodsell, *op. cit.*, pp. 508–9.

point so as to bring to a nation the supposed blessings of a stable population? France did not long remain at this point and before the present war it had passed over to a declining population.[45] Neither its stability nor its decline could be looked upon as a boon when it was attacked by Germany with its population on the rise, and neither stable nor declining. Can we in the United States assure ourselves that we can stop the vast falling mass of the population at a point of zero increase, or that if we do our stabilized population can live forever in peace and tranquillity undisturbed by nations whose numbers are ever increasing and who prowl about seeking whom they may devour?

There are signs that some among our intellectual classes are commencing to realize the peril which the agitation for birth control has brought upon the educated in particular and on our nation in general.

Houdlette in a study program meant for intelligent parents writes as follows:

"The problem of voluntary parenthood is one that faces us in the final analysis. Confronted with a national trend which experts agree is serious, will individuals weigh social against personal situations and choose to have larger families? If women are economically free, will they choose to bear more children rather than fewer? When the significance of present trends is fully appreciated by intelligent people, will there be no further need to fear a declining birth-rate among them? Will there be no need of such drastic criticism as that quoted by Harold Ward: 'To the writer it seems that the selfishness, apathy, and prejudice which prevent intellectually gifted people from understanding the character of the present crisis in civilization is a far greater menace to the survival of culture

[45] Cf. Joseph J. Spengler, *France Faces Depopulation*, Durham, N. C.: Duke Univ. Press, 1938, p. 53. Germany in 1934, 1935, and 1936 more than doubled its natural increase of population of 1933.

than the prevalence of mental defect in the technical sense of the term.' "[46]

The present crisis, which is now being realized by thoughtful students to be acutely impending, has been brought about by an attempt to make the marriage contract anything that the individual pleased it should be, without regard to the fundamental nature of man as an individual or in his social relations to the family and the state.

Marriage must flow from a mutual love and admiration which is on an essentially higher plane than sexual attraction. This mutual attraction results in a perfect friendship which demands the permanence of the marriage and excludes the thought of separation and divorce.

The biological purpose of marriage is the procreation of children and it becomes a moral duty of the married partners to look forward to the procreation of children in sufficient number to ensure the stability and development of the nation, and to develop a home in which there will be transmitted to the children the religious, moral, and intellectual culture of the centuries. It is sometimes said that the home formerly was the chief means of *imposing* on the child the concepts of the past. It is even more inappropriate to speak of imposing culture on a child than to say that a father imposes on his children the inheritance he has acquired by years of labor.

In the home the law of charity must reign supreme. The children must realize that they were wanted in the beginning and are secure in the future in virtue of an all-pervading charity that stabilizes and perpetuates the home.

To plan a marriage without children is in itself a crime. It is true that marriage is essentially a pact of perfect friendship and because of this fact circumstances may arise that would justify a marriage when children would not be possible. But

[46] Harriet Ahlers Houdlette, *The American Family in a Changing Society: A Guide to Study and Research*, Washington, D. C.: Am. Assoc. Univ. Women, 1939, p. 44.

speaking of ordinary conditions, a marriage without children is not to be contemplated. Mechanical methods of contraception are inherently wrong and one is not allowed[47] to practice the biological method of rhythm merely to avoid the burden of children.

Reasonable as are these principles of the home, in all quarters we hear advocated the practice of birth control and limitation of the family to a small number of children. If the studies of Raymond Pearl and others are a valid guide, no married woman can look upon herself as having done her minimum duty till she has brought four living children into the world.

If, however, married women in general are going to do this, then there must be a rightabout face in the propaganda that proceeds from our universities, medical centers, social workers, and organized societies that work for the limitation of the family by the practice of birth control. We may have some hope that this change in the present trend will come in the near future. But even though the change should come soon, it will be very difficult to undo the harm that has already been done and put an end to the selfishness that is now so common, and the low ideals that now exist which make of marriage a mere opportunity for sex satisfaction, precluding children or doing away with them by abortion so that parenthood may be avoided and the married partners may still attend night clubs and spend the evenings as before at cocktail parties and various amusements without the burden of looking after the children at home. But unless this change comes about and selfishness ceases to recruit devotees from all ranks of society, there will be many unhappy husbands and wives who have failed in the sacred duties of the home and before this century draws to a close our country, which now seems to have such a wonderful, beneficent role to play in the history of the world, may have to hand over its heritage to another.

[47] We are dealing here with mental hygiene and do not enter into the discussion of the ethics of this problem. Cf. hereon T. V. Moore, *Principles of Ethics* (ed. 4), Philadelphia: Lippincott, 1944, pp. 216 ff.

9. INTERPERSONAL RELATIONS IN THE FAMILY

If the foundation of marriage is a suprasensual love of friendship, there will be an abiding all-inclusive charity existing in every one of the members of the family. Incidents will naturally occur from time to time and angry words will be in the air, but incidents pass and charity remains and the difficulties of the moment are soon forgotten. If, however, there never was a true friendship between husband and wife and the marriage was based purely on a sensory sexual attraction that never passed into anything of a higher nature, many difficulties are likely to arise between husband and wife and grow in magnitude and lead eventually to their separation or to various unwholesome attitudes of mind towards the children. As a result of these unwholesome attitudes of the mind on the part of parents, the behavior of the children will be profoundly affected and so various problems and difficulties between parents and children arise.

Certain unwholesome attitudes of mind are found in parents who seek help at a child guidance center with an almost monotonous frequency of repetition.

Mohr thus classified the more common attitudes observed among mothers who encounter difficulties with their children:

1. Mothers who overprotect their children
   a) Pure overprotection—a genuine overconcern for the welfare of the child. . . .
   b) Compensatory overprotection. Here an overprotective attitude masks some rejection of the child.
2. Mothers who are closely attached to their children for reasons not related to the children's needs, but the mother's.
   a) The emotionally deprived mother who turns to the child for gratification of her own need for affection.
   b) The ambitious but frustrated mother who seeks to gratify her own ambitions through the child's accomplishments.
3. Mothers who reject their children consciously or unconsciously.
   The numerous reasons for such rejection cannot here be discussed adequately. They range from fundamental resentment at being forced

to accept a feminine role, to specific traumatic experiences, e. g., having herself experienced rejection in childhood.

4. Ambivalent attitudes, i.e., conflicting attitudes of acceptance and rejection.[48]

Let us now consider some of these attitudes in more detail.

[48] George J. Mohr, "Influence of Mothers' Attitudes on Mental Health," *J. Pediat.* **16:** 641–46, 1940 (cf. pp. 643–44).

CHAPTER XI

THE OVERPROTECTED CHILD

LEVY thus describes the symptoms of the overprotected child: "Disobedience and impudence at home, characteristic of the entire group, follow maternal weakness in compelling respect, and submission to ordinary household requirements. The child refuses to come to meals, finally coaxed to the table he refuses to remain until the meal is over, or to eat what is placed before him; he refuses to come when called, to answer when spoken to. He keeps his own bedtime, goes to bed late, stays up late, refuses to wear what is required, throws his clothes anywhere, refusing to comply with numerous injunctions from either parent concerning neatness or routine. He is impudent, tells his mother to shut up or go to hell."[1]

This description of a child's behavior will awaken in a number of mothers the exclamation: "That's my child all over." And then the query, "What am I going to do about it?" The first thing to do is to ask yourself: "Did I attempt to protect my child to such an extent that I tried to satisfy his every whim, and let him have his own way hoping perhaps that he would thereby learn to love me so much that he would always obey and do just what I want just because he loves me? Did I try to keep him away from all other contacts and keep him for myself, rationalizing my real selfishness by saying I was keeping my child away from every possible harm?" As a matter of fact, keeping the child entirely for yourself, you commenced to stand in the way of even his lawful and legitimate craving for companionship and then like any little animal he commenced to rebel against restraint. And so he fought you and did not learn to love you. And then because you loved him and wanted always to let him have his own way, you unconsciously taught him that if he made a fuss he could get what

[1] David M. Levy, "Maternal Overprotection," *Psychiatry* 4: 393, 1941.

he wanted and so he commenced to tyrannize over you by tantrums and display of temper.

Perhaps in your difficulty you can make use of the good advice a child psychiatrist gave to the mothers of overprotected children. This consists "in helping them to ignore attention-getting behavior; in changing coaxing and nagging into direct commands; in breaking up the pattern of infantilizing care by direct refusals; and in encouraging the child to become more responsible and independent. Specifically, mothers stopped dressing the child, waiting on him at table, coaxing, babying, explaining everything, shining his shoes. They refused to argue every point and ignored tantrums. They stopped complaining about what a headache the child gave them. They allowed the child to make friends of his own, to go on errands, to go to school alone. Mothers were encouraged also to speak sharply to the child and to use methods of punishment of their own devising. They were encouraged also to bring the father more and more, not only in a friendly but also in an authoritative relationship."[2]

One child who had been overprotected by his mother and apparently neglected by his father improved when his father took more interest in him—"became friendlier, helped him with a stamp collection, went places with him, assumed generally more responsible paternal behavior—in fact aroused his wife's jealousy."[3]

It will be noticed that Mohr in the passage cited above distinguishes a group of cases in which mothers "are closely attached to their children for reasons not related to the children's needs, but to the mothers." Here belong a group of cases in which this overprotection or attachment continues into adult life and the mother looks upon the child as bound in conscience to regard the mother-child relationship as supreme and exclusive of any other human attachment whatsoever.

[2] *Op. cit.*, p. 420.
[3] *Ibid.*, p. 417.

The marriage of her child is something inconceivable to such a mother. I remember a woman of about 50 who had broken three engagements to marry because of her mother's attitude. On each occasion the mother said to her: "Of course you may marry, my child, and leave your dear old mother who has cared for you for so many years. I will never stand in your way—so marry, my child, and leave me alone." And the dutiful daughter each time broke her engagement that she might remain faithful to her mother and settled down to life as nursemaid, from which death alone could deliver her. When she wanted a day off her mother would say: "Go, my child, but remember your poor mother won't be with you forever. But of course I won't stand in the way of your pleasures. You may go and leave your poor old mother alone." And so the day's outing would be given up and the dutiful daughter served her mother her coffee in bed, opened her mail for her, read her the morning paper, took her to lunch, shopped with her in the afternoon, dined with her and then played cards with her unless the two went out together for the evening.

This is an extreme example of a condition that occurs all too often, in which the parents forget that the family is like the grain of wheat, which, unless it loses its individual existence and undergoes an apparent death, itself remaineth alone. The family is born to grow and develop in order that it may eventually disintegrate and give rise to a number of independent but related families. The parents who wish to keep the children to themselves and continually put off the marriage of their children if it is in any way possible, are guilty of a sinful selfishness. It is strange that one can love a child in such a selfish manner. But such instances occur with sufficient frequency to make it important to call attent on to this manner of self seeking when discussing the mental hygiene of the home. I remember a physician who said to me: "I was perfectly delighted when my daughter was born and I made up my mind I was going to spoil her 'good and proper' and make her love me so much that she would never be interested in any boy. She is a young lady now and she is my girl and no boy can ever stand between us."

Let us consider a case in which the mental difficulty of a young woman in the middle twenties arose from a selfish overprotection. The chief complaint was that she was always taking her pulse and had attacks of palpitation of the heart that gave her a sense of impending death, giving rise to periods of acute anxiety. At about 16 years of age she had chorea and there was at that time an apparent conflict of opinion about the condition of the heart. One specialist assured the mother that there was no heart disorder present, another that the heart was affected by some kind of toxic condition. At all events the child was kept in bed for over a year. At about this time the child's father died, and his death may have had something to do with centering the child's attention on her own illness and crystallizing the fear that her heart might suddenly stop beating and she would die suddenly.

The result of her condition was that she did not finish high school and for ten years lived alone with her mother with few other associations. Being neither in school nor at work, and having learned to drive an automobile, she was naturally requisitioned whenever her mother wanted to go out. The loneliness of her life and the tediousness of her duties as "chauffeuse" eventually led to a situation that was mentally intolerable. That this weariness of living was the crux of her difficulties did not at once appear from the history. An examination by two physicians showed no disorder of the heart, and that she was in good physical condition.

Analysis, because of the paucity of associations and laconic brevity of all answers, was very difficult. But eventually the attempt was made to find out what advantage the patient reaped from her disability. A hidden, unconscious motivation sometimes perpetuates psychoneurotic conditions that would otherwise fade away and cease to be.[4] So in the course of one interview I asked:

[4] Cf. T. V. Moore, *The Nature and Treatment of Mental Disorders*, p. 142.

"What's attractive about staying home?"   No answer.

"You don't like to leave home, do you?"

"No, I don't!"

"What do you get out of being home all the time?"

"I feel better.   I don't like to go out."

"What do you do when home?"

"I listen to music.   I do as I want to, read and relax."

"What do you fear about going out?"

"I don't know.   I was never frightened."

I had been expecting the disclosure of some kind of traumatic episode as a possible cause of the condition, but to my surprise she went on to tell me that when she had been able to go out her mother absorbed her time.   She had to take her around to see all her friends, people in whom the patient was not at all interested.   She did not like to go to places where her mother took her and found the daily trips unbearably tedious and monotonous.

"I was just tied to my mother," she said, "I could go no place without taking her around."

"You wanted to get out of it in some way."

"Yes, I did," she said with emphasis.

"And you found a way, you developed a disability."

"Yes, I have," she replied.

I went on to explain that sometimes people simply make up their minds to pretend they are sick in order to get out of doing something they do not want to do.   At other times they are not conscious of pretending but in some way, without voluntary effort on their part, a disability of some kind appears and prevents them from doing what they find distasteful.

"You don't pretend, do you?"

"No, I don't," was the emphatic reply.   But she remembered how her heart would beat when she went out with her mother, not in earlier years, but during the latter part of her "captivity" until she quit going anywhere at all.

Furthermore she had been telling her mother recently that she could not go out with her, because if she should her heart would beat.

In a later interview we returned to this situation again and she told how in those days she felt emotionally rebellious because she was tied to her mother. I remarked: "If you get angry your heart beats."

"Yes," she replied, "but you have to be awfully angry." She went on to recall how very rebellious she felt on those occasions.

I then went on to explain the concept of the conditioned reflex and pointed out that if going out was associated often enough with palpitation of the heart it was psychologically possible that after a time the very idea of going out, no matter with whom or where, might be followed by a rapid beating of the heart. "But," I remarked, "a girl does not like to admit to herself that she is selfish to her mother and so you did not realize the true cause of the palpitation of your heart."

The girl seemed to understand that her fear of going out could have developed as a rebellion against her mother's selfishness. I asked, "If you got well would the old situation revive?"

She answered, "I don't know, maybe I fear it might."

She wanted to go to a wedding that night, but had given up the idea for fear that her heart would beat. I suggested that this analysis should help her to go. She went. Her heart did beat a little as she went out but she carried on and it subsided and she had no more trouble that evening, enjoying the function very much. From time to time in later interviews, I would ask about the palpitation of the heart and to my surprise found it had practically ceased. Only occasionally later did it recur. Nevertheless the fear of going out persisted, unaccompanied by the palpitation. A dream that I managed to analyze later may throw some light on the continuation of the disability.

She dreamed about buying a hat made out of a big bird. There was a price tag on it: $12.50. She did not finish the bargain, neither accepting nor rejecting it.

A bird in her mind was associated with being a rascal and

the association seemed to indicate that she was on the fence about being a rascal, a kind of roguish, independent child. She could not complete the bargain, could not make up her mind either way. And then in some manner the price tag seemed to indicate the cost of being free. Not knowing much about the value of women's hats I asked if $12.50 was much to pay for a hat. She said, "It's not so much."

"Perhaps," I remarked, "your dream is telling you it won't cost so much to get free from your phobia."

"It would be wonderful to come out!"

"The dream tells you you can't come out without paying something, but it is not so much to pay. Had you not better conclude the bargain?"

"I would like to."

But she did not. In the meantime a great deal had been accomplished. She had taken up a business course and held a good position. At first she worked at a distance from her home but demanded that someone in the family take her to work and bring her back. Later she worked nearer home and went to and fro by herself.

It is hard for any of us to realize our own selfishness. So let us not blame the parents who unconsciously use a child for their own advantage, nor the child who sometimes does not understand and appreciate all he owes to his parents. But the parents must learn the hard lesson: when we have done all those things we know we ought to have done, then to say we are unprofitable servants. The home lives that the home may die and what more can anyone do than play his part well on the stage of life and then leave the scene and appear no more. However, grandparents can and are meant to play a useful role in the home and in a normal family where charity reigns supreme and where there is a fairly numerous offspring, the children's children enliven the latter days of the grandparents and many a child is thankful for having known and been helped by the self-sacrificing, kindly parents of his father and mother.

CHAPTER XII

THE REJECTED CHILD

I T IS strange that so many children come to our child guidance centers because of behavior problems arising out of the fact that they are not wanted by their parents. The term "rejection" is used to designate the essential underlying cause of many a child's abnormality of conduct and indicates that in some way or another one or both parents have made the child feel that he is not wanted. Symonds thus defines the concept: "By rejected we mean the child who is unwanted by either mother or father. Either mother or father or both fail to give the child adequate care, protection or affection, or they may make invidious contrasts with other children in the family or with children outside the family, and in general the child is neglected in one or more ways. Sometimes the mother or father compensates for the guilt which they may feel for their rejection by lavishing affection on the child and overprotecting it."[1]

It is strange to what extent rejection will go. Burgum[2] cites the case of a father who with the aid of a midwife friend of his bound up his wife's breasts so that she would be unable to nurse their child.

Taking the group of mothers who bring children to child guidance centers as a class, it is fairly easy to find among them a fair number who did not feel that they should fondle their children, who fed them in a perfunctory manner when they were little and were ingenious in devising punishments when they were old enough to move about and make trouble.

Take for instance the following description given by a mother of her child and her account of how she attempted to discipline him:

[1] Percival M. Symonds, "Study of Parental Acceptance and Rejection," *Am. J. Orthopsychiat.*, vol. 8, 1938.

[2] *Am. J. Orthopsychiat.* **10**: 314, 1940.

"Lack of cooperation; lack of concentration; nothing interests him for any length of time; very destructive; cruel to his younger brothers and sisters, that is, he slaps or hits them with a toy, pulls hair and bites; inconsiderate of everybody and disobedient; doesn't respond to punishment. I have used every measure and nothing helps. I deprived him of small pleasures, left him behind when the others went out, and locked him in his room, but he destroyed things. Then, I took everything out of the room and left him alone. I whipped him, and locked him up alone in the garage, but nothing helps."

Much of the child's behavior was due to the fact that he wanted to get back at his mother for punishing him. Much to the father's surprise, when the mother had to go to the hospital for some weeks, there was a marked improvement in the behavior of the child.

Then there is the father who does not want to be bothered with the children. Sometimes a Navy or an Army officer tries to make the family stand about like the men under his command, with the result that his furloughs are dreaded by the children. One young girl in high school was brought to the clinic for stealing. She had a very domineering, antagonistic father. Her stealing exasperated him to fury. The child had no lack of spending money, and merely asking her mother for the things she stole would have gotten them for her in no time. Whether consciously so motivated or not, her stealing enabled her to "get back" at her father for many whippings and angry scoldings. Encouraging her to a different attitude towards her father and awakening her to an appreciation of the values, dangers, and opportunities of life by letting her read vocational novels put an end to her stealing.

Then there is the parent who is always telling her impossible Jimmy what a fine boy his little brother Billy is and how he should try to be like Billy, with the result that from time to time Jimmy beats up Billy and gives ever more and more proof of his inherent wickedness. In fact the mother is likely to prove to the psychiatrist some fine day the fact that she rejected the child from the beginning by saying: "You know Jimmy was never a nice cuddlesome baby like little Billy."

Children don't imitate children they are told to imitate, but promptly reject the model. Some parents find it hard to realize this principle. It is very illogical in the children but their behavior is psychologically true to form. If you want a child to imitate, you must first find a model that he admires. He will imitate *you* if you act so that he loves and admires you. He will imitate the heroes he learns to reverence from his reading. But he won't imitate anyone, in the family or outside of it, whom you hold up to him so that he can see how wicked he is himself.

Naturally the best treatment here is prophylactic. Parents must want a family from the outset and when there are two or more children, do their best to show no preferences but manifest equal kindness and affection to all.

When, however, rejection has already taken place the parent is the primary one to treat. This is often impossible because the rejecting parent will not come for treatment. But even when the parent will come the outlook is not bright.

Clothier points out that one method is to attempt to give "a mother insight into the tensions and conflicts that lie behind her child's problems."[3] But while a mother is glad to have her child treated she is often unwilling to be treated herself and soon stops coming.

Again, "an effort is sometimes made to diminish a mother's hostility toward her child by encouraging her to give vent to her aggression during clinic interviews—trying at the same time to discover and interpret to her the original sources of her hostilities. By a process of catharsis, it is hoped that aggression will be drained off and the child's situation alle-

[3] Florence Clothier, "The Treatment of the Rejected Child," *Nervous Child* 3: 93 (Jan.), 1944.

State Teachers College Library
Willimantic, Conn.

viated.   But seldom does this approach bring about the hoped-
for results."[4]

In fact the author continues: "One is inclined to feel that
in the case of the rejecting mother, little or no permanent
modification of fundamental attitudes toward her child can
be accomplished by direct clinic psychotherapy."[5]

This means that at times we will have to adjust the child himself to his impossible situation.   Too little attention has been
paid to a direct psychotherapy of the child aimed at changing his
attitude and helping him to bear what seems impossible to
endure, by attempting to introduce into his mind sound principles of mental hygiene more or less specific to his present
situation.

Furthermore, rejection need not always be empty of any
advantage to the child.   It is an ill wind that blows no one
any good.

Burgum has attempted to show that parental rejection is
not an unmitigated evil.   The children whom she studied,
however, were all serious behavior problems but they did
develop a fearless self reliance and the capacity to meet
frustration by making use of their own resources.   Many
learned to amuse themselves and some found for themselves
acceptance and a welcome outside the home.   "You can't
stump me" was the attitude taken by some.   In whatever
way such an attitude developed, we must regard it as a wholesome asset.   However, rejection must be looked upon as the
occasion for these wholesome reactions rather than the cause.[6]

But whereas a mother might resent having her attitude of
mind changed by any psychiatrist, and any attempt to do
so might fail, she can if she wills take another point of view
and alter her treatment of the child.   She must, however, in

---

[4] *Ibid.*, p. 94.

[5] *Ibid.* See, however, the case reported in T. V. Moore, *The Nature and
Treatment of Mental Disorders*, p. 178 ff.

[6] Mildred Burgum, "Constructive Values Associated with Rejection,"
Am. J. Orthopsychiat. **10:** 312–26, 1940.

some way first become conscious of the fact that she rather than the child may be responsible for the behavior difficulties. Should any mother who has a child manifesting behavior difficulties read these pages she might ask herself: Did I ever tell my child to be good like so and so? Have I been ever devising ways of punishment? Have I ever shown more affection to one of my children than to another? Perhaps she might try to see what more affection and less scolding would do for her problem youngster and let the results speak for themselves.

Usually at a child guidance center one treats both mother and child. Sometimes, however, when it is impossible to treat the parent, good results can be obtained from dealing with the child alone.

Margaret was the last child of a rather elderly mother and a father who at times would be angry and unreasonable. Whether justifiably or not, Margaret got the idea that her father did not love her. At all events he was far from being the child's friend and confidant, he showed affection very coldly if at all and at times spoke to her in an unreasonable, angry manner. She came to the clinic originally because of epileptic seizures and spells of vomiting. School anxieties seemed to be a factor in the situation. She was afraid of examinations, wanted to live alone by herself, and had stopped school because of vomiting after meals.

Psychotherapy helped the situation very much. The child's vomiting ceased, she returned to school and managed to make up for what she had missed, passed her final examinations, and was promoted to a higher grade. Just before the school opened in the autumn she had a violent scene with her father. It had started with a fuss between her father and her grandmother in the course of which he told her grandmother to get out of the house. Margaret stuck up for her grandmother and told her father that he had lived with his mother all these years and had no right now to tell her to get out of the house. So the father turned on his daughter and told *her* also to get out of the house.

When she came to the child center for her next visit after this stormy episode, its memory filled her consciousness and was the main topic of her conversation.

"I'm sixteen," she said, "and I'm going to get out and get a job and have my own little room all to myself."

No amount of persuasion or argument could shake her in this resolution. It was then that I turned to bibliotherapy, a technique that we have developed at the child center, where we have a small library for children for carrying it out.[7]

And so I suggested a compromise:

> Go to school just for two weeks
> Read a book
> Write me what you think of it
> And see me at the end of the two weeks

I let her take home *Land Spell* by Gladys Hasty Carroll. Some days later I received the following letter:

I read the book and now I see what you mean. I must have my education in order to go out and face the world. I realize now that I must take a step down for happiness. I know now that the man who said "Pride goeth before a fall" was really right. I have gone to school now for a week and I can truthfully say that I have never had a better time. Dr. Moore, I think my daddy really loves me now and doesn't want me to leave.

I hope you are well and happy and please say hello to your nice secretary for me. Lots of love!

---

[7] Some time ago it occurred to me that children might be helped by giving them a book to read which would touch upon their specific problem and illustrate principles of conduct that they might absorb and be guided by in the determination of their behavior. I spoke about the matter to Miss Clara Kircher, a member of the staff of the Newark Public Library, and she prepared for me a bibliography of children's literature classified as to school grade, with a subject index giving captions in alphabetical order designating various foci in the behavior of problem children. This bibliography has been published as *Character Formation Through Books, A Bibliography*, Washington, D. C.: Catholic University of America, 1944. By means of it I was able to pick books for this child that had to do with leaving home when difficulties with parents became acute.

When she returned we had a general talk about home and school problems and on leaving I loaned her *A Bend in the Road* by Margaret Raymond. At the next visit I asked her what she got out of the book. She told me that it was a story of a girl who left home because her father beat her when she came home late at night. She got a factory job and boarded with two other girls and had a pretty tough struggle.

"And what did you learn from it for yourself?"

> It shows me losing my temper is pretty silly.
> I don't think I should leave home.
> I learned that my father loves me even though he is gruff on the outside.

In a previous interview I had suggested that she should make up with her father and give him a big hug and a kiss and so at this point I queried:

"Did you ever give your father that big hug and kiss?"

"O no," she answered, "he would never let me get that near him."

Unfortunately a number of fathers have an attitude towards their children which makes them stand aloof and seek advice and companionship outside the home.

We went on with our conversation:

"Are you really learning to be unselfish and give up your own way?"

"I am trying to."

"When your father or mother or sister want you to do something, you say: 'I don't want to'?"

"Yes!"

"Could you give in to them a little more easily?" No answer.

"It would be wiser."

"It would."

"You know life is a time in which we learn to be reasonable."

"I never looked at it that way. I always thought I could live *my* life *my* way."

"It is better to lead life a reasonable way."

"O, yes, but I never looked at it that way before."

I then loaned her *Long Winter* by Laura Wilder and when she came again I asked, "What did you get out of *Long Winter*?"

"You have to learn patience. The little blind girl and the children's father made me think of patience."

"How would you apply this idea of patience to yourself?"

"I get mad awful quick. I haven't tried to stop it."

"Why not try?"

"It would be O.K. if it would work. I have a temper and it won't calm down."

"What else did you learn?"

"I learned also not to be selfish. It came from reading how the family always lived together. They got along. There was a sense of balance there. We fight like the devil at home."

And so we went on and instead of running away from the home where she felt rejected, she stayed and continued her schooling and though emotional episodes were by no means entirely banished from her life, there was some attempt on the part of the child to deal with them reasonably and there was a worth while improvement in the interpersonal relations of the family group.

The case we are now about to present is a mixture of over protection and rejection, but a mixture so typical that many parents will recognize therein a situation they have often met and perhaps must meet in dealing with their own children.

Every good parent attempts to give to his children the religious, moral, social, and educational inheritance that is their due. And it is a most important matter that he should do so. To make no attempt to transmit this valuable inheritance would be a most serious delinquency on the part of the parent. But to transmit this inheritance is to bring about an inner assimilation of many valuable ideals and principles on the part of the child. The ease and success of the process of transmission and assimilation are going to depend largely on the stability and the personality of the parents and their freedom from blind emotional drives.

In their attempts to secure conformity with standards on the part of their children, parents of necessity place certain restrictions on the free activity of their children. They must at times also mete out some kind of punishment. For a child who is always allowed to do what he pleases when he pleases and is never punished in any way for any type of behavior is not likely to develop a stable, normal personality. At times in an attempt to preserve the child from any and all dangers there arises an attitude of overprotection: and when the child rebels against an extreme limitation of liberties, the parent reacts by the mechanism of rejection and seeks revenge by punishment. And so out of the very necessary process of discipline and training we reap the evils of overprotection and rejection. Our conclusion should not be to give up all discipline and training as some writers suggest, but to train and discipline in such a way as to develop a normal, stable personality and strengthen rather than weaken the bond of love between parents and children. The way in which this is to be done is the crux of the problem of child guidance. The following case history may give some suggestions as to what to do and what not to do with a troublesome adolescent.

Some time ago we were asked to see Alice, a 16-year-old girl who had wandered away from home during an attack of amnesia.[8]

We shall give an account of the episode as reconstructed from the history and the associations obtained later from the patient.

The patient's mother and stepfather were both honestly interested in the patient and attempted to do the very best they could for her. But there had been a number of episodes between mother and daughter prior to the attack of amnesia, all arising out of an honest though at times emotional attempt to secure proper behavior.

[8] That is to say, a loss of memory accompanied by wandering.

Among these incidents was the following: A few days before the onset of the amnesia, Alice wanted to go to the high school prom. But she felt that she would have to have a new dress. Apparently the relationship between Alice and her parents was such that she could not go and talk over her problems with either one of them. At the same time she wanted to shine at the high school prom. The temptation was too great, and so she stole $13.65 from her mother's purse and bought herself a dress. The mother missed the money, found the dress, and concluded to give Alice a lesson that stealing does not pay, so that she would remember it for the rest of her life. So she took Alice and the dress back to the store where she bought it, made known the theft, returned the dress, and got her money back. Alice, as her mother said, "blew up completely" and told her stepfather and her mother that they would be sorry for what they did. Apparently the whole affair was noised about to the neighbors, for in one of the mother's interviews at the child center, she later related that the lady next door told her: "I was shocked that you could do such a thing to Alice. I can understand how terrible Alice felt in that humiliating incident. I have known you for twenty-five years and I never imagined you could do such a thing to Alice."

I think that most thoughtful students of the child mind will agree that the mother was cruel, though her intentions were perfectly good. Many less drastic procedures would have been less harmful and more beneficial. But Alice had commenced to question whether or not her mother was really her mother, and thought perhaps her own mother had died when she was very young.

Later in the therapeutic interviews Alice spoke of how she and her mother used to quarrel. The mother hardly said a word that was not nasty. "I can't stand any more of it with her," she exclaimed with some vehemence. "I often thought of going out, going away from home because it got on my nerves. Mother was always more or less cross. She would take it out on me more than on Jim."

"Whom did she like more?"

"I think Jim."

"Did she like you?"

"I guess she did, but I always had it in my mind she didn't. It seemed as though I was the black sheep of the family. My mother did not know how to be a mother."

And so after the violent emotional shock that followed the exposure of her theft, she brooded over what had happened and had been happening for years. About three mornings after the humiliating episode, she forgot to eat her breakfast. Her mother noticed she had fixed up her hair in a peculiar manner. She left the house apparently to go to school, but got on a bus to go to the place where she worked in the afternoon after school. In one of the later therapeutic interviews she could remember getting on the bus and meeting the lady who lived next door, who asked if they were out of school for the day and she answered, "I work in the afternoon," though it was then only a little after 9 in the morning. For things from that time on until she came to in a mental hospital, there is an amnesia. A few vague memories remain. From these and data given by others it appears that she wandered about in a clouded state of mind. In this clouded state of mind she asked some young boys to take her home and offered them her billfold, in which was her identification card. But the boys ran away with the pocketbook and so she was left without any means of identification. Later she wandered into a large apartment house saying she wanted to see someone but could not remember the name. She was given the list of the people living in the apartment and finally picked out a name but the lady was out. Alice waited till the lady returned. But when she did return she did not know Alice at all, and so the police were notified.

After coming to "she remembered things that had happened since she 'came to' "; but all persons and events of her life prior to the given morning were apparently obliterated from her memory. She did not recognize her mother and sister, the neighbors, people in various stores, etc. She had also apparently forgotten various social acquisitions. She did not dare to go out to dinner because she did not know how to behave at table; she could not go to church, because she did not know what the people did in church. She did not know how to go to confession or communion and so she was cut off from the whole world and all manner of social contacts.

After about three weeks in the hospital with no essential change, she was taken to a psychiatrist, who after attempts at hypnosis gave her three electric shock treatments which apparently in some measure restored her memory. She was then allowed to go to a moving picture and when she returned her memory was gone again. This was followed by three more shocks without any amelioration of her condition and the psychiatrist gave up further treatment. About two months later she came to the child center in a kind of dazed condition with an apparent complete amnesia for all events prior to the morning she forgot to eat her breakfast, did up her hair in a strange fashion, and started to wander.

The treatment consisted in merely suggesting that if she would allow her mind to wander she would remember everything that happened in her past life, for nothing had really been forgotten beyond recall. At first very little was recalled and there were continuous digressions into her present troubles. In one of the early visits she was in acute mental distress because a boy who had been taking her out quit showing up in the evenings. The depression increased and it was decided to treat it as an organic depression and administer eschatin.[9] In the meantime we went on with the attempt to trace back our way to past events by the channels of association. In one of these periods she remarked: "I am afraid that if I get back into my other state of mind in which I remember things I

[9] See T. V. Moore, *op. cit.*, pp. 262 ff.

would have to go back and live with my mother and there would be arguments. I can't stand her. She is having change of life and everything falls on me. I would like to go off alone where there is nobody."

The girl was at that time living with her cousin and was taking care of the latter's children. It is worth while noting how the patient referred to "my other state of mind" in which she remembered things. This suggests that we are dealing here with an incipient doubling of the personality. Any attempt to dwell on her "other self" might complete the split and lead to two well-defined personalities each with its own separate memory chain without any connnecting links to bridge the split.

Memories of difficulties with her mother about her boy friends, prior to the attack of amnesia, came back in various interviews. Also various other memories. In one interview apparently apropos of nothing else she suddenly remarked: "I feel as though I can swim," and then added hesitatingly, "but I don't remember swimming," and then a moment later, "Last summer I did go swimming. My cousin and I swam all last summer." Then she recalled working in the afternoons before she "got sick," then many quarrels with her mother, "when she got angry and slapped me." Then she complained that her mother did not try to look for her when she disappeared: "She could have gone to the police, but she did nothing till she saw my picture in the paper."

In the meantime her mother was surprised at various signs of Alice's returning memory. She had gone to a store and talked to the shopkeeper for the first time since her "sickness" as if she had known her all her life. Up to the recent present she had stood bewildered in the store as if in a strange place.

I began trying to awaken an interest in reading. She had spoken of never going to school again. One book awakened an interest in becoming a nurse. I pointed out that that would be a fine career, but it would require a high school diploma. She said she never wanted to go to school around home—evidently feeling that people knew about her loss of memory and wandering. At first she did not want to appear on the streets or go anywhere because she felt ashamed and as if everybody were looking at her.

In one interview she spoke of having paid a visit to her mother and said: "We got along all right. When mother started in, I kept quiet. When I let her talk that way a bit, she gets all right." A profound bit of family philosophy. If more mothers would talk less and more children would keep quiet and let their mothers talk that way a bit, more families would get along all right.

By this time, to her mother's great surprise, she was interested in reading. From *Mary Karstens, M.D.*, by Mildred F. Mees, she learned the importance of cooperation and realized she had never cooperated. "But," she added, "I am getting along O.K. now."

In the meantime another physician at the clinic had been interviewing the mother and the mother commenced to realize that she had been at times a bit harsh and gruff with Alice. And she tried to do better. When Alice's birthday rolled around she bought her a whole new outfit, dress and shoes and everything. Alice was just lovely at home and even the neighbors said that she had never looked so nice and sweet. Alice even said of her own accord that she would go back to her mother when the cousin with whom she was living went away for a couple of weeks. "And you know," said the mother, "I feel much better myself and when I went to see the doctor the other day he told me that my high blood pressure had all disappeared. And what do you think, when Alice was here she kissed me and wanted to kiss her father, a thing she hasn't done for a long time."

And when Alice came to her next visit with me she said: "Mother seems changed now. Before she was always so cross and would take things out on me. And I took it out on my daddy. I was so cross to him. But I can't get over how my mother has changed. I feel as though I can talk to her now about my problems. Now she seems to understand. I can tell her about the boy who quit coming to see me. Before, I could not say a word to her about a boy. I can talk to her now. It makes you feel good to have someone to talk to."

I asked a question about when she had first thought of leaving home but she was not interested, said it must have been several years ago and then continued: "I can't get over how she has changed. I feel better. She feels better. I can talk to somebody. Before, I did not feel I had anybody close to me."

And that is precisely what the rejected child feels, no matter what may be the cause of the rejection. If parents would only realize how much their children need to feel that someone is close to them and how real is the necessity of their having someone to whom they can go and talk over their troubles and, if you will, tell all about the details of the tempest in the teapot—and if they would only understand that a dress, a pair of shoes, or baseball bat, or any other thing given as a sign of love and acceptance would make them recipients of their children's confidences—many a storm in family life would be dissipated before the distant thunder could roll and the lightning strike.

But the course of true love never does run smooth. Alice likes to wear shorts when she works in the garden and even on the street. Now her mother does not approve of shorts and Alice has actually shortened her shorts which the mother thought were already too short. And so the mother gave her a piece of her mind and told her that it was downright indecent to wear her shorts as short as they now were. And Alice replied: "That's the way I like to wear them."

The psychiatrist in the course of interviewing the mother pointed out to her that a great deal depends on the way in which matters are placed before a child. If you say to a child in an angry manner, "You have shortened your shorts so much that it is indecent now for you to wear them," the child may look upon this as just one more sign of the fact that you don't love her, want to be mean to her, and may react by insisting on wearing her clothes the way she wants to wear them just to get back at you. But you might smile and say: "I wonder if boys and people of good taste would like to see you dressed in that way? Do you think you really look pretty the way you are now?" Then after a bit her own judgment on the matter will mature and you will guide your child to better standards which she takes and keeps to because she has adopted them herself.

But the little difficulty about shortening the shorts did not disrupt readjustment to the mother. "I can still talk to her," the girl said, "about many things I could not mention before. Everything is going all right now and I am going to do my best to get along. I can take things better. I was nasty to the children. When I get irritated now I can hold my breath and let it pass."

There is now no loss of memory for things prior to the onset of wandering. For the actual period of wandering there is only a vague memory of a few incidents. But there is good rapport with the mother and the child looked forward with interest to her return to high school in the autumn.

The incident is a good example of a loss of memory due to mental causes. An organic loss of memory due to a blow on the head, for example, would have been more likely to affect the power to store new impressions and would have left intact the ability to recall the data of past experience. The patient fled from home and the memories of the past not by voluntary effort but from an unconscious drive to escape surroundings that had become unhappy owing to a good mother's good intentions of forcing her daughter to be what she should be. The way back to the memories of the past and a happy home adjustment was not found by mere verbal association, though this did lead to islands of recall that spontaneously expanded till they joined the whole continent of past experience. This expansion was made possible by the psychiatrist who worked with the mother and brought about a change in her attitude and conduct, so that the patient found that she was really close to somebody to whom she could talk and who in spite of the past really loved and cared for her.

Chapter XIII

HOME ORGANIZATION AND THE PROBLEM OF DATING

THE HOME is a social unit and as such must have a stable organization. Whenever a group of human beings constitutes a social unit, there must be authority to guide and direct, and cooperation and obedience on the part of those who constitute the unit and live under authority. The two evils that must be guarded against are an arbitrary inconsiderate imposition of authority on the one hand and on the other an individualism that goes its own way and utterly disregards the lawful demands of authority.

There are homes in which everyone lives in terror of the father and every child seeks the first opportunity of leaving the parental home and living elsewhere. On the other hand there are homes which are nothing more than sleeping quarters. Family life has ceased, everyone departs in the evening to go about his own affairs, comes in when he pleases, eats a hurried breakfast in the morning and rushes off to work.

The ideal home has a family life and the main recreations of each member of the family are found within the family group. The father loves to return from work and play with the little children when the family is in its infancy; and, later on, all like to sit and talk together in the evenings when the day's work is done. When anyone, still living under the family roof, wants to go out, he acquaints the family with what he is going to do and where and with whom he intends to go. This is true not only of adolescents but even of older children who have grown up and still live in their father's house. When there is love and trust and affection, this imposes no burden. If it is true of the adult child, it is particularly true of the adolescent. And yet in our days the boy and girl who are growing up sometimes think that they should be allowed to go and come as they please and that parents should not ask questions about their going out and coming in.

A young girl, for instance, feels that she would like to get married at the earliest opportunity and that she should be allowed to go out with a "date" whenever she is asked and come home when she pleases. From her point of view she sees no objection to going out in the evening and returning at 12 or 1 o'clock in the morning or perhaps even later. In fact, she has done so a number of times and everything was quite innocent and she enjoyed the dancing and had a bully good time, and why should her parents want to place restrictions and make things so uncomfortable and awkward? Who wants to leave a dance anyhow before the others do and why can't one stop in on the way home and have a drink or two like so many other girls?

On the other hand, parents do get worried about their beautiful young girls and they know much more about the dangers of dating and drinking and being out late at night than their children. Furthermore, they feel responsible and are responsible for allowing a daughter to go out with this or that young man, supposedly to this or that place, and to remain out till this or that hour at night—or in the early morning. If they sanction the evening's outing, should they not be reasonably certain of the good character of the young man who takes their daughter out and know enough about the function she will attend and the people she will meet to have a fair assurance that no harm is likely to befall their daughter? Should not a young girl try to look at things from the point of view of her parents so as to appreciate the responsibility which they feel for her safety?

As to these evening outings, many are indeed perfectly good innocent amusement. Much depends on persons and circumstances; but quite often an evening party or a high school outing involves much more than innocent amusement.

Judge Lindsey's investigation will bear this out. He found

that about 90 per cent of the youth who go to high school parties indulge in hugging and kissing[1]; and "at least fifty per cent of those who begin with hugging and kissing do not restrict themselves to that, but go further, and indulge in other sex liberties which, by all the conventions, are outrageously improper"[2]; and "fifteen to twenty per cent of those who begin with hugging and kissing eventually 'go the limit.'"[3]

He goes on to say that out of 495 girls of high school age who admitted to him that they had sex experiences with boys about 25, or 5 per cent, became pregnant. About three-fourths of these girls came to him of their own accord. "Some were pregnant, some were diseased, some were remorseful, some wanted counsel and so on."[4]

Is not prevention more important than cure?

An adolescent girl having her own personal mental hygiene at heart should ask herself: Would it not be better for me to allow my parents to guide my life, for the next few years at least, rather than take risks and rush blindly into situations which may at any time get beyond my powers of control?

What principles have we to guide us in the present problem? After all, principles are our best guides in the complex maze of the interpersonal relationships of the home. Let us look at the matter from this point of view. The home is a social unit on a small scale. Every social unit, whether the state, the municipality, a business orgainization, a small store, must have a leader with power and authority to direct and organize the social unit. If there is no such leader, or if the leader's regulations are utterly disregarded, there will soon result a condition of chaos and the social unit will disintegrate. The same is true of the family. The family must have a leader with the power and right to organize the household. This

[1] Ben B. Lindsey and Wainwright Evans, *The Revolt of Modern Youth*, New York, 1925, p. 56.

[2] *Ibid.*, p. 59.

[3] *Ibid.*, p. 62.

[4] *Ibid.*, p. 64.

power ordinarily centers in the father, though much of it is frequently delegated to the mother.

Sometimes there is a bit of foolish vanity in a family about who should be the boss of the house. No serious difficulties arise when the father and mother have good common sense, love each other sincerely, and are frank and open one with the other about all the details of their lives. In general they will discuss matters and come to a reasonable agreement. If the father assumes responsibility in place of asserting authority, all will run smoothly.

The father, therefore, talking over things with the others and taking into consideration the duties, needs, and legitimate desires of all concerned, as the head of the family, fixes the hours for meals, the time for rising, etc., and so organizes the whole household regimen. As long as the child remains a member of the paternal household, even though grown to adult years, he should try to fit in with the ordinary routine of the household and so make all things run smoothly. Certainly an honest attempt by every member of the family to "fit in" is going to make for the happiness of the whole household. Now let our adolescent look at matters from this point of view. Is it reasonable, is it wise, is it for the adolescent's own good to go his or her own way without regard to the process of "fitting in" with the family regimen?

When now the adolescent girl "goes out," what rules should govern her conduct? Perhaps it would be well to let our adolescent draw up the rules. And so I will present the following case of a 17-year-old girl whose mother was very much disturbed about her and had her come for a few visits to see what might be done.

The mother was quite naturally anxious about her daughter's "running around" with a boy. She felt that she came home too late, at about 11 o'clock, and then insisted on staying with him in the parlor until midnight. It was stipulated that I would see the girl only after she herself wrote and asked

for an appointment.   A few weeks later the letter was received
and Louise was given an appointment.

In the first interview we started to talk about the possibilities
that life held out for her and the various careers in which she
might be interested. She thought a job as "dental assistant"
might be something different from the ordinary and was given
several references by which she could orient herself as to ways,
means, and probable openings in this line of work. She very
soon commenced to talk of her boy friend, whom she praised
very highly, and said that her affection for him was different
and far stronger than any love she had previously known. She
said that this was her real difficulty and she and her mother
could not agree on the solution of the problems that arise out of
"dating." She asked my advice about these problems and I
suggested that it would be well to think the matter over, do a
little reading, and work out her principles, and we could discuss them together. I suggested that she read Maureen
Daly's novel *Seventeenth Summer*[5] and use the scenes and characters in that book to work out her principles. She took the
book and eventually presented me with the following principles
to govern a girl's conduct when "dating." They are given in
her own words:

Good Principles

What is a man's opinion of a woman without principles?
What is a boy's opinion of a girl without principles?
The opinion is not high.
Young girls first beginning to date should establish some principles, good
principles, to follow through the life of dating.
Dating principles are important to every young girl. Some of these which
could be established are:
1. No drinking. This habit may be obtained even though the girl is not in
   the company of a boy. There may come a time when she would be.
2. Stay with the crowd. To stay with a crowd is evading temptation.
   Stay *with* a crowd and you'll stay *away* from temptation.
3. Staying away from night clubs and from places tolerating sin.

---

[5] New York: Dodd Mead, 1943.

Burlesque shows are not for young people, in fact they are not for good Catholics.

4. Indulging in excess hugging and kissing. Prolonged hugging and kissing brings into the picture too much sexuality. Things may get out of hand, so why take chances.

5. Get interested in clubs and organizations to occupy your time wisely. These are only a few good principles to follow. There are lots of girls who have no principles. They wish they had!

In the meantime she had been loaned *Famous Mothers and Their Children*[6] by Anna Curtis Chandler. In this she enjoyed most the story about Edison, who seemed at first unlikely to succeed in life. She also liked the story of St. Francis of Assisi and how his mother spurred him on to do great things by calling him a knight and expressing the hope that he would be a knight of God. "These mothers," she said, "guided their children and saw them through thick and thin. They established in the child's mind what was right. St. Francis' mother taught him to pray."

I asked what is the most important thing to pray for, and she answered: "That I will lead a good life and do what's right and go to heaven."

I asked what is the first thing we ask for in the "Our Father" and she answered, " 'Hallowed be Thy Name.' "

"Do we praise God only by our words?"

She looked puzzled and I went on to point out that we praise God most of all by what we are. If the heavens show forth the glory of God, how wonderful is the praise that you can give to God by becoming a strong, noble, beautiful, moral, and spiritual creature. She thought that this was really worth while.

In closing the interview I asked: "Can you recall anything in the conduct of the famous mothers that seemed to you to be an example worth imitating?"

She answered: "Their patience. They knew what they wanted their children to be—someone to be looked up to; and they kept on trying to bring that about."

[6] New York: Stokes, 1938.

Evidently, I said, the good mother must herself be someone to look up to. By the nobility of her personality she must, like the heavens, show forth the glory of God.

These are but sample notes of things that transpired in some half-dozen interviews. The mother told me that one thing was accomplished at which I had not specifically aimed. The girl gave up trashy reading, commenced to select of her own accord really worth while books. The mother was not at all pleased with Louise's best boy friend. This is a situation that very often appears. Parents should remember, however, that while they have a duty to feed, clothe, shelter, and educate their children, they have not a right to insist that the child enter this or that career or marry this or that person. The child, not the parents, must live out the career and live with the married partner. On the other hand, children should treat their parents' opinion with great respect and go against it in these important matters only after mature deliberation and consultation with others capable of giving good advice on the point. In general the psychiatrist takes neither side. He knows but little about the unseen partner. Furthermore, certain children will be driven to do what they want to do whether it is wise or not, merely because everybody is lined up against them. In the last interview Louise expressed the idea that she had learned a great deal and would be able to manage herself and her problems much better. I asked: "How are you and the boy getting along?"

She smiled and from what she said I gathered that her interest in this particular boy had waned and other "best" boy friends were appearing on the horizon.

Chapter XIV

THE IDEAL OF FAMILY LIFE

1. The Coordinating Principle of the Home

THE FAMILY has by its nature a twofold root in the mind of man, namely:

1) The desire of man for true and perfect friendship.
2) The natural craving to have and to care for, to protect, and to educate a number of children.

There is, however, an ethics floating around in the minds of some and finding philosophical exponents in such men as Bertrand Russell, which would call in question the fundamental character of these two cravings.

According to this "new morality," "the average man in all ages has had as many children as it paid him to have, no more and no less,"[1] and according to this philosophy, the main driving force in bringing about a marriage is the craving to satisfy sexual desire. As we have pointed out above, such concepts are based on a theory of human nature that sees in man only sensory and affective elements and leaves out of consideration the intellectual and spiritual values in human life.

It will suffice here to point to the fact that many partners in the marriage compact are friends in the true sense of the word and that they would still want to be united in matrimony even if for any reason the sexual element were eliminated entirely. Furthermore, there are many who do marry and look forward to a family of children to love and care for and make happy, and find their own happiness in fulfilling the duties of parenthood.

And here where we are delineating the ideal marriage we

---

[1] George Ernest Newsom, *The New Morality*, New York: Scribner, 1933, p. 124.

must point to the craving for and the finding of true friendship as the psychological factor which normally brings a marriage about in the first place. Furthermore, the ideal marriage is going to look forward to a number of children and the establishment of a happy social group living together in peace and harmony, preparing to serve God and the social order by their life and work.

That many marriages fall short of the ideal and are even diametrically opposed to it there can be no doubt. But it does not take a very deep philosophic insight to decide which type of marriage is more likely to be a permanent happy union and a contribution to the welfare of society. For centuries the ideal outlined has been cherished by Christian thinkers.

But the Christian concept of the home was an inheritance from the Jewish people, in whom it had developed as a result of centuries of training in Old Testament tradition.

Edersheim thus pictures the Jewish home in contrast to that of other nations: "The Gentile world here presented terrible contrast, alike in regard to the relation of parents and children, and the character and moral object of their upbringing. Education begins in the *home*, and there were not homes like those in Israel; it is imparted by influence and example, before it comes by teaching; it is acquired by what is seen and heard, before it is laboriously learned from books; its real object becomes instinctively felt, before its goal is consciously sought. What Jewish fathers and mothers were; what they felt towards their children; and what they received, is known to every reader of the Old Testament. The relationship of father has its highest sanction and embodiment in that of God towards Israel; the tenderness and care of a mother in that of the watchfulness and pity of the Lord over His people."[2]

Christianity carried with it from Judaism this concept of

[2] Alfred Edersheim, *Life and Times of Jesus the Messiah*, London: Longmans, 1884, pp. 226–27.

the family and St. Paul naturally expressed the concept of
the ideal love that should exist between husband and wife
by saying: "Husbands, love your wives as Christ also loved
the Church and delivered Himself up for it."[3]

And so there arose that concept of the *caritas conjugalis*
as something of another nature and transcending in its dignity
mere sexual attraction.   St. Augustine speaks of it as being
essentially different from *libido* and constituting the essence
of the marriage union.[4]   Again he speaks of the union of Mary
and Joseph as one "not of lust but affection, not a mingling
of the corporeal but a union of minds, which is something of
higher value."[5]

And so we get the concept of the home as a social unit but
at the same time a truly living organic whole, and the principle
of its life is charity.   This charity extends not only from parents
to children but also to all those, even servants, who live together
in the same household.   According to St. Augustine there is
no essential difference in how the father of the family treats
his own children and how he treats servants living under his
roof: "Those who are true fathers of a family take care of all
those in their family as if they were their own children, that
they may praise God and serve Him, live worthily in His favor,
desiring and wishing to come to the heavenly home where there
will no longer be any necessity of commanding mortals."[6]

2. The Home and the State

Furthermore, the ideals of the home are the seeds from which
spring the ideals of the state; and the peace of the home is
the beginning from which develops the peace of the state.
Therefore we may conclude: As charity is the formal organizing
principle of the home, it should also be the formal organizing

---

[3] Eph. 5:25.

[4] "Quasi uxorem libido faciat et non caritas conjugalis": Sermon 51, "De
concordia Matt. et Luc.," 21.

[5] *Contra Faustum*, bk. 23, chap. 8.

[5] *De civitate Dei*, bk. 19, chap. 16.

principle of the state and the supranational social order in which all men should live in peace and harmony.

"Hence therefore the home of a man should be the beginning of or a small particle of the state.   Furthermore, every beginning is referred to some end like unto itself and every part to the integrity of the whole of which it is a part.   It is therefore sufficiently clear that the peace of the home is referred to the peace of the state, that is, that the coordinated harmony of commanding and obeying of those who live in the home, is referred to the coordinated harmony of commanding and obeying of the citizens of the state.   So that it behooves the father of the family to derive from the law of the state the precepts by which he so rules his household that it contributes to the peace of the state."[7]

And what is this law of the state?   St. Augustine writes: "For men loving one another and loving their God Who dwells within them make a city unto God.   For a city is held together by its law and the law itself of these citizens is charity, and charity itself is God."[8]

And again: "What is the power of this city?   Let him who desires to understand the power of this city, understand the power of charity.   This is the power which no one conquers."[9]

When one builds an edifice it is necessary to lay one stone after another until the whole structure is finally completed by putting in their proper places a large number of appropriate units.   The family is the unit out of which the state is constructed.   What the state will be is determined by what the family is.   If then we want to work for the mental hygiene of the state we must start with the family and develop one after another family units permeated by the spirit of charity.

But it is one thing to hold up before the mind a true ideal worthy of attainment, and it is another to accept the ideal and attempt to realize it in practice.

[7] *Ibid.*
[8] *Enarratio in psalmum*, bk. 98, chap. 4.
[9] *Ibid.*, bk. 47, chap. 13.

Let us now consider the difficulties of realizing in practice the concept that true and perfect charity should dominate all the interpersonal relations of family life.

The difficulties of home life arise to a large extent from native human selfishness. Sometimes this selfishness is rooted in the character of the mutual attraction which was the driving force leading to the marriage in the first place. Sometimes a marriage is brought about by the attraction of pure sensory sexual charm and a selfish desire for its satisfaction. There is no mutual admiration born of insight into the spiritual beauty of human personality. There is no desire to serve and help and work with one who is loved by the pure love of perfect friendship; and so when the novelty of sensory satisfaction wears off, antagonisms develop, quarrels are common, and are witnessed by the children, who in their turn become selfish and quarrelsome like the parents and so we have the unhappy home.

To avoid this a marriage should be carefully planned in the first place and should grow out of the development of a perfect friendship and should aim at the bringing of children into the world and establishing a school of the service of God in which charity will reign supreme and each member of the household will serve the others because he loves them truly.

3. THE CENTER OF PARENTAL AUTHORITY

Every social unit as we have pointed out must have a head and be directed by some one who exercises authority. The fact that authority is sometimes abused does not justify us in deprecating all authority, but only in urging that authority be used properly and not abused.

According to the general tradition and various reasons of propriety, the husband is the head of the family. It is also definitely the Old Testament and scriptural tradition: "Let women be subject to their husbands as Sarah was obedient to Abraham."[10]   And St. Paul writes: "As the church is

---

[10] I Pet. 3:1–6.

subject to Christ, so should women be to their husbands in all things."[11]   But the wife is not by any means subject to her husband as a servant or a slave but as a loving companion who has equal rights and privileges in married life.[12]

A certain foolish vanity in our day, while rightfully asserting the fundamental equality of man and woman, husband and wife, does away with the concept of the husband's authority in the home and replaces it by nothing else.   The introduction into the home of a discussion as to the center of authority in the family may give rise to many domestic difficulties.

Granted a love of perfect friendship between husband and wife, all matters of any importance will be discussed and usually agreed upon without any difficulty.   When after a friendly discussion a difference of opinion still remains, the wife should in general ask the husband to assume the responsibility for the decision.   A man who loves his wife will do everything in his power to make her happy and contented, and a woman who loves her husband will make every sacrifice that conscience can make to work with her husband with unselfish cooperation.

4. THE MOTHER'S PLACE IS IN THE HOME

From time immemorial there has been a sharing of duties in the home.   Until recently the husband went out to work and the wife stayed home and cared for the children.   But in recent years, particularly since our entry into the present war, both parents have gone out to work and the children are allowed to shift for themselves till the parents return or, if they are too young, a neighbor or a servant is asked to look out for them during the absence of the parents.

The salaries of both husband and wife enable the family to live in better circumstances than they could if only the husband worked and the wife stayed home and managed the children.

But there are two serious difficulties which result when

[11] Eph. 5:24.
[12] Cf. I Cor. 7.

both mother and father leave the home and go out to earn
money:

1) Delinquency naturally develops in children who are left alone to their
own devices.
2) The size of the family is limited till it is below the level for maintenance
of the population. When both parties work from the beginning of married life, it often happens that no children at all are allowed to come
into the world.

The White House Conference on Child Health and Protection found increased delinquency when mothers were
employed outside the home. "The mothers of fully 50 per
cent of the delinquent girls were employed outside the homes.
The mothers of 43 per cent of the delinquent boys were employed. But the mothers of only 24 per cent of the combined
group of public school children were employed."[13]

In the very nature of things a home cannot be properly
cared for when the mother is absent all day long. The present
tendency of women to enter business and industry is most
deleterious to home life and the moral welfare of the children.
It is to be hoped that the termination of this war will call
wives and mothers back to the duties of the home.

5. The Monastic Ideal and Family Life

There are various analogies between a home and a monastery.
What the abbot is to the community, the father is to the family.
What the procurator, or brother cellarer, is to the monastery,
the mother is to the home.

The father of the family like the abbot "should know that
it behooves him to be of use to the family rather than to rule
over them. . . ."[14]

[13] *The Adolescent in the Family: A Study of the Personality Development in
the Home Environment*, Report of the Subcommittee on the Function of Home
Activities in the Education of the Child (E. W. Burgess, chair.), White House
Conference on Child Health and Protection, New York: Appleton-Century,
1934, p. 221.
[14] "Sciat sibi oportere prodesse magis quam praeesse": *Rule of St. Benedict*,
(transl. by D. Oswald Hunter Blair), Ft. Augustus, Scotland: Abbey Press,
1914, chap. 64.

"And even in his corrections, let him act with prudence, and not go too far, lest while he seeketh eagerly to scrape off the rust, the vessel be broken. Let him keep his own frailty before his eyes, and remember that the bruised reed must not be broken."[15]

The father of the family like the abbot must realize that he is to train and teach those committed to his care and that this teaching is best accomplished by being in all things the ideal father he should be; "that is, he should shew forth all goodness and holiness by his deeds rather than his words."[16]

It does little good for the father to tell the children not to get angry and quarrel and use bad words and let them see just the contrary example in his own dealings with them and their mother.

The father like the abbot must realize that he must give an account to God of the conduct of his children and that he may well be held responsible for much of the delinquent behavior of the children.

"Let the Abbot be ever mindful that at the dreadful judgment of God an account will have to be given of his own teaching and of the obedience of his disciples. And let him know that to the fault of the shepherd shall be imputed any lack of profit which the father of the household may find in his sheep. Only then shall he be acquitted, if he shall have bestowed all pastoral diligence on his unquiet and disobedient flock, and employed all his care to amend their corrupt manner of life."[17]

What has here been said primarily of the father, applies in large measure to the mother also and much of what we shall now say of the mother as the analogue of the cellarer wil hold also of the father.

St. Benedict says of the cellarer: "Let there be chosen out of the community as Cellarer of the monastery a man wise and

[15] *Ibid.*, p. 167.
[16] *Ibid.*, chap. 2, p. 17.
[17] *Ibid.*

mature of character." And so one might say, if looking for a good wife to be the mother of a household, one should seek a person who is wise and mature of character.

The concept that St. Benedict had of *sapiens* was no doubt the classical one which is thus expressed by Forcellini: "He is said to be wise who is endowed with the knowledge of things human and divine, and organizes his life and conduct in accordance with this knowledge so as to keep himself free from vices and evil emotions and adorns his mind with moral virtues."[18]

The young girl who is looking forward to the day when she will be married and have her own house and children will do well to hold before her mind and strive to attain the ideal of true wisdom.

What does St. Benedict mean by *mature in manner*? An ancient abbot writes that "those are said to be of mature character who are courteous, restrained, and have settled down to an even temperament after a long and varied experience." And then lest one should think that only at the end of a long lifetime could one be "mature in manner," Smaragdus quotes the passage from the book of wisdom which says that "a spotless life is old age"[19] (chap. 6). One can readily see how very important it is for the mother of a family to be *mature in manner* and our experience with mothers will teach us that young girls are sometimes much more courteous and restrained and have developed in some way a more even temperament than some mothers who are ever quarreling with their children.

Here again is an ideal which the young girl, and the young boy too for that matter, must hold before the mind and do everything possible to attain to, before they enter into a contract to be faithful unto death and to develop a home and educate a family.

The cellarer of the monastery is a person in a position of

[18] Forcellini, *Latin Lexicon*, under *sapiens*.

[19] Smaragdus, *Commentaria in regulam sancti Benedicti*, in Migne, *Patrologia latina*, vol. 102, col. 856.

subordinate authority. "Let him have care of everything," says St. Benedict, "but do nothing without leave of the Abbot."[20]

If the position we have outlined above is correct, then the wife, though an equal, is in a position of subordinate authority. She should not do anything of importance without consulting her husband, particularly in regard to incurring debts. And the same thing is true of the husband. St. Benedict says of the abbot: "As often as any important matters have to be transacted in the monastery, let the Abbot call together the whole community, and himself declare what is the question to be settled."[21]

Many troubles arise from husband and wife acting independently and not consulting each other. Thus a woman periodically bought expensive furs and dresses and charged them to her husband and he only learned of the transactions when he received the bills. This caused a violent emotional scene, but after a few days of storming the husband paid the bills and settled down again to the even tenor of his ways until the next extravagance of his wife. The case might serve as an example of blind repetition of the same emotional behavior without any attempt at its reasonable modification. On the other hand, there is the husband who keeps his wife in utter ignorance of his financial circumstances and gives her so much every week wherewith to run the house. He does not treat his wife as an equal but as a servant and that is contrary to one of the fundamental principles of the family.

A mother must often have to deal with unreasonable requests from her adolescent children. She might well pay attention to what St. Benedict says to the cellarer: "If a brother ask him for anything unreasonably, let him not treat him with contempt and so grieve him, but reasonably and with all humility refuse what he asks for amiss. . . ."[22]

[20] *Rule of St. Benedict*, chap. 31, p. 91.
[21] *Ibid.*, chap. 3, p. 25.
[22] *Ibid.*, chap. 31, p. 91.

"Let him above all things have humility; and to him on whom he hath nothing else to bestow, let him give at least a kind answer, as it is written: 'A good word is above the best gift' " (Eccles. 18:17).[23]

Take for example the adolescent boy who comes in and says to his mother in a demanding tone: "Mother, I want ten dollars." The mother might well say: "Well, you are not going to get it." But though certain things may be lawful, they may not be expedient. If the mother speaks to him sharply, as indeed he richly deserves to be spoken to, he becomes sour and antagonistic, feels badly treated, and goes away with a grouch. After a few such episodes the mother loses her influence over the boy and he no longer pays attention to what she says. Logically he is quite wrong, but psychologically his conduct is true to human nature as it now exists. But suppose she says: "Come here, my son, sit down for a moment and let's talk things over. You know, I have so much money with which to pay the rent and meet all our bills. If I give you ten dollars now, it is going to cause me considerable difficulty. Do you really think I should do so?" The boy might growl a bit and go away, but in all probability he would soon come back and say: "Mother, maybe I was all wrong. I should not have spoken and acted as I did." And the little incident would end in a hug and a kiss and the mother would deepen rather than lose or weaken her influence over her son.

If a girl has not attained that even temperament which characterizes one who is mature in manners before she marries she must certainly strive to develop it before her children attain the age of making unreasonable demands. Perhaps if she deals with them from their infancy in the spirit of emotional maturity they too will attain to evenness of temperament and not make unreasonable demands.

The good cellarer arranges all things in the monastery so

[23] *Ibid.*, p. 91.

that everything is well organized, the meals are ready promptly at the proper times, the clothing is properly cared for, the house kept in order, and he does all this quietly without imitating the methods of a drill sergeant.

"Let him distribute to the brethren their appointed allowance of food without arrogance or delay that they may not be scandalized: mindful of what the Word of God declareth him to deserve, who 'shall scandalize one of these little ones': namely, 'that a millstone be hanged about his neck and that he be drowned in the depths of the sea' " (Matt. 18:6).[24]

Parents who through anger, coldness, or irritability tend to do or to say things that children should not see or hear would do well to ponder on this passage from St. Benedict. Parenthood demands virtue and sanctity and a judicious understanding by which ideals of conduct are transmitted to children by word and example.

6. The Home Is a School of the Service of God

There is a fairly common prejudice in certain circles against teaching the child any definite principles of religion whatsoever. The attitude is taken that one should let the child grow and develop and when his mind has attained to its maturity, let him choose freely in religious matters whatever he thinks best. It is even suggested that all types of religion should be presented to him in order that he may make a wise choice.

Popular notions often find advocates in scientific circles and so one is not surprised to find this common prejudice against teaching religion to children given expression to by a psychiatrist:

"We hold that it is a duty to the child to avoid one-sided dogmatic doctrines and 'pious lies.' In religious metaphysical questions of faith, the child should learn to know all views and should make up his own mind in a really perfectly free manner. It is a deep injustice to filter into his mind a one-sided faith

---

[24] *Ibid.* ⲅ. 93.

which often stands in direct contradiction with the science which will be taught him a little later at the higher institutes of learning. But still more objectionable is it during his minority to force upon him a public profession of faith, before he possesses the time, the power and the independence to come to a truly free conviction."[25]

Now all this has a superficial aspect of logical common sense. But let us look at the matter from the point of view of child psychiatry. How does the child learn? By asking questions and getting simple, clear answers. In the early years of his life he must of necessity take on faith what his parents tell him. Should they say to him that some have this view on the matter, others that, and still others hold quite a different concept, the mind of the child would be confused. He would learn nothing. He could not weigh the evidence and take sides. It is utterly out of the question to teach the child *all* views on religion and metaphysical questions of faith.

And yet he should have the fundamentals of religious and moral teaching. Without moral principles he will get into all manner of trouble in his contacts outside the home. Sometimes a child is sent to school and after a little is expelled for stealing. His parents never gave him any instruction on property rights. At home toys and playthings were common to all and when he went to school he had the same concept and just took whatever he wanted and so got into trouble.

The adolescent needs a philosophy of life to meet its trials and sorrows. It is a crime against the child when he is given no mental preparation for the various storms of human experience.

It is therefore the parent's duty to face seriously the great problems of religion and morality, to live honestly in accord with his principles, and to teach his children his own honest convictions. He gives them his very best, the product of

[25] August Forel, *Hygiene der Nerven und des Geistes* (ed. 4), Stuttgart: Moritz, 1914, pp. 297–98.

years of thought and practice, and it is a high moral duty that he should do so.

Some, unlike Forel, who would have the child taught *all* views on religious metaphysical problems, would postpone all teaching on these matters till the child has grown up and possesses a mature judgment. To attempt this would be to deceive oneself. The child learns from his daily life in the home what the parents think about important matters. They teach him by their conduct and by remarks made from time to time, whether or not they resolve to postpone any teaching in the problems of life until the child grows up. Why not then be honest and teach the child as best you can by word and example?

But how about teaching children "pious falsehoods?" A pious falsehood is a contradiction in terms and nothing false should ever be taught to anyone.

And how about teaching them a faith which stands in contradiction to the science they will later be taught at higher institutions of learning? There is no real contradiction between the truths of faith and the established principles of science. There would be less difficulty between religion and science if certain scientists would confine themselves to teaching their sciences and not react to their emotional complexes by building a metaphysics of their own on what they know of science in order to fight religion.

The fundamental truths of religion find confirmation in science. We see material energy, conserved indeed, but playing itself out. All forms of energy tend to be degraded to heat, and heat tends to diffuse itself so that all things will be at an equal temperature and at some time in the distant future the "heat death" of the universe is inevitable. The universe as science reveals it is like a clock that is running, but must run down and stop. If that is so, then at some time in the finite past it was wound up by a power outside the totality of all natural energy. The universe then was started on its present course, obeying laws imposed upon it in that primeval act of creation or disturbance of equilibrium from which necessarily resulted the present order governed as it is by the laws of nature—laws which science has been investigating for centuries, and still there is far more to learn than has yet been discovered. The Extramundane Power from which nature and its laws have proceeded is therefore a Being of incomprehensible intelligence—the Supreme Intelligence in this world of intelligent beings. St. Augustine's "City of God" is the society of intelligent beings who love one another and love also and adore the Supreme Intelligence, the Source and Origin of all.

The family is a social unit in this City of God, and, as such, must be a school of the service of God—a place where children are reared to know God and love Him and go forth to do the work God calls them to do in His social order.

Unfortunately in our day few parents have the ideal of establishing a school of the service of God. But what a profound difference it would make in society if this were the the common ideal! But the true philosophy of history points out to us that this is the ideal, and we must set about accomplishing it.

If this is the ideal, then there is one more analogy between a monastery and a home. As in a monastery there is a "corporate carrying out of the functions of religion," so in a home there should be family devotions in which all participate. Such homes have not altogether disappeared from the world by any means, but in former centuries they were far more common.

Schmiedeler, basing his description on a study by Cardinal Gasquet, gives us a glimpse into the inner life of the old English home. "There were such practices as morning and evening prayers in common in the home, grace before and after meals, frequently even assistance at the daily Mass, the evening blessing asked of their parents by the children, the inculcation of filial reverence and respect, etc., all showing how close, in those days, was the supernatural to the natural—how God was ever present and how the sense of this real, though unseen, presence affected the daily life of all in the Christian home."[26]

"Work," writes Cardinal Gasquet, "was everywhere insisted upon as necessary in God's service, and work was savored, so to speak, by the remembrance of God's presence. The two orders of the natural and the supernatural were not so separated as they are generally supposed to be today. Of course there are many in our day who no doubt keep themselves in God's presence, but whilst I believe that most will allow that this is the exception, in the ages of faith it was apparently the rule: and if we may judge from books of instruction and other evidence, God was not far removed from the threshold of most Catholic families in pre-Reformation days."[27]

And back in the early days of Christianity Clement of Alexandria wrote: "The whole life (of a perfect Christian) is a solemn festival. His sacrificial offerings are prayers and hymns of praise and the holy reading to which he devotes himself before meals, the psalms and hymns during the meal, and before he goes to bed at night, for at night he prays again. In this way he joins himself to the divine chorus, devoted to unending contemplation in unceasing mindfulness . . . . Therefore, he prays in every place, but not so that it appears openly to everybody. But when taking a walk, or conversing with others, when at leisure, or during reading, or when at intellectual work, in every place he prays."[28]

When one listens to these echoes of the past, one feels that something of great value has departed from the life of our day. Or has it not disappeared utterly but only hidden itself in out of the way nooks and crannies? May it reappear and become common again in the life of the family of our own

[26] Edgar Schmiedeler, O.S.B., *An Introductory Study of the Family*, New York: Century, 1930, pp. 52–53.

[27] Aidan Cardinal Gasquet, O.S.B., *The Christian Family in Pre-Reformation Days* (quoted from Schmiedeler, *op. cit.*[26]).

[28] *Stromata*, bk. 7, chap. 7, in Migne, *Patrologia graeca*, vol. 10, col. 469.

times so that every household will become a school of the service of God.

7. The Cloister of the Home

There is one more analogy between the home and the monastery. The law of cloister leads the monk to live in his monastery and find therein his life's work and his social contacts. His recreations are taken with his fellow monks, seldom with outsiders. And so there is a cloister of the home which brings it about that the members of the family not only eat and sleep in the same house but find their main companionship and social life within the family. The father looks forward to his evenings with his wife and family. He loves to play with his children and when they grow to adult years he still takes pleasure in spending his evenings in one way or another with the members of his family. It is always a calamity when any member of the family edges himself outside the family circle and finds all or most of his social contacts outside the home. When a parent does this he loses the influence he should exert over the lives of the children. When a child does this he loses the protection of the cloister of the home. Now this does not mean of course that neither parents nor children ever go out in the evening except with members of the family. But there is in an ideal home a continuous unbroken family life to which each member of the family is ever glad to return even though he often enjoys wholesome social and business contacts outside the home.

Between all of the members of the family there should exist a relationship of perfect friendship. What is a friend? Cardinal Newman in one of his sermons compares a friend to a master violinist who takes his violin and awakens its sleeping melodies. So a friend should play upon the soul of his friend and bring forth its hidden possibilities.

And thus the family lives together within the cloister of the home. And what is the main work that goes on within the cloister? The rooting out of vice and the acquisition of virtue. And as a workman has all his tools in order and uses first one and then another, so the laborer in the cloister devotes himself now to this exercise and now to that in the acquisition of virtue. St. Benedict in the fourth chapter of his *Rule* enumerates a number of these exercises which he terms "instruments of good works." Many of these instruments can be used with profit in the home as well as in the monastery.

"In the first place to love the Lord God with all one's heart, all one's soul, and all one's strength: then one's neighbor as oneself. To keep the commandments. To relieve the poor. To console the sorrowing. Not to give way to anger. Not to harbor a desire for revenge. To do no wrong to anyone, yea to bear patiently wrong done to oneself. To keep one's mouth from evil and wicked words. To love chastity. To hate no man. To make peace with an adversary before the setting of the sun. And never to despair of the mercy of God."

And so one studies his faults of character and tries to correct them and endures patiently the imperfections of others for the sake of family peace. And he works at it patiently and perseveringly all the days of his life. "And the workshop where he is to labor at all these things is the cloister of the home and stability in the family."[29]

[29] Adapted from *Rule of St. Benedict*, chap. 4.

Chapter XV

MENTAL HYGIENE AND THE SCHOOL

WHEN we approach the problem of mental hygiene and the school, it is important that we should include in our consideration the teacher as well as the pupil. The study of behavior problems by psychiatrists in the various child guidance centers has broadened our knowledge of children's difficulties. Before the days of the child guidance center, the "bad boy" was treated as an isolated human being and perhaps looked upon as an inherently wicked creature, or at all events a delinquent who had to stand alone and bear the full responsibility for his crime. Few ever looked into the home and parent-child relationships in an attempt to understand the bad boy. And fewer still perhaps ever cast the least suspicion on the prim, sedate, well-intentioned and perhaps pious teacher who had to suffer so much from the innate depravity of the bad boy.

Leaving aside the problem of the home and mental hygiene, let us focus our attention on the school.

Teachers may be divided roughly into three classes—the "Quietists," the "Jansenists," and those who lie in between. The Quietists would eliminate entirely the purgative way from the field of education. The child must always be allowed to do what he pleases. Discipline and correction must be banished from the classroom. In fact, they are supposed to become unnecessary when each child picks his own project and does what he pleases. Should discipline become necessary, the parents are told that the child should be sent to another type of school.

The Jansenists see to it that their conduct is always logically correct. It is reasonable, they say, to punish promptly and adequately every offense whatsoever. Charity with with them takes second place to the law of making full and adequate satisfaction.   It is logical also, they think, to frighten children by letting them know all the dire consequences of doing wrong.   And they conceive of it as their duty to lay down the law and see that it is observed.   The Jansensists have a high sense of their own personal integrity and would be very much surprised if anyone held them responsible for the delinquent behavior of any child.   They often prepare thoroughly every class.   They work hard.   Many children make good progress under their training, but others rebel and are expelled eventually as trouble makers or, being crushed by severity and reprimands, remain as discouraged students in the school, and perhaps graduate; and if the school is a Catholic school, these are likely to have little interest in their religion forever afterwards, or perhaps become actively anti-religious.   The Jansenistic teacher, however, assumes no responsibility for the loss of faith of these students and should the fact ever be called to his attention, he would feel no guilt or responsibility whatsoever but would say: "So-and-so was always bad, always doing the wrong thing.   In spite of being exposed to the best of influences, nothing good ever left the least trace in his mind or in his conduct."

A good teacher is neither a Quietist nor a Jansenist.   It is not necessary for him to attain cooperation by allowing the child to do what he pleases.   He can present whatever he wants in a way to make it interesting and so awaken interest and secure attention.   He has discipline, but he never hurts a child's feelings, or frightens him into obedience by a formalistic recountal of the dire consequences of his behavior.

Let me take an example of the Jansenistic trend to show what I mean here.   Gertrude was a 15-year-old girl in an orphan asylum.   The social worker who brought her told me that she was sulky, sullen, always contradicting.   She could not be satisfied and could not get along with anyone.   She turned on one in anger.   She was failing in her school work and, though 15, still suffered from nocturnal enuresis.

I learned further that the child's father had recently died of tuberculosis. He was said to have been always quarreling with the mother. He destroyed discipline in the home by telling the children that they did not have to obey their mother.

The mother also had tuberculosis and was said to be unstable and inadequate. The mother had for some reason become ashamed of Gertrude and the child's aunts also were antagonistic to her and while they were willing to take Gertrude's sister into their home, they refused to have anything to do with Gertrude.

And so we have a child who is rejected at home and looked upon as dull and incorrigible in the orphan asylum where she had to go because the home that rejected her disintegrated.

When one with a little experience looks at the list of charges brought against Gertrude, he may well suspect that they derive from someone who has what I have termed here a Jansenistic trend. I am not of course taking the word in its full theological significance, but using it as it were to serve my own purposes. However, the Jansenists placed self-denial above charity and some teachers seem to forget about kindliness and sympathy in their formalistic rigorism.

Though suspecting that my patient had been misunderstood, I rather expected to be confronted with a nervous, irritable type of youngster. I was much surprised to see a quiet, refined girl with nice, lady-like manners come into the office.

We started to have a chat on what she was going to do when she got out of school. She said that she had wanted to be a nurse, but had given up the idea because they told her that she could not because of her bad disposition. "My disposition blocks everything."

We talked about her school subjects and she said: "You know, I can't learn algebra." And so she said: "I can't be a nurse and I can't learn in school, so I guess I'll have to be a government worker and make some money for my mother, who needs it."

Then she added: "I want to leave the orphan asylum with the other girls of my class and go to the high school where they are usually sent, but they say I cannot because of my disposition."

I tried to find out something about the external manifestation of this bad disposition and I heard of doing things wrong and getting scolded, of a locker that was always mussed up, of getting nasty when told to do something, and "taking my time when I really should hurry."

"It's all," she said, "due to my disposition. Sometimes they say I killed my daddy."

Here she commenced to sob as if her heart would break, then looked up between sobs to force out the words: "They say I will put my mother in her grave. Do you really think so? Did I really kill my daddy?"

Of course I hastened to say "No" and I tried as well as I could to reassure the child. We chatted on after the tears had stopped and I learned that the one dream of her life had been to become a nurse and with the salary she could command as a nurse, to make a home for her mother and live with her and so do for her what her father had never been able to do because of his tuberculosis. "But," she said sadly, "you know, I can't because of my disposition."

In spite of the charges against the child, are we not here face to face with a really beautiful personality, a fine type of 15-year-old girl? But unfortunately this is a child who no longer has any hope for herself or her power of accomplishment because she has been mishandled by teachers who have dealt with her without regard to the sound principles of mental hygiene in school life.

Anyone who has any familiarity with the emotional problems of school children will recognize in the history of our little patient a common type of mishandling of a child's problems which has wrought havoc in many a life.

A consciousness of the sound principles of mental hygiene and an earnest attempt to carry them out in practice would prevent tragedies of this nature. Treatment is not a part of mental hygiene, but it may be worth while to speak of what we did in regard to the problems of this child.

The enuresis was successfully overcome in the course of about six weeks by injections of follutein, suggestion, and persuasion. The clearing up of this difficulty helped the general situation a great deal.

The girl came to our child center for about nine weeks. What did we do for her? Let us now briefly outline the mental treatment. What was done for Gertrude may be taken as an example of what could be done for many a child if the services of a child guidance center were available. Every school system should have a child guidance center to deal with special problems of this nature.

In one of the early interviews Gertrude remarked, as we noted above: "They say I can't learn algebra."

This was one reason why she could not go to high school for the basic training necessary to become a nurse and finally carry out her ideal of making a home for her mother. As a psychologist and a psychiatrist I would like to shout from the hilltops: Never tell any child that it cannot learn. If you implant in the child's mind the idea: "I can't learn," it soon ceases to attempt what it is convinced it can never accomplish. There is ample experimental evidence to prove that the will to learn is a most important factor in learning. Take away that will to learn by discouragement or in any other way and you have done a serious injury to the child.

So I said to Gertrude: "Let's see."

It did not take long to find out that she was hopelessly astray in the simple maze of powers and coefficients; but it did not take more than a few examples to enable her to find her way successfully in that same maze.

We spent the time of one interview on the fundamentals of algebra. I showed Gertrude's work to her algebra teacher, who seemed very much surprised. This and the fact that

Gertrude's behavior seemed to improve almost from the very start, gained her the privilege of going with other members of her class to the high school she so much desired to enter.

Usually in our Child Guidance Center we try to treat the parent as well as the child; but this is not always possible and it is usually even more difficult to get a teacher to come in regularly with the child. At all events, Gertrude alone was treated in this case.

And now we come to a point which is often neglected in the modern child guidance program of treatment. Conduct is profoundly influenced by principles which the mind has definitely accepted as practical guides of conduct. Normal behavior to a very large extent depends on sound religious and moral principles which exist in the mind not merely as abstract generalizations, but also as well established controls of behavior. Not all accepted principles control or even help to control behavior; but some do. A good cashier in a bank for instance never stops to think about whether or not he will transfer some of the money in the cash drawer to his pockets. "I never appropriate money that does not belong to me" is a principle which controls his conduct in the ordinary affairs of daily life, not by rising into focal consciousness, but unconsciously and as it were by reflex action. Most all the world keeps at least some of the Ten Commandments without reflection and without hesitation. Who of my readers, for instance, has ever for a moment seriously considered murder as one way out of present difficulties?

In the course of one's lifetime, by thoughtless imitation or rational selection, the mind becomes imbued with a number of principles of conduct. Some of these principles become in time quasireflex determiners of conduct—but not all. Even those who develop high and noble ideals are not willing to make the full and complete sacrifice of self that is necessary in order to make every item of daily behavior actually conform to the ideals that have been consciously adopted. One haggles over many sacrifices. There is no real resolution to give up once and forever certain pleasures incompatible with the ideals. If that were not the case, moral temptation would have become a practical impossibility. The great sacrifice has not been made and therefore temptation continues to be possible and its issue doubtful. In the hour of temptation one hesitates to be true to principles; and it is then that free will and personal responsibility come into play. The instincts drive to action contrary to the ideals; and the ideals themselves tend to slip into the depths of the unconscious. One enters another world in the hour of temptation, often a world of excitement, action, and pleasure, quite foreign to the even tenor of one's normal ways. In this world of sensory charm, impulses and instincts reign supreme. Ideals are banished. Impulse will triumph and dominate conduct if one remains in it but a little while. The will alone can lead the mind back till it comes face to face with its ideals and sound principles of conduct in another mental world, and in this world the impulses vanish from the scene. But if there are no worth while ideals and no sound principles of conduct, there is no haven of peace and holiness into which the mind can retire. Furthermore, instead of worthy aims and wholesome principles of conduct, the mind may harbor false ideals and a set of vicious principles of conduct, not dictated by sound reason but following the drive of mere sensory impulses and desires.

It becomes a matter then of good educational mental hygiene to develop in the mind of the child true ideals and sound principles of conduct. And when a child with a behavior problem comes to a child guidance center, and particularly when the child itself must be treated, a technique of bringing principles of conduct to bear on the child's problem will be of very great value.

For some time we have been attempting to do precisely this at our Child Guidance Center by means of bibliotherapy. Let us see how the method was used in treatment of the behavior problems of Gertrude. We did not attempt to treat directly the faults charged to her: "Sulky, sullen, always contradicting, can't get along with anyone." She was in an orphan asylum and was going to another school, so we loaned her *A Wagon to the Star*, by Mildred Foulke Mees. When she returned for the next visit I asked her how she liked the book. She told me she had read it every chance she got and finished it in two days. She then went on to tell me that it was about a girl in an orphan home who was growing up and had to be transferred to another school. Thus it was very easy for Gertrude to identify herself with the heroine. She roomed with another girl who was lonely like herself. Gertrude too for various reasons has been lonely. At the end, the the heroine went to college and Gertrude is looking forward to going through high school and then starting training to become a nurse.

So far we have heard of only certain elements in the narrative. Much reading is done for the story only. Unless guided, most children read for interest only, but even then we have evidence that from time to time they gather unwittingly ideals and principles of value. To discover some possible ideals, I asked her: "What did you find that was good in Mary [the heroine]"? Gertrude answered:

"She was considerate and thoughtful of others. She tried to make friends. She was ambitious. She tried to make up with others when she did wrong or offended anyone and to forgive and be friendly. She thought some girls did not like her."

We had a little talk, the burden of which was that we ought to try to absorb into our own personalities the good points of those we read about in books.

As a matter of fact, when one reads an interesting novel he becomes for a time the hero or heroine of the story. In psychiatry, one speaks of identifying oneself with the hero and thus his ideals become for the time being at least our ideals and they may become a permanent acquisition of the mind. It is on this account that the child far more easily makes his own the ideals of the hero in whose exploits he becomes absorbed than the principles one might preach to him and lay down for him with logical cogency.

After all, Gertrude has absorbed from *A Wagon to the Star* a set of principles which will be of distinct value when she leaves her orphan asylum to enter the high school academy. As a matter of fact, whether *post hoc* or *propter hoc*, there was decided improvement in her conduct before she left the orphan asylum and she made an excellent record in the academy.

To sum up briefly, in our further attempts at bibliotherapy we loaned her *Into the Wind* by H. Mallette, a story of nursing from which she crystallized the principle, "It pays to work hard and do right," and *Forty Faces* by H. Urmston, the story of a girl who wanted to be a teacher but was "scared stiff" when she had to face her first classes in practice teaching. From this she crystallized the very valuable principle: If you keep on working you can get used to anything.

Gertrude was allowed to go to the high school academy. She went and made good. She even got a B+ in algebra. The enuresis did not reappear. She made friends, gave no trouble to teachers or those in authority, regained confidence in herself, and manifested a great deal of the exuberant happiness of a normal adolescent.

There are two things that stand out in our study of this child. One is psychological—the fundamental importance of a mutual understanding between teacher and pupil in which the teacher has confidence in the essential value of the pupil and tries to be personally helpful as a true friend. The other is at once psychological, ethical, and religious. The psychological element is the realization of the importance of ideals and principles in the direction of conduct. The ethical and religious elements consist in the formulation and choice of the true ideals and principles.

Let us dwell upon these points a little further.

It has sometimes been thought that the creation of the friendly, helpful attitude of the teacher towards the child is the creation of modern pedagogy, psychology, and psychiatry. But for an illustration of what is meant by the true psychiatric attitude in pedagogy, I will go back to St. Anselm, the father of scholastic philosophy.

Eadmer in his life of St. Anselm tells us how a certain abbot visited St. Anselm and mentioned to him the serious difficulties he was having with the children reared in the cloister. "What, I beg of you, is to be done with them?" said the Abbot. "They are perverse and incorrigible, I never leave off whipping them day and night, and they are getting even worse than their very selves."

Anselm wondered at these things and said: "You never leave off whipping them? And when they have grown up what kind of men will they be? Stupid beasts."

"What then," said the abbot, "is the use of spending money on their upkeep, if we are going to develop beasts out of men. We restrain them in every way possible in order to help them and we get nowhere."

"You restrain them!" said St. Anselm. "Tell me, my Lord Abbot, if you were to set out a young tree in your garden, and bound it up on all sides so that it could not send out a branch in any direction, when you unbound it years later, what kind of a tree would you then find? Surely a useless thing with its gnarled branches all bent in. And whose fault would this be but your own who tied it up so tightly? This certainly is what you are doing with your children. They were planted by oblation in the garden of the Church, that they might grow and bear fruit for God. But you by frightening them and threatening them and whipping them have tied them up so completely that they are allowed almost no freedom at all."[1]

---

[1] Migne, *Patrologia latina*, vol. 158, col. 67, from *Sancti Anselmi vita auctore Eadmero*.

St. Anselm then goes on to point out that a sculptor does his fine work with gentle touches rather than heavy blows and remarks that a baby must be fed on milk, not on meat and bread. A strong soul is capable of taking punishment and makes spiritual progress out of humiliations and suffering. But, he says, the baby needs the milk of infants, that is, to use his own words, "the gentle helpfulness of others, kindness, mercy, friendly consultations [*hilari advocatione*], charitable support and many things of this nature."[2]

If we consider these words and ponder their meaning we shall see that St. Anselm expects that everyone who has to deal with the children in a school will be personally interested in doing everything in his power to mould the character of each and every pupil into an ideal but real structure of great value. In these dealings with the pupils, threats, scoldings, bitter words—"You killed your father, you are killing your mother"—none of these things has any place. Instead we have a *gentle helpfulness*—"Are you having trouble with your algebra? Let me see if I can explain this to you"—and *kindness*: how many a child will do anything in the world for the teacher who greets it with a smile and shows a real interest in its welfare and happiness. *Mercy* will usually do far more than punishment and never embitters the heart of the child. And then there is that which St. Anselm speaks of as a *hilaris advocatio* and which I have translated "friendly consultation": "Let's sit down and talk things over," one says to a child who is giving trouble. Much can be accomplished by the *hilaris advocatio*. And the charitable support: one speaks kindly to the dull student, tells him that if he works hard he can get the matter, that in general more is accomplished by a hard worker than a lazy genius. Such were St. Anselm's principles of how to train the young. They have never been surpassed in our age or in any other.

He kept up his interest in his students after they left the

[2] *Ibid.*, col. 68.

Abbey of Bec, as his letters show. In a letter to his former student Mauritius, he wrote as follows: "I have always desired that you should be loved by God and by good men and with all my power, as far as I can now see, I tried to bring this about, all the time that you were with me."[3]

The passage speaks to us of a true teacher who throughout his years of contact with his student studies his faults of character and the ways in which he might help him to correct them. And though the school is a monastic school, St. Anselm looks forward to the day when his pupil will be face to face with the conflicts of life. He wants him not only to keep the law of God but also to be able to make a wholesome adjustment to life and its problems and so to be loved by God and good men.

If we cast a glance at medieval education as expressed by St. Anselm we will see that it takes ample care of the emotional problems so much discussed at the present time. The Anselmian system lays great stress on the importance of the personal interest of the teacher in his pupil. This personal interest by its very nature eliminates all the emotional difficulties that arise between the teacher and the child. If now some types of abnormal behavior derive not from the teacher but from the attitudes ingrained by faulty parental discipline, the teacher studies his child and his faults of behavior and from time to time there is a *hilaris advocatio* and the two sit down in a friendly manner and talk things over.

In the modern mental hygiene of the school this attempt to bring about what is termed a satisfactory emotional adjustment exhausts about completely the actual work of educational mental hygiene. Little else is ever attempted.

"Most schools," says Percival M. Symonds, "do too little in setting ideals and standards for their pupils."[4] Furthermore,

---

[3] Letter 60 to Mauritius, in Migne, *Patrologia latina*, vol. 158, col. 1132.
[4] Percival M. Symonds, *Mental Hygiene of the School Child*, New York: Macmillan, 1934, p. 123.

later maladjustments have been recognized as due to faults in the early training of the child. "It is quite generally accepted," says a United States Public Health Report, "that the imperfect mental adjustment exhibited by a number of individuals who are incapable of the highest citizenship, though not insane in the proper interpretation of the term, is largely due to the lack of proper mental training during childhood."[5]

Symonds points out that there is no reason why this proper mental training should be lacking in childhood; for "the teachers can redirect a pupil's attitudes by setting before him high ideals and ambitions and encouraging and stimulating him to worthwhile activities."[6]

But what are these ideals and by what standards are we to judge what is essentially worth while in any activity?

Averill also recognized the importance of ideals and also the necessity of rational self control in the management of life. "There is no mental health and serenity apart from consistent self-management and control, and there is no controlling force in human experience greater than that of loyalty to great ideals. One who has accepted such domination by principle and ideal will find it not difficult to choose the desirable conduct, even though such choice may mean monotony, hard work, the pursuit of reason and even renunciation."[7]

And so, though many writers lay little or no stress on intellectual ideals and volitional control, we do find sporadic references to the higher forces that control the conduct of a normal man. But with Averill, this is accompanied by a rejection of all the religion and moral philosophy of the past. He then points to the "rise into power of philosophies and of social movements which encourage freedom and teach self-realization, even at the cost of license," and then complains:

[5] *Mental Hygiene Leaflets for Teachers*, Reprint 518, Pub. Health Rep., Apr. 25, 1919, Washington, D. C.: Gov't Print. Off., 1919, p. 3.

[6] Symonds, *op. cit.*, p. 236.

[7] Lawrence Augustus Averill, *Mental Hygiene for the Classroom Teacher*, New York: Pitman, 1939, p. 50.

"Having cast men adrift from their sometime shallow anchorages, we have been slow in substituting safer moorings where water is deeper and darker—and perhaps more treacherous."[8]

What is this philosophy that has risen in our day? There runs throughout many a psychiatric interview and many works on psychiatry and mental hygiene a tendency to deny the existence of any stable moral principles and to lay aside anything that approaches a moral ideal and to question all authority, whether human or divine, in the home, in the state, or in any human relationship whatsoever. Sometimes the attempt is made to make adherence to any eternal religious truths or stable principles of morality appear akin to the ideas of a fascist dictatorship and therefore as elements to be eliminated from a sound democracy.

And so the attempt to imbue the minds of the young with the eternal religious truths and stable principles of morality is confused with the activity of "pressure groups" in American politics and the activities of "a handful of bankers who know little of the technical problems of the industries they manage or of the social implications of their decisions."[9]

And the complaint is made that the professor in the modern university is the paid agent of a corporate body and his experience and judgment do not count in determining the social standards to which students and professors are required to conform.[10]

Objection is taken to the fact that even in the grammar school, information is presented in a preorganized form. And it is said that moral principles as manifested in matters of discipline "are often so oriented as to create a spirit of docility and blind acceptance of authority."[11]

[8] *Ibid.*, pp. 61–62.
[9] Harold H. Anderson, *Mental Hygiene in Modern Education* (ed. by Paul A. Witty and Charles E. Skinner), New York: Farrar & Rinehart, 1939, p. 174.
[10] *Ibid.*
[11] *Ibid.*, p. 175, quoting from Laura Zirbes Hilda Taba, *Teacher and Society* (ed. by W. H. Kilpatrick), New York: Appleton-Century, 1937, p. 104

Even the authority of the mother over her child is regarded as something to be destroyed and it is said: "Although the divine right of kings was exploded some time ago, one still hears the refrain 'Mother knows best.'"[12]

In spite of the fact that young children learn naturally by asking questions of one whom they trust, and that they cannot learn all things or even most of the important things they must learn by their own personal investigations, we are told that "the crying need of human beings today is to develop techniques for problem solving,"[13] and it is implied that this method of learning must commence in the grades and morality and its fundamentals must emerge from a series of annoying and satisfying experiences. And so one no longer speaks of right and wrong conduct, but of satisfactory and unsatisfactory behavior. And so it is held that the psychiatrist cannot be supposed to succeed in making the child's behavior satisfactory to society, but only to himself.

Thus Helen Witmer writes that "psychiatry cannot take upon itself the responsibility for altering the conduct of its patients, since the chief tool of its trade is a non-condemning attitude."[14]

And so instead of the moral man with his fine ideals and principles of conduct, there are those in psychiatry who would substitute an anarchical individual with no standards, no principles, and no ideal but to attain his own personal satisfaction.

But does a noncondemning attitude necessitate this anarchy of mental and moral life? Can we not refrain from showing the patient any form of disapproval while we are waiting for the time when he will see and accept and perhaps formulate spontaneously, under proper guidance, true principles of conduct and a wholesome plan of life destined to lead to an end that is truly worth while?

[12] Anderson, *op. cit.*, p. 177.
[13] *Ibid.*, p. 173.
[14] Helen Leland Witmer, *Psychiatric Clinics for Children*, Commonwealth Fund, 1940, p. 285.

Because there is discussion about some moral problems, must we reject all moral principles and standards of right and wrong? Even the "common law" was better than no law at all.

It is perhaps because so many men of our day have lost religious principles and can find no sound philosophy that psychiatrists and educators confine their therapy to emotional adjustments, to a study of the rejected and overprotected child, to feelings of inferiority, to the study of sensitive children, to fears and timidity, to daydreaming and boasting, to rigid discipline and the unhappy child, to sex behavior and satisfying companionship, to play, antagonism, truancy, cruelty, and many other problems of like nature; and all the technique of psychiatry is marshalled to deal with these things without delineating or attempting to crystallize in the child's mind those true principles of conduct and noble ideals, loyalty to which Averill terms the greatest controlling force in human experience.

But with St. Anselm, emotional adjustment formed only a part of the whole picture. Perhaps we should term it the background, for in the foreground of the child's character, set off by a halo of peace and emotional security, stood out those ideals fidelity to which truly constitutes the greatest controlling force in human experience.

Nor was he at a loss to formulate them: "At first one commands the child to believe in God, then to love Him, then to fear Him, then to do good, then to suffer with patience, and after that one is able to place before him with security any command whatsoever."[15]

These are but the strokes of a sketchy outline. How wonderful must have been the picture that he unfolded to his students. From little things he led them on to the philosophy of the Passion so beautifully expressed by St. Augustine:

[15] P. Ragey, *Histoire de St. Anselme*, Paris: Delhomme & Briguet, 1889, vol. 1, p. 99.

"Let us speak to Him therefore with a clear conscience: On account of the words of Thy lips I have kept to the ways that are hard. Why do you fear the hard ways of sufferings and tribulations? Christ Himself passes by along this road. You answer perhaps: But it is He. The Apostles pass by. And still you answer: But they are Apostles. I grant it. But give me a reason now. Then there pass many mere men also. Blush. And women pass by. Have you arrived as an old man at the threshold of suffering? Fear not death even though you are near to death. Are you young? The martyred youths pass by also, who were still hoping to live. And the children pass by and the little girls. How can that path be any longer rough, worn smooth by the feet of so many?"[16]

One who can ascend with Christ to his cross on Calvary can meet any trial, no matter how great; but strange to say, someone else must often lift the head bowed with sorrow till it can see the Cross of Christ.

But all religion is banished from modern psychiatry and social work; and we are sometimes told it must be so or we shall cease to be scientific. The fact that this attitude is possible and exists points to the necessity of introducing religion into psychiatry and the psychiatric clinic. Don't think that I suggest anything like what St. Anselm would term an attempt to feed babes on bread and meat. We must treat the patient in accordance with his mental level. Modern psychiatry has evolved many valuable therapeutic procedures. We must not neglect them. But without ideals and with no moral and religious principles, modern psychiatry has many most unfortunate limitations. There is a crying need for Catholic psychiatry and for Catholic clinics.

The present day limitations of psychiatry merely reflect the disorder of society itself. It has lost its moral principles. Because the modern state no longer has any moral or religious principles, man's rights to life, liberty, and the pursuit of happiness are denied and wars result. And for the very lack

---

[16] St. Augustine, *Homily Read on the Feast of St. Placid*, lesson 12.

of moral principles a war once started cannot be terminated by a treaty of peace but only by extermination, for no treaty has any binding force in the minds of those by whom they are now negotiated.

And so it is incumbent upon all men of sound intelligence to do everything possible to introduce religion and morality not only into psychiatry but also into the school and the social order of the present day, that society itself may live and our rights to life, liberty, and the pursuit of happiness may be preserved.

Chapter XVI

RELIGIOUS VALUES IN MENTAL HYGIENE[1]

A WELL-KNOWN writer on mental hygiene takes the following attitude toward religion:

Primitive man found his environment saturated with fear born of his ignorance, and in his efforts to escape from the dangers that faced him on every side he was irresistibly drawn toward the supernatural, pulled both by his yearnings and his need of security. This interpretation is at least closest to the attitude that mental hygiene has to take as it deals with religious experience in the modern world.[2]

The passage may be cited as a typical expression of the current concept of religion in a rather wide circle of intellectual men and women. Consequently, when one raises the problem of the value of religious concepts in mental hygiene, it is likely to be confused in the minds of many with asking whether or not it is helpful to dwell upon ideas born in the infancy of the race from ignorance and fear and perpetuate them in the modern world.

But before we rest satisfied with this current concept of religion, we should pause to consider certain questions:

1. Are current concepts about the origin and nature of religion in primitive society established scientific facts?

2. On the supposition that our information on the matter has really passed beyond the stage of problematic conjecture, would the concept of religion prevalent in certain early races be the one of greatest mental hygiene value in the present day and therefore the attitude which psychiatric workers must take when dealing with religious experience in the modern world?

[1] Reprinted by permission from (Am.) *Ecclesiast. Rev.* **89**: 13–27 (July), 1933.

[2] Ernest R. Groves and Blanchard, *Introduction to Mental Hygiene*, New York, 1930, p. 308.

It is quite clear that before we can speak of religious values in mental hygiene we must clarify the atmosphere around the concept of religion.

But should that be done, there would still remain a further difficulty of a practical nature, and that is this: Let us suppose that we have come to the conclusion that for this particular patient religion is the essential element in our prescription. It is easy enough to write the prescription; but how are we going to administer the medicine? One thing is certain: it cannot be administered at any time and to anybody as one would take a pill or so many drops of a tincture.

I remember a lady of intelligence and education, who had some difficulty in adjusting to her problem in life, who said, "I have tried about everything else. I think I will try a little sublimation." The concept behind the remark was that without having any genuine religious convictions she wanted to see what religion might be able to do for her in her difficulties.

And then a psychiatrist said to me some time ago: "How do you make use of religion in psychiatry? I once tried it on one of my patients and failed. He was a manic-depressive and we were both at our wit's end in our attempts to cope with his alternating periods of excitement and depression. So we finally determined to try religion. On my advice he took a good drink of whisky and went to a Salvation Army meeting. And he really got religion at the meeting, but it lasted only a week or so and we were then confronted with the same old problem."

Now without attempting to go deeply into the matter, I am going to call attention to what appears to me to be a self-evident assumption. Religion as a therapeutic aid in mental difficulties is applicable only to those who have sincere and honest religious convictions. If a patient has no religious convictions he cannot be aided by religious concepts until he sees their truth and honestly adopts them. Consequently when I speak of the mental hygiene value of the religious attitude of mind, I shall hold to the assumption that a patient has honest religious convictions. Let us now proceed to clarify the concept of religion in order that we may see what mental hygiene value it has.

Every intelligent human being should formulate to the best of his ability a philosophy of life. What is meant by a philosophy of life? An interpretation of life, a view, provisional at least, of the purpose of life and a body of principles to govern conduct in the more or less serious problems and difficulties of life. Certainly, if we are going to cope successfully with these difficulties we must be prepared to meet them when they come. And so we need a philosophy of life in order to deal with life's interior mental problems and to govern our external relations with other human beings.

Every serious philosophy of life involves a positive or negative attitude toward God and religion. So that a philosophy of life may be termed religious when the concept of God holds therein a central and all-important place. A philosophy of life is nonreligious when some other concept takes the position of central and supreme importance.

We shall conceive of religion for the moment in the broad sense of a religious philosophy or view of life, asking the privilege of extending the concept of "philosophy" or "view" so as to embrace both natural and revealed religion. Furthermore, religion is conceived of also as a moral virtue that really dominates conduct, and is not a mere external profession of religious belief.

We have already pointed out the necessity of an intelligent human being working out to the best of his ability an honest philosophy of life. We have also called attention to the fact that this cannot be done by any serious-minded man without taking some attitude towards God and the relation of man to God. It is not for us to enter here into the relative merits of a religious or nonreligious philosophy of life. We must now assume an individual who has worked out a religious view of life, one to whom religion is the supreme moral virtue dominating his interior life and external relations to other human beings, and ask ourselves: Has this man's religion any mental hygiene value; and if so, what?

When we conceive of religion as an honestly developed philosophy of life, we can readily see what it does for one to whom this philosophy has become the dominating principle of thought and conduct. It provides what is essential in the life of every man, a *Zielvorstellung*, an end, a purpose, an object in living. Let us try to see how this is brought about, by describing or mentioning facts of religious experience, without attempting to justify and establish the fundamental truths from which they proceed.

To the religious-minded man God is the Supreme Intelligence in a universe of intelligent beings. And as the Supreme Intelligence in this universe of intelligent beings, He is directing all minds to an end conceived by Himself and worthy of His own transcendent powers. We might perhaps make use of an analogy to bring out the force of this statement. Take the great minds and the little minds in human society and let us ask: Which class is composed of the greater number of individuals working with a purpose and devoting their energies to the carrying out of some well thought out plan of action? Unquestionably, the great minds. The idlers on the street corner who make no attempt to accomplish anything are not as a class composed of men of great intellectual ability. In fact, the greater an individual's intellectual power, the more likely is he to devote his life and energy to the accomplishment of some kind of end that intelligence can conceive and human ability can bring to realization. And so we may say that the Supreme Intelligence in this universe of intelligent beings exerts His omnipotent power to bring to its realization an end that in its fulness only Infinite Intelligence can conceive, but in which finite intelligent beings can participate.

It is perfectly evident that the divine plan for the whole

universe cannot be clearly apprehended by any human intelligence in any period of the world's history. We are much like the rank and file of the infantry in a big battle with a front extending for many a bloody and thundering mile. What soldier in the midst of the battle can apprehend the general's plan of action? Who can tell that an advance here and a retirement there may mean victory or defeat? Who knows but that a division which seems to be idly hiding in a line of trenches is holding the all-important position in the whole line of battle? And so in the warfare of the centuries between good and evil, who knows the value of his own or any human life? Little did Monica dream that her unhappy home in an obscure hamlet in Africa and her worthless, good-for-nothing boy Augustine were to contribute much that was of supreme importance in the battle of the centuries. And so one who has really made a religious philosophy of life the great living force in his mental activity can view his own humble lot with patience and contentment. He realizes that in order to live and accomplish something worth while he need not attain to any position of great political importance, nor become a man of great wealth and influence, or even be blessed with good health and freedom from trial and sorrow. But it is necessary to submit his mind to the guidance of the Supreme Intelligence and devote his energy day by day to accomplishing in the most perfect manner possible the duties that each day imposes.

And so the religious philosophy of life leads to fruitful production, to patient persistence in one's plan of life in spite of difficulties and discouragement. There have been thousands and thousands of individuals who have failed in life, not because they lacked ability or were unfortunate in finding opportunities, but because they had no *Zielvorstellung*, no purpose in life, no sense of value, no ideal of doing something worth while in the great scheme of things. They wavered for the very lack of an ideal and changed from one thing to another, following whims, seeking personal satisfaction, unwilling to endure with patient self denial the hardships, disappointments, and monotony that one must suffer to the end that a life's work may be finished and an unselfish contribution made to the welfare of humanity and to that eternal order which the Supreme Intelligence is establishing in a world of intelligent beings.

I have in mind a young man on whom considerable money was spent to give him an engineering education which was successfully completed. But after a few years of work he entered into a state of lazy indifference. In this condition he came to the clinic. It was soon seen that he belonged to the class of individuals who have no purpose in life and no desire to accomplish anything. He had no sense of a duty to make use of a valuable mental equipment on which money and years of labor had been expended. He was thinking of taking up bookkeeping and becoming some kind of a clerk, not because he had any definite plan for the future, but merely to try something new. He had no seriously worked-out philosophy of life, either religious or nonreligious. He was merely sailing aimlessly on the sea of life and unhappy because he was not getting anywhere.

But who are those who are capable of such a lofty idealism? Is not a religious philosophy of life possible only to a select circle of the intelligent and poetic few? As to the thousands who must grapple with a prosaic world as it is, how can they derive from such ethereal notions the solid substance of their daily bread?

In answer to this I would say that there is much more poetry and idealism in the lives of plain, ordinary people than the pessimism of some can possibly imagine. When Elias the Thesbite thought that he alone had been left of all those who served the Lord (III Kings 19:16), there were still seven thousand men in Israel who had never bowed their knees to Baal (III Kings 19:18). And so the privileged few in our days sometimes think that they alone can relish the higher things in life; but in factories and offices, in tenements and hovels, thousands know and appreciate truths of which even the better classes have little or no understanding.

Then too the casual observer often fails to see the idealism in many a prosaic life. What can be more prosaic than a factory, or a crowded thoroughfare, or a rainy day, or an excavation? But let a true artist make an etching of one of the prosaic things of ordinary everyday life and it lives with action and purpose worthy of the ideals of humanity. And so it is with the honest everyday life of the honest everyday man. The idealism is there. He does not see it himself, but when he has lived out his life faithful to the end, a poem has been written, a work of religious value has been accomplished, and a contribution made to the divine order that God is bringing out of the chaos of human sorrows and perplexities, wanderings and doubts, labors and strivings that seem, but only seem, to end in failure.

Religion alone can enable the toiling thousands to understand the meaning and value of life's monotonous drudgery and so to endure sorrows that would otherwise be unendurable and to carry burdens that would otherwise be insupportable. It is after all only human to endure gladly when endurance leads to something that is worth while and to collapse under burdens for which there seems to be no "why" or "wherefore" of any kind.

Let us take an example. I have in mind a young lady whose home life is intolerable and whose adjustments outside of the home have been a series of disappointments and failures, accompanied by periods of depression of almost pathological intensity that are associated with a strong drive to suicide. In these moments she seems to fall into a state of mind so common to many, which Shelley says he experienced in himself and which was well described by a stanza of poetry written by one of his friends.

> Man's happiest lot is not to be;
> And when we tread life's thorny steep
> Most blest are they who earliest free
> Descend to death's eternal sleep.

A religious conversion changed her attitude towards life and for some time she lived a life radiant with joy and hope. But from time to time the old depression comes back. God seems to depart from her life and like a pouty child she becomes angry with God, and life again seems a hopeless burden and she has to struggle with her depression and drive to suicide. Such periods are now terminated by a new insight into the meaning of God and life, a sudden sense of shame and repentance and a sudden return to joy and peace. Her readjustment was facilitated by study and preparation for a worth while career in the world. This period of preparation was not without its time of stress and trial. Her religious reaction to these difficulties is expressed in the following extract from a letter.

> Of myself I can't study and I am not accurate in work; but He can bless with success the real effort I am going to make; and if I work conscientiously and hard (it isn't a hardship because I like it so—in fact it will take an effort to put work in the secondary place and keep God always in the foreground, first and last), then should I fail—it will be that God has other designs for me. I hope He hasn't; but I am going to say *Fiat* from now on, so that if failure comes I'll automatically say—"Thy will be done."

The religious attitude of mind is of great value in enabling a person with a manic-depressive constitution to carry on and fill a place in life instead of being forced to give up and go to a mental hospital, lest he should be unable to cope with a suicidal drive.

Quite contrary to the attitude of enduring all for God's sake is the drive to make a show of sorrow, and play upon the sympathy of others. It would be an interesting thing to find out how the idea got abroad in humanity that it is a noble thing to be overwhelmed by sorrow even to the point of suicide. In individuals much depends on the ideals that have been instilled into the mind of the child by parental example. Why do parents make such a demonstration of grief before their children? A certain type of literature is in part responsible. True literature is what it is because men are what they are. There is an interaction between literature and life. But we may say that certain literature leads to faulty mental adjustments and that good authors in the future should be conscious of the harm to humanity that may result if they hold up for admiration examples that from the mental hygiene point of view are wrong in principle.

It is probable that Spanish tales of romance have exerted an influence far beyond the southwestern peninsula of Europe. At all events I would exemplify from a Spanish novel, or rather drama, a heroine whose mental hygiene is utterly wrong in principle and the extreme contrary of the religious attitude of mind that beareth all things and endureth all things.

Melibea, the only daughter of her parents and the heroine of the Spanish drama *Celestina*, written about the end of the fifteenth century, is overcome with a profound depression by the murder of her lover Calisto. Her father tries to console her, in vain. Desperate with grief, she goes to the roof of her house and there addresses her father watching her from below: "I am forsaken by all. The manner of my death has been well prepared. Already I feel some consolation in seeing that I and my beloved Calisto will be so soon united. I intend to lock the door that no one may come up to prevent my death. Let them not hinder my departure. Let them not block the path by which in a short time I shall on this very day be able to visit him who last night came to visit me . . . . O my love and lord Calisto . . . do not blame me for the delay I am making by giving this last account to my old father, for I owe him so very much. O my much beloved father, if thou hast loved me in this miserable life, now spent, I beseech thee that our burying places may be together, and together our funerals may be held. Salute for me my dear and beloved mother. May she learn from you at length the sad reason why I die. How glad I am I do not see her now . . . . May God be with you and you with her. To Him I offer up my soul. And do thou place in its coffin this body there below." Thereupon she throws herself from the roof.[3]

[3] Quoted from Cesar Barja, *Literatura española*, Libr. autores clasicos, Brattleboro, Vt., 1923, p. 147.

It is evident that Melibea is making a demonstration of grief that is largely an appeal for sympathy. She even extends her dream of sympathy beyond the grave and looks forward to the moment when the bystanders will throng about her bruised and mangled body and say, "Poor child, how shamefully she was treated, how bitterly she suffered."

I remember a patient who after a sarcastic remark made by her brother went to her room and shot herself in order that the family might see how badly they treated her. She aimed at her abdomen rather than her head in order that she might be conscious when they gathered about her after hearing the report of the pistol. By accident she recovered and so I was enabled to learn the motivation of the deed. On the other hand, an Italian shoemaker after a few harsh words from his wife went to his room and put his mouth over the muzzle of a shotgun, pulled the trigger with his toe, and blew the top of his head off.

It will be an important moment in the life of any man when he commences to realize that to suffer and endure in patient silence is far nobler than even the most poetic demonstration of grief and dramatic appeal for sympathy. This matter is so important in mental hygiene that I would illustrate the principle from pagan philosophy, lest any one should say that he cannot rise to the sublimity of religious ideals. Marcus Aurelius has given us a picture which illustrates admirably how we should strengthen ourselves in the time of trial: "Be like a headland of rock on which the waves break incessantly; but it stands fast, and around it the seething of the waters sinks to rest."[4]

The figure is an excellent one and it leads to a wholesome attitude of mind. One who in every storm of trial and sorrow of whatever kind takes the attitude of standing upright with such strength and solidity that the waters of life's calamities will break upon him rather than that he should be broken,

[4] *Meditations* iv. 49.

is developing a much more wholesome type of mentality than one who is ever whining for sympathy and showing to all who will stop to look, how badly he is treated and how keenly he suffers.

The attitude advocated by Marcus Aurelius after all appeals to a wholesome sense of self respect, which, however, is likely to weaken in storms that are exceptionally prolonged and are of extraordinary severity. One who has honest religious convictions has elements of reinforcement in which the purely ethical point of view is lacking. Standing one's ground and carrying out one's daily duty, rising serenely above the billows of life's trials as they break one after another, silent fidelity utterly free from whining or boasting or vain appeals for sympathy, all this is a duty to God, the Supreme Intelligence, in the war of the centuries between good and evil—a test of faith in which we prove our fidelity to One whom we love as a servant loves a kind master to whom he has given the labor of a lifetime.

Not only is religion of value in the sorrows of life, whether or not they may happen to be accentuated by a manic-depressive constitution, but it is also of particular importance in all mental conditions that are derived from the lack of a plan of life that is an integral part of one's mental equipment. Let us recall that we have defined religion as a view of life, a *Weltanschauung* or a philosophy of life in which God holds a position of supreme importance. We have assumed also that religion has become the supreme moral virtue dominating thought and conduct. When this has come about in any individual his life is coordinated and directed to an end that has acquired in his mind a value with which nothing else can be compared. A life with no purpose, one that aims only at pleasure, usually is soured with discontent or darkened by depression long before the days draw near of which one must say: They please me not.

The inadequacy of a life that aims only at pleasure and not at an end worthy in itself which has pleasure as a by-product, is set forth by no less a person than John Stuart Mill. He bears witness to this truth in his autobiography, where he tells how one day he mused as follows:

> Suppose that all your objects in life were realized; that all the changes in institutions and opinions which you are looking forward to could be completely effected at this very instant; would this be a great joy and happiness to you? And an irrepressible self-consciousness distinctly answered, "No!" At this my heart sank within me; the whole foundation on which my life was constructed fell down. All my happiness was to have been found in the continual pursuit of this end. The end had ceased to charm, and how could there ever again be any interest in the means? I seemed to have nothing to live for.[5]

He then tells of months of depression and how the cloud was gradually lifted, but with something of a change in his ideas.

> I never indeed wavered in the conviction that happiness is the best of all rules of conduct, and the end of life. But now I thought that this end was only to be attained by not making it the direct end. Those only are happy (I thought) who have their minds fixed on some object other than their own happiness; on the happiness of others, on the improvement of mankind, even on some art or pursuit, followed not as a means but as an ideal end. Aiming thus at something else, they find happiness by the way. The enjoyments of life (such was now my theory) are sufficient to make it a pleasant thing when they are taken *en passant*, without being made a principal object. Once make them so, and they are immediately felt to be insufficient. They will not bear a scrutinizing examination. Ask yourself whether you are happy, and you cease to be so. The only chance is to treat, not happiness, but some end external to it as the purpose of life.

Religion provides the attitude of mind that Mill here advocates. It makes one see a value in the patient fulfillment of homely duties in the everyday world. It obliges us to something that is worth while to God and man. It turns us aside from the unwholesome pursuit of selfish pleasures. It directs our minds to the noble purpose of life and in so doing it does not deprive us of pleasure but gives it in abundance and permanence as we attain the great purpose of life in the service of God and man.

If religion has become an essential element of one's mental

[5] *Autobiography*, 1873, chap. 5, pp. 133–34.

equipment, if it constitutes a plan of life that the individual has made a real part of his daily existence, if it is a practical ideal that he has adopted with enthusiasm, then it becomes a powerful inhibitory force in the development of unwholesome mental conditions. No constitutional psychopath of the wandering, dilettante type could remain fixed in his type if he developed profound religious convictions and conceived of himself as having a duty to fulfil in the world, a duty not merely to his fellow men or to himself, but also and above all to God. For when this comes about one must ask himself: How can I reasonably expect to be of service to God? One must then use his energies in some form of productive activity. He must work hard every day whether he likes it or not. He must in a word sacrifice those pleasures that lead to the aimless pursuit of trivialities and devote himself heart and soul to the doing of something that is worth while. Nor need we think of lofty, unusual idealistic ends. A bootblack who conceived of shining shoes as his contribution to the world and as the fulfillment of a duty he owed to God could work on, day after day and year after year, in fidelity, peace, and happiness, with his whole mind suffused with a joy in living which religion alone can give to those whom the world despises.

So far we have spoken more or less in generalities, as if we were pointing out how one might conceive of religion as of some value in the difficulties of life.

It would be much more interesting if we could show how it actually does enable one who is in some kind of mental stress, to deal with his difficulties. To do this I have drawn on some unpublished material that I have been gathering. I commenced to amass it with the idea of getting some idea of ordinary religious experience. The work of James in the *Varieties of Religious Experience* lays too much stress on the extraordinary. I wished to find out what is the nature of ordinary religious experience in the ordinary person. I, therefore, asked various individuals apparently of the ordinary type of religious-minded person to keep an account of their religious experience. From this rather extensive material I have selected a few instances which show the effect of a definite experience of a religious character in dissipating some kind of a mental trial.

A young nurse had developed a great friendship for another girl of about her own age The attachment was of such a character that it seemed to stand between herself and God. Difficulties arose between them; and the young nurse in question felt very bitter. She wrote the following account of how an acute crisis was tided over by a religious experience.

Last night I felt all wrong about N——. I wanted to hurt her for ignoring me and felt like throwing everything up, as I could not be mean and lead an interior religious life. When I commenced my mental prayer, which I resolved recently to make every single day, my mind was in a turmoil. I started to cry with temper and self-pity. I don't remember how I was praying, but suddenly, quite clearly, I saw or felt (I don't know how to express it), *If you had had N——, you would never have had God;* and for a moment I experienced more peace than I ever did before. I started to thank God for not letting N—— care. After a while I again felt rebellious, and I have felt rebellious today, but I remember that sentence and so I continue to thank God.

Another writes as follows:

One evening "when so sad I could not sadder be," I noticed the *Autobiography of the Little Flower* on a friend's table. I had read it more than once, but not at all for several years. I borrowed it and read from it that night, opening it at random. I cannot describe what happened as I read. It was as if a person who had been confined in a dark, noisome prison were suddenly brought into the light and sweetness of home, or a person in delirium suddenly restored to clearness.

This experience is quoted as an example of how a religious experience may act as a specific in an acute mental condition.

And the following shows how a religious experience dissipated a little trial which, however, was bitter enough to the nun who had to put up with it.

This morning I covered our altar with white cloths, that it might not be spattered with paint by the men who were decorating our chapel. The Blessed

Sacrament was in the tabernacle. My heart was burning with indignation because I was required to use cloths which were not even clean. Tears came to my eyes, and with them a realization of how weak our faith is, and a'so of the depths of the abandonment of the Son of God, the Spirit which made Him wear the white robe of a fool in Herod's court. Has He not reduced Himself even to a more helpless state here? My own pride and sensitiveness loomed up as more horrible than ever, in contrast with the meekness of Our Lord. I think I can never again resent an injury. I long to learn of Him who was meek and humble of heart. I know I shall often fail, but when I do, Lord, let me feel as I do today, that shame may melt my pride.

Another person who consented to give an account of her inner religious life was once in great sorrow and agitation. She writes as follows of how the trial was lifted in a sudden manner by a definite religious experience.

I was kneeling one morning at the altar rail waiting to receive my Saviour— my mind and heart filled with anxiety and sorrow, and a humiliating fear that I should fail to fulfill my offer of sacrifice. Suddenly I heard a voice say very gently: "You have Me." I only dimly realized what had happened but the words remained with me and my agitation gave way to a feeling of numbness. This lasted for some months. Then, as I was making my thanksgiving after Holy Communion one morning, I realized with a flood of joy the wonder and significance of those precious words. It was so stupendous I have hardly dared to face the glorious fact fully.

It will be readily seen that the experiences I have just quoted differ from the ethical considerations of a Marcus Aurelius or any similar manner of activity dealing with the perplexities and sorrows of life. Both ethics and religion provide concepts that one may hold in mind by sheer force of will and grim determination and so find assistance in the acute struggles to which life subjects us all.

But it seems to be a rather common thing for a religious-minded person to receive a sudden insight that has no sign of coming from his own spontaneous efforts. It comes and though at times it persists as an aid in the struggle that follows, it will at other times suddenly and entirely do away with sorrow, anxiety, agitation, and flood the mind with peace and joy and consolation that seem produced *in* the mind rather than fashioned *by* the mind.

It is quite remarkable how such experiences tend to the moral perfection of the one who has them. They give him a better mode of adjustment in his relations to other human beings, a spiritualized conception of the nature of some mental trial so that he is able to stand like the headland of rock, but without effort or painful exertion.

And so we see how religion has a mental hygiene value peculiarly its own and more powerful than a potent drug in dissipating the unhappiness of life's emotional crises. Its mode of action speaks strongly in favor of the fundamental concept in a religious philosophy of life—namely, the great truth that we live in a social order, in a world of intelligent beings in which God is the Supreme Intelligence. There is a true light which enlighteneth every man who cometh into the world and by that very enlightenment guides, consoles, transforms, and develops the finite mind till it attains the moral end and spiritual ideal by which alone it will be able to fill its place in the universal social order, in which Infinite Intelligence lives with, illumines, and fills with spiritual joy a world of intelligent beings.

CHAPTER XVII

UNWHOLESOME DRIVES: FAME AND FEMININE CHARMS[1]

DANTE Gabriel Rossetti (1828–1882) was the son of an Italian revolutionist who escaped from his own country, settled in England, and married an English governess, half Italian and half English by birth, Frances Polidori.

His father's home was a center for discontented Italian revolutionists of all classes from organ grinders to the nobility. Rossetti once had the little group of the Pre-Raphaelite Brotherhood meet at his house and Holman Hunt has left us a description of what he saw—no doubt a characteristic evening of the Rossetti household. A motley group was gathered around the fire. "The conversation was in Italian, but occasionally merged into French, with the obvious purpose of taking into the heat of the conference refugees unfamiliar with the former tongue. The tragic passions of the group around the fire did not in the slightest degree involve either the mother, the daughters, or the sons, except when the latter explained that the objects of the severest denunciations were Bomba, Pio Nono, and Metternich, or in turn, Count Rosso and his memory; with these execrated names were uttered in different tones those of Mazzini, Garibaldi, and Louis Napoleon, who as a refugee had once been their visitor. The hearth guests took it in turn to discourse, and no one had delivered many phrases ere the excitement of speaking made him rise from his chair, advance to the center of the group, and then gesticulate as I have never seen people do, except upon the stage. . . . When it was impossible for me to ignore the distress of the alien company, Gabriel and William shrugged their shoulders, the latter with a languid sign of commiseration, saying it was generally so."[2]

[1] Reprinted from *Dublin Rev.* 200: 345–60, 1937.
[2] W. Holman Hunt, *Pre-Raphaelitism and the Pre-Raphaelite Brotherhood* (ed. 2), 1914, vol. 1, p. 108.

Dante Gabriel was destined by his father from childhood to be a painter—perhaps because of the talent he manifested in drawing pictures of his toys. The father felt this so definitely that he once reprimanded him for wasting his time on poetry when he should be preparing himself for earning a living by studying painting.

The study of poetry commenced with his games with his sister, Christina, in which they tried out their skill in rhyming. When only 6, he wrote a drama in blank verse which he entitled "The Slave."[3] When only 17 he was, according to his brother, a "practised and competent versifier."[4]

Rossetti, however, was one of those individuals who never learned to settle down to work and do all the things one has to do in order to attain an end that is worth while. He did what he wanted, when he wanted, and that was all.

Thus, when in 1842 he left the King's College School to take up regular training in art at Sass's Academy, he seems to have attended or not attended, as he pleased. Tradition has it that when the professor asked why he did not come to school the day before, Rossetti replied simply and candidly, "I had a fit of idleness."[5]

And when subsequently he attained the ambition of every young student of art and was admitted to the Antique School of the Royal Academy, he was no more serious in his efforts to get down to business and learn the fundamentals. He came or not, simply as he pleased, and finally gave up altogether, disappointed and disgusted with the work he was called upon to do. The methods of the Academy of that day have been severely criticized, but still they gave Holman Hunt his foundation and perfected the genius of Millais. Rossetti never learned anatomy and perspective and was hampered all his life by the imperfections of his technique.

[3] William M. Rossetti (ed.), *Collected Works of Dante Gabriel Rossetti*, London, 1890, vol. 1, p. xxviii.

[4] *Ibid.*, p. xxix.

[5] R. L. Mégros, *Dante Gabriel Rossetti—Painter Poet of Heaven in Earth*, London, 1928, p. 43.

Having left the Academy, he became the private pupil of Ford Madox Brown; but when the master tried to teach his pupil perspective and gave him the uninteresting task of drawing a group of bottles, the pupil again gave up in disgust and eventually went to Holman Hunt, under whose direction he finished his painting "The Girlhood of the Virgin."

The same spirit of *dolce far niente* dominated his after-life and interfered with his financial prospects. When given an order to paint a picture, even though he needed the money, he would put off the work and spend his time as he chose, doing what attracted him at the moment.

His intimacy with Holman Hunt brought him into contact with John Everett Millais. Millais and Hunt were thoroughly dissatisfied with the artificiality of the Royal Academy. Holman Hunt had been captivated by the writings of Ruskin, feeling that they expressed essentially his own ideas of art. He converted Millais and the enthusiasm of Rossetti made a movement out of what might have remained mere chatting among friends. With a few others, they made up their minds to form a secret society which they termed the Pre-Raphaelite Brotherhood and agreed to s gn all their pictures with the cryptic monogram P.R.B.

Holman Hunt thus expresses the fundamental concepts of this society[6]: "Despite differences, we were agreed that a man's work must be the reflex of a living image in his own mind, and not the icy double of the facts themselves, *for we were never 'Realists.'* I think Art would have ceased to have the slightest interest for either of us had the object been only to make representation, elaborate or unelaborate, of a fact in nature."

Still they tried to paint true to nature with a wealth of detail as actually found in nature. They deprecated the slavery of modern imitation of Raphael. They criticized Raphael and their fellow students said: "Then you are pre-Raphaelite." And Hunt and Millais accepted the designation.[7]

[6] Hunt, *op. cit.*, vol. 1, p. 105.
[7] *Ibid.*, p. 69.

One day Walter Deverell broke into the studio of Hunt and Rossetti telling of the beautiful model with reddish golden hair whom he had recently persuaded to sit for him as Viola in *Twelfth Night*. This beautiful creature, Elizabeth Siddal, became eventually the wife of Rossetti after a long period of engagement. But Rossetti, because of his thoughtlessness, his unbridled temper, and his infatuation for his mistress, Fanny Schott, made her life intensely unhappy.

Violet Hunt, who claims that her information is based on oral sources and an intimate acquaintance with the chief actors in the scenes, says that Rossetti refused one night to stay with his wife when she pleaded with him to remain, and that while he was out she took laudanum. When Maddox Brown came to her bedside, he removed a little piece of paper pinned to the dead wife's nightgown, which read, "My life is so miserable I wish for no more of it."[8]

Perhaps Rossetti referred to another note when he told Hall Caine that "on the night of his wife's death, when he returned to her room from his walk, he found a letter addressed to himself lying on the table by her side"[9] and that "it had left such a scar on his heart as would never be healed."

He never did recover from the realization that was forced upon him that fatal night, and an element of sadness is ever recurring in his poetry and painting.[10]

Rossetti's little story, *Hand and Soul*, written entirely in one night in 1849,[11] is a revelation of his own inner life. It is a tale of an Italian painter, Chiaro, who as a child loved art and "endeavored from early boyhood towards the imitation of any object offered in nature." He tells how he heard of a famous painter, Giunta Pisano, and went to him and begged to become

[8] Violet Hunt, *The Wife of Rossetti*, New York, 1932, p. 305.

[9] Hall Caine, *Recollections of Rossetti*, 1928, p. 198.

[10] Helen Rossetti Angeli has called in question Violet Hunt's story about this little piece of paper: *Dublin Rev.*, vol. 201, pp. 364–67.

[11] Rossetti (W. M.), *op. cit.*, vol. 1, p. 524.

his pupil—just as Rossetti asked to become the pupil of Maddox Brown. But when he saw the master's studio he was much disillusioned. "The forms he saw there were lifeless and incomplete; and a sudden exaltation possessed him as he said within himself 'I am the master of this man'" (p. 7). Can this be the expression of his own attitude toward Maddox Brown when he left him because Brown insisted on his learning perspective by drawing a group of pickle bottles?

He then tells of how he continued to work and eventually attained to fame.

But while he was seeking his own fame, he felt that his work was a service to God. And he offered his work to God that he might make amends for self seeking in pursuit of fame. "There was earth, indeed, upon the hem of his raiment; but this was of the heaven heavenly" (p. 15).

But as he studied and worked[12] he realized that life offered other channels for the satisfaction of desire. "And when, in his walks, he saw the great gardens laid out for pleasure, and the beautiful women who passed to and fro, and heard the music that was in the groves of the city at evening, he was taken with wonder that he had never claimed his share of the inheritance of those years in which his youth was cast" (pp. 8–9).

But after a little the pursuit of fame and pleasure no longer satisfied his soul. "But now (being at length led to inquire closely into himself), even as, in the pursuit of fame, the unrest abiding after attainment had proved to him that he had misinterpreted the craving of his own spirit. . .so also, now that

[12] "In these early days, with all his headstrongness and a certain want of consideration, Rossetti's life within was untainted to an exemplary degree, and he worthily rejoiced in the poetic atmosphere of the sacred and spiritual dreams that thus encircled him, however some of his noisy demonstrations at the time might hinder this from being recognized by a hasty judgment": Holman Hunt, quoted by George Birkbeck Hill, *Letters of Dante Gabriel Rossetti to William Allingham*, 1898, p. 28.

he would willingly have fallen back on devotion, he became aware that much of that reverence which he had mistaken for faith had been no more than the worship of beauty."[13]

And so he sought another aim for life. "From that moment Chiaro set a watch on his soul, and put his hand to no other works but only to such as had for their end the presentment of some moral greatness that should impress the beholder."[14]

But, though his works were "more laboured than his former pictures, they were cold and unemphatic" (p. 20). This passage is perhaps a criticism of the ideals and work of Holman Hunt.

But one day the two great houses of Pisa fought out their feud within the very entry of the church where Chiaro had painted his frescoes presenting the moral allegory of Peace, and spattered his paintings with their blood. And Chiaro thought within himself: "Fame failed me: faith failed me: and now this also...the hope that I nourished in this my generation of men" (p. 28).

Chiaro fell sick and "the fever encroached slowly on his veins. . . . The silence was a painful music that made the blood ache in his temples: and he lifted his face and his deep eyes [p. 3]. . . . A woman was present in his room, clad to the hands and feet with a green and grey raiment, fashioned to that time [p. 32] and she said to him:

"'I am an image, Chiaro, of thine own soul within thee. See me and know me as I am. Thou sayest that fame has failed thee, and faith failed thee, but because at least thou hast not laid thy life unto riches, therefore, though thus late, I am suffered to come into thy knowledge. Fame sufficed not, for thou didst seek fame: seek thine own conscience (not thy mind's conscience, but thine heart's), and all shall approve and suffice' [p. 34].

"'Why shouldst thou rise up and tell God He is not content?

[13] Dante Gabriel Rossetti, *Hand and Soul* (repr. from the German) (ed. 2), Portland, Me.: 1900, pp. 17–18.
[14] *Ibid.*, p. 18.

Had He, of His warrant, certified so to thee?... What he hath set in thine heart to do, that do thou, and even though thou do it without thought of Him, it shall be well done; it is this sacrifice He asketh of thee, and His flame is upon it for a sign. Think not of Him, but of His love and thy love. For with God there is no lust of Godhead[15]: He hath no hand to bow beneath, nor a foot, that thou shouldst kiss it [pp. 37–38]. Know that there is but this means whereby thou mayst serve God with man:—Set thine hand and thy soul to serve man with God'" (pp. 41–42).

And then she said to him: "Chiaro, servant of God, take now thine Art unto thee, and paint me thus, as I am, to know me: weak as I am, and in the weeds of this time; only with eyes which seek out labour, and with a faith, not learned, yet jealous of prayer. Do this; so shall thy soul stand before thee always, and perplex thee no more."

And thus Chiaro painted the woman that was the image of himself. This little story is not entirely the figment of his imagination but really tells us a great deal about Rossetti's inner life.

Holman Hunt bears witness to the marked change that appeared in Rossetti's paintings in the exhibitions in 1857 after he had spent some time in drawing and water co'or work.

When the first collection was brought together, Gabriel sent two excellent examples of his last oil work. He had now completely changed his philosophy, which he showed in his art, leaving monastic sentiment for Epicureanism, and after a pause, which was devoted to design in water-colour, he again took to oil painting. He executed heads of women of voluptuous nature with such richness of ornamental trapping and decoration that they were a surprise, coming from the hand which had hitherto indulged in austerities.[16]

Let us now follow Rossetti's development in poetry and painting and see how again and again he painted the woman that was the image of his soul.

[15] " 'For God is no morbid exactor' is the original reading."
[16] Hunt (W. H.), *op. cit.*, vol. 2, pp. 111–12. This exhibition was in 1857. Cf. Marillier, *Dante Gabriel Rossetti*, London, 1899, p. 50.

His youthful aspirations are expressed in a poem entitled "World's Worth" which was published in the *Germ* in 1850. A somewhat modified version appeared in the *Collected Works* edited by his brother.[17]

> He stood within the mystery
>   Girding God's blessed Eucharist:
>   The organ and the chaunt had ceas'd.
> The last words paused against his ear
>   Said from the altar: drawn round him
>   The gathering rest was dumb and dim.
> And now the sacring-bell rang clear
>   And ceased; and all was awe,—the breath
>   Of God in man that warrenteth
>   The inmost, utmost things of faith.
> He said: "O God my world in Thee."

And so in these early days Rossetti looked at the world about him.

> The obscure deafness hemmed him in.
> He said: "O world, what world for me?"
> . . . .
> The ripples set his eyes to ache
> He said: "O world, what world for me?"

And then he had a glimpse of the utmost things of faith and

> He said: "O God, my world in Thee."

He could understand the vision of perfect loveliness found in the Mother of Christ and could sing to her pleadingly:

> Oh when our need is uttermost,
> Think that to such as death may strike
> Thou once wert sister sisterlike!
> Thou headstone of humanity,
> Groundstone of the great mystery,
> Fashioned like us, yet more than we![18]

---

[17] Rossetti (W. M.), *op. cit.*, vol. 1, pp. 250–51. Both versions are given in Elizabeth Luther Cary, *Poems by Dante Gabriel Rossetti*, 1903, vol. 1, pp. 117–20. We quote the modified version as giving the clearer meaning.

[18] "Ave": Cary, *op. cit.*, vol. 1, p. 113.

And then he commenced to feel the temptations in the world about him. But at first he would not yield. Time passes and the world will be no more. Why tarry with what is mortal when one can be faithful to the eternal ideal of truth and beauty? This idea he expressed in a sonnet written in 1847 and its accompanying picture.

Retro Me, Sathana!

Get thee behind me. Even as, heavy curled,
   Stooping against the wind, a charioteer
   Is snatched from out his chariot by the hair,
So shall Time be; and as the void car, hurled
Abroad by reinless steeds, even so the world:
   Yea, even as chariot-dust upon the air,
   It shall be sought and not found anywhere.
Get thee behind me, Satan. Oft unfurled,
   Thy perilous wings can beat and break like lath
   Much mightiness of men to win thee praise.
   Leave these weak feet to tread in narrow ways.
Thou still, upon the broad vine-sheltered path,
Mayst wait the turning of the phials of wrath
   For certain years, for certain months and days.

Rossetti's idea of relinquishing all and finding his world in God never took the form of a strict religious asceticism, but rather of disdain for a world that could not appreciate the beauty of poetry and art. He became absorbed in drawing and poetry, turning from one to the other. But finally he commenced to taste also of that which the world enjoys and, once having tasted, could never become again the innocent, idealistic lover of art and beauty that he was in early youth.

This he expressed later in life by the picture and poem entitled "Proserpine." When we look at the picture of Proserpine, we must realize that in this series of pictures, Rossetti is trying to portray the image of himself. To interpret it we must recall the legend of Proserpine. She was the daughter of Ceres captured by Pluto and taken to the nether regions. Ceres obtained an order from Jupiter for her release on condition that she had eaten nothing. But she had tasted of a pomegranate and so she was never to be entirely freed from the lower regions over which Pluto ruled.

And so Rossetti, having in early youth been true to mystical and poetic ideals and kept himself free from gross sexual indulgence, followed finally the lure of pleasure and, descending from the pure regions of a chaste and holy art, came to realize at last that he was held a prisoner like Proserpine in the realms of Pluto. Had he only passed through the dark trials of life without tasting, he could have risen again to his former self. But he had tasted and felt he could never again be what he was in the early days of his mystic idealism.[19]

With these thoughts in mind, we can appreciate the pathetic appeal of the picture and the poem.

> Afar away the light that brings cold cheer
> Unto this wall,—one instant and no more
> Admitted at my distant palace door.
> Afar the flowers of Enna from this drear
> Dire fruit, which, tasted once, must thrall me here.
> Afar those skies from this Tartarean grey
> That chills me: and afar, how far away
> The nights that shall be from the days that were.
>
> Afar from mine own self I seem, and wing
> Strange ways in thought, and listen for a sign:
> And still some heart unto some soul doth pine,
> (Whose sounds mine inner sense is fain to bring,
> Continually murmuring)—
> "Woe's me for thee, unhappy Proserpine!"

Rossetti's life is like that of everyone, a conflict between good and evil. In early youth the good definitely dominated in Rossetti's life. Then there came a time of trial, and goodness yielded to wickedness. Just as in some, good dominates and evil is repressed and becomes unconscious, by a reverse process in Rossetti evil dominated and the good tended to be repressed. The good, however, never became utterly repressed and wholly

---

[19] P. T. Forsyth gives this interpretation to the picture and poem in *Religion in Recent Art*, London, 1901, p. 4. The first study of the picture was made in 1871: Cary, *op. cit.*, vol. 2, p. 69.

unconscious but was ever in one way or another rising into consciousness.

This conflict is expressed in a drawing he made in 1858 of Mary Magdalen at the door of Simon's house. The head of Christ is seen at a window gazing at Mary Magdalen. She feels that Christ is calling her and is tearing the roses from her hair before she enters and comes into the presence of the Saviour. Her companions are pleading with her to remain, but her mind is made up, and she, as it were, leaving her companions says to them:

Oh world, what is the world to me?

and turning to Christ says:

O God, my world is in thee.

It is the figure of the conflict that went on throughout life in the mind of Rossetti—the face of Christ seen as it were in the darkness symbolizes the appeal that rises up in spite of repression.

The voice of Mary Magdalen's lover:

Why wilt thou cast the roses from thine hair?
Nay, be thou all a rose,—wreath lips, and cheek.
Nay, not this house,—that banquet-house we seek
See how they kiss and enter; come thou there.
This delicate day of love we two will share
Till at our ear love's whispering night shall speak.
What, sweet one,—holdst thou still the foolish freak?
Nay, when I kiss thy feet they'll leave the stair."

The voice of Mary Magdalen:

Oh loose me! Seest thou not my Bridegroom's face
That draws me to Him? For His feet my kiss,
My hair, my tears He craves today:—and oh!
What words can tell what other day and place
Shall see me clasp those blood-stained feet of His?
He needs me, calls me, loves me: let me go![20]

---

[20] Cary, *op. cit.*, vol. 1, p. 262. William Rossetti ascribes this poem to 1859, Cary to 1869.

The poem entitled "Lilith" was written on the frame of the picture "Lady Lilith," which was painted in 1866.[21] The first model for the picture was Fanny Conforth—Mrs. Schott. But later he repainted the face from another model. Fanny Schott was the evil genius of his life. He met her about 1852 and his love for her marred the short two years of his married life. She profoundly affected his later life and she haunted his dying days, trying to induce him to make a will in her favor.[22]

Lilith, the inhuman witch, is the embodiment of sensual charm.

> . . . Ere the snakes, her sweet tongue could deceive
> And her enchanted hair was the first gold.
> And still she sits, young while the earth is old,
>   And, subtly of herself contemplative,
>   Draws men to watch the bright web she can weave,
> Till heart and body and life are in its hold.[23]

And so he expressed the thraldom from which, he complained in "Proserpine," he could never be freed.

And again, in a translation from Goethe:

> Hold thou thy heart against her shining hair,
>   If, by thy fate, she spread it once for thee;
> For when she nets a young man in that snare,
>   So twines she him he never may be free.[24]

In a companion poem and picture, "Soul's Beauty," Rossetti again attempts to picture "the fair woman that was his soul."[25]

> Under the arch of Life, where love and death,
>   Terror and mystery, guard her shrine, I saw
>   Beauty enthroned; and though her gaze struck awe,
> I drew it in as simply as my breath.
> Hers were the eyes which, over and beneath
>   The sky and sea bend on thee,—which can draw,
>   By sea or sky or woman, to one law,
> The allotted bondman of her palm and wreath.

---

[21] Cary, *op. cit.*, vol. 2, p. 256.

[22] Fanny Schott, now bereft even of her physical charm, had come to the Vale of St. John with one purpose, to induce Rossetti to make a will in her favor. Cf. Evelyn Waugh, *Rossetti: His Life and Works*, London, 1928, p. 219.

[23] Cary, *op. cit.*, vol. 2, p. 257.

[24] Rossetti (W. M.), *op. cit.*, vol. 2, p. 469.

[25] *Hand and Soul.*

This is that Lady Beauty, in whose praise
   Thy voice and hand shake still,—long known to thee
   By flying hair and fluttering hem,—the beat
   Following her daily of thy heart and feet,
How passionately and irretrievably,
   In what fond flight, how many ways and days![26]

He here expresses the purpose of his life—the search for and the perfect expression of beauty. He thus writes in *Hand and Soul*:

"In all thou dost work from thine own heart, simply; for His heart is as thine when thine is wise and humble; and He shall have understanding of thee. One drop of rain is as another, and the sun's prism in all: and shalt thou not be as He, whose lives are the breath of One?"[27]

And so Rossetti strove to picture human nature by picturing himself; and conceiving of his soul as essentially an image of God and therefore beautiful, and beauty as the property of woman, he again and again strove to give expression to "the fair woman that was his soul." And so his life commenced as the pursuit of an aesthetic ideal but it ended by his being ensnared in the network of sexual charms, and he followed his own sensuality

   . . . passionately and irretrievably
   In what fond flight, how many ways and days.

Let us now approach the problem of the value and truth of Rossetti's philosophy of life.

Can the end of man be conceived of as the expression of himself?

Rossetti himself has placed the problem on a philosophical basis in a phrase of poetical prose. "One drop of rain is as another, and the sun's prism in all: and shalt thou not be as He, whose lives are the breath of One?"

If man is the image of God, then the end of man must be the outward expression of the divine likeness within himself. Therefore, the end of man is to express himself.

[26] Cary, *op. cit.*, vol. 2, p. 255. Said to have been written in 1866.
[27] *Hand and Soul*: Rossetti (W. M.), *op. cit.*, vol. 2, p. 394.

But when we say that the end of man is the expression of himself, an ambiguity is likely to arise and a false concept to slip into one's mind. And that is precisely what happened in the mind of Rossetti and the result was the ruin of his life.

We must all realize that within us there are two selves striving for expression—one the divine ideal of eternal beauty, and the other our own selfishness which is but the mocking caricature of a human being. And so when we say that the end of man is the expression of himself and set about realizing the purpose of our own lives, we must ask ourselves what is it that we are going to express: the divine ideal of eternal beauty, or the mocking caricature of a human being?

And here we are so likely to be deceived. If the divine ideal is going to find expression, it is necessary to hew away great masses of disfiguring selfishness. But this means work and effort. And nature rebels against what seems to be the marring of the beauty of human nature. But such an outcry is but a defense reaction of the mind against long and painful effort. It is so much easier to conceive of the expression of oneself as giving free outlet and ample manifestation to natural emotions as they arise.

And so in this dream the image of Chiaro's soul said to him: "Seek thine own conscience (not thy mind's conscience, but thine heart's), and all shall approve and suffice."[28]

That is, follow the promptings of your emotions, give expression to yourself by satisfying the desires of your heart, and all shall approve and suffice. And so Rossetti laid aside the restrictions of his somewhat puritanical home and forgot the ideals of his childhood, and gave expression to himself in following the emotional drive.

He was seeking beauty, but only what appeared to be beauty, but in reality was not. He seems to have been vaguely conscious of the self deception when he wrote that "much of

[28] Rossetti (W. M.), *op. cit.*, vol. 1, p. 392.

that reverence which he had mistaken for faith had been no more than the worship of beauty."[29]

And we might say that the worship of beauty became in his own personal life nothing more than the sensuous selfishness of sexuality. He strove to attain his aesthetic ideals by painting that which is beautiful, and so woman after woman was drawn adorned with all that art could imagine as the background and embellishment of feminine charm. It seems as if he sought to attain beauty and make it his own by painting it on a canvas.

But no external portrayal of the beautiful can beautify the artist himself. And if one attains to the aesthetic ideal, it must be by an inner transformation of one's own personality. No dream can ever be a reality unless it leads to action in everyday life. One does not become beautiful by thinking of aesthetic ideals. One must conform his life and action to the ideals of beauty, if his own soul is really going to possess the beauty of its dreams. Nor can the beauty of the soul be pictured on a canvas, for it is spiritual and only the spiritual is capable of receiving it.

Rossetti clung to his ideals. True to the principles of the Pre-Raphaelite Brotherhood, he strove to express ideals by painting reality in such a way that it would be no mere mirrored image of a thing but the embodiment of a concept. And he attained his end in many pictures of exquisite drawing and wonderful charm. He painted a woman whose beauty symbolized the beauty of which he dreamed; but the woman he painted was not the image of his soul but of the empty figment of his dream. What he should have striven to be, he made no effort to become. In trying to give expression to himself, he followed the desires of his heart, and lost all beauty and virtue in the mires of sensuality. His infidelity to his wife, his outbursts of temper, his thoughtless neglect led to her suicide. The note she left and which he read beside her deathbed overwhelmed him with

[29] *Hand and Soul:* Rossetti (W. M.), *op. cit.*, vol. 1, p. 387.

remorse; and in expiation, he buried the little manuscript volume of his poems in her coffin. He wanted it later and had the body exhumed to recover it, and ever after his mind was tormented by what he looked upon as the crime of the exhumation. But this was only a defense reaction which kept him from thinking of the real crime of his infidelity and neglect which drove her to suicide.

His last days were profoundly unhappy. They are thus pictured by Hall Caine, who attended him in his latter years: "If Rossetti's days were now cheerless and heavy, what shall I say of the nights? At that time of the year the night closed in as early as seven o'clock, and there in that little house among the solitary hills, his disconsolate spirit would sometimes sink beyond solace into irreclaimable depths of depression. Night after night we sat up until eleven, twelve, one and two o'clock, watching the long hours go by with heavy steps, waiting, waiting, waiting for the time at which he could take his first draught of chloral, drop back on his pillow, and snatch three or four hours of dreamless sleep."[30]

As early as 1863 he painted a picture of a woman which was the truest image of his soul that he ever executed. It was entitled "Beata Beatrix" and was nominally a representation of Dante's Beatrice in a trance before her death. But it is the picture of his dead wife and it expresses the agony of soul which his own infidelity and neglect had made her suffer, and it also reveals his own agony of remorse which abided and became more intense and intolerable as his powers failed long before their time and death approached.

In his later years nature herself seemed dark and dismal to him and he wondered if ever again he would be forgiven and united with his Beatrice in a paradise beyond the grave.

> The sky leans dumb on the sea,
> Aweary with all its wings;
> And oh! the song the sea sings

---

[30] Caine, *op. cit.*, p. 185.

Is dark everlastingly.
Our past is clean forgot,
Our present is and is not,
Our future's a sealed seedplot,
And what betwixt them are we?—
We who say as we go,—
"Strange to think by the way,
Whatever there is to know,
That shall we know one day."[31]

He dabbled in spiritualism but gave it up, thinking the phenomena were due to evil spirits attempting deceit,[32] but he longed for an immortality when he would attain in reality to the love and dreams of his younger years. He thus writes to his dead wife:

Alas, So Long!

Ah! dear one, we were young so long,
It seemed that youth would never go,
For skies and trees were ever in song
And water in singing flow
In the days we never again shall know.
Alas, so long!
Ah! then was it all spring weather?
Nay, but we were young and together.

Ah! dear one, I've been old so long,
It seems that age is loth to part,
Though days and years have never a song,
And oh! have they still the art
That warmed the pulses of heart to heart?
Alas, so long!
Ah! then was it all spring weather?
Nay, but we were young and together.

Ah! dear one, you've been dead so long—
How long until we meet again,
Where hours may never lose their song
Nor flowers forget the rain
In glad moonlight that shall never wane?
Alas, so long!
Ah! shall it be then spring weather,
And oh! shall we be young together?

---

[31] "The Cloud Confines": Cary, *op. cit.*, vol. 2, pp. 24–25. Written in 1871.
[32] Caine, *op. cit.*, p. 237.

Judging Rossetti's philosophy of life by its results, it was most unfortunate. Self expression alone is an inadequate guide because of its ambiguity. There are two selves within us all, the higher and the lower: the perfect man, the image of God, and the fiendish ego in which there is no vestige of divinity. Rossetti truly saw that we must be as He and realized that in some measure we are now as He is. And thus he said: "I need but be myself and I shall be as He." But he did not clearly perceive that as long as we are on earth we are not wholly as He is, but to a large extent as He is not. And if we say: "I shall be as I am" this may mean either that I shall be as He is or as He is not. *Facilis descensus averno et per aspera ad astra.* If we avoid all effort, and all his life long Rossetti shrunk from effort, we shall never become as He is, but more and more as He is not. The true philosophy of life is to shrink from no labor, refuse no sacrifice, spare no pain and no effort to become as He is. By sacrifice and unselfishness alone can we give expression to that image of oneself which is like unto God. And when we make ourselves as He is, all our work shall of necessity reveal Him who worketh all in all, and when our days draw near their close, the consciousness of having drawn our picture of Him, who is all Beauty, all Truth, and all Goodness, will not only make us rejoice in what we have done, but urge us to spare no effort not to mar, but to put the final touches on our picture before we present it for judgment to Him whose Judgment makes perfect that of which He approves.

Chapter XVIII

UNWHOLESOME DRIVES: THE LURE OF PLEASURE AND ITS RATIONALIZATION [1]

Every man slips by accident or is guided more or less by design into a philosophy of life which commences to be formulated in childhood and is fairly well developed before he arrives at the legal age of manhood. This does not mean that philosophies are never tried out and discarded and new ones adopted, but merely that the exigencies of life lead to acting in accordance with more or less clearly defined principles.

These principles of conduct become the actual guides of human lives and are to a large extent responsible for the happiness or unhappiness, success or failure, that blesses or mars an individual's life. Some guides lead men to the realization of noble ideals and a life of valuable accomplishment; others lead them into blind alleys where nothing is to be found and nothing can be done, or into pitfalls of ruin and destruction.

The life and work of any individual is a fruitful lesson to those who follow, if they can see the principles of guidance and control by which his life was developed and the end results, the happiness, peace, contentment, and accomplishment of him who lived out his life under direction of these principles—or the misery and failure that can be attributed to a false philosophy of life.

Algernon Charles Swinburne is an example of a man with great natural gifts who, by the use of these gifts, attained fame, but whose life cannot be described as happy nor as a contribution of positive value to future generations. However, his life and life's principles have a distinct negative value, for they show us what to avoid, and make us realize that with a nobler philosophy he would have been a greater poet.

[1] Reprinted with permission from *Character & Personality*, vol. 6, no. 1 (Sept.), 1937.

That his poetic genius was native, that is, spontaneous in its manifestations, is evident from the history of his early childhood. The love of poetry came to him with the ability to read. No one, apparently, guided him or led him into poetic lore. Even as a child a fat Shakespeare had to be with him at meals and especially at tea-time.[2] And when he went to Eton, he could discourse "at large about Elizabethan dramatic poets, of whose plays he knew pages and pages by heart."[3]

He seems to have had a native ability in rhyming. Mrs. Leith recalls the following incident. "I recollect one evening he said of a name casually mentioned, 'I wonder if one could find a rhyme to Atkinson,' and then immediately spouted

'A tree with all its catkins on
Was planted by Miss Atkinson.'[4]

And so we have in Swinburne's childhood a boy with a native love of poetry and a drive to rhyme; that is, the foundations of the technique and appreciation of the poetic art were already being laid.

In spite, too, of his later antireligious tendencies, he was as a young man religiously minded, as the following quotation from a letter shows. On July 18, 1855, he wrote thus to his mother from Cologne:

The old priest was very nice, I think you would have liked him; he was so gentle and reverent that I took a great fancy to him, he showed me all the work and all sorts of things in different parts; and he said I could see St. Ursula's tomb if I waited till the service was over, which I did, and I felt quite miserable, it was such a wretched feeling that while they were all praying, old men and tiny children kneeling together, I was not one of them, I was shut out as it were. I could have sat down and cried I was so unhappy. How I do trust that some day all will worship together and no divisions and jealousies "keep us any longer asunder."[5]

---

[2] Mrs. Disney Leith, *The Boyhood of Algernon Charles Swinburne*, London, 1917, p. 6.

[3] Letter of Reverend Father Congreve in Leith, *op. cit.*, p. 244.

[4] Leith, *op. cit.*, p. 20.

[5] Letter in Leith, *op. cit.*, p. 42.

But even prior to this, the beginnings of revolt against authority and all that it stands for had already commenced. Lafourcade says:

We are, however, forced to the conclusion that, whatever happened afterwards, during most of his childhood and adolescence there existed a strong antagonism between the poet and his father.[6]

Swinburne's novel in letters is, as he himself says,[7] autobiographical, and the letter of Captain Harewood to his son Reginald represents Swinburne's own idea, albeit emotionally overdrawn, of his father's attitude to himself.

You must be very well aware that for years back you have disgracefully disappointed me in every hope and every plan I have formed with regard to you. . . . At school you were incessantly under punishment; at home you were constantly in disgrace. Pain and degradation could not keep you right; to disgrace the most frequent, to pain the most severe, you opposed a deadly strength of sloth and tacit vigour of rebellion. . . . What the upshot of your college career was you must remember only too well, and I still hope not without some regret and shame.[8]

At all events, Swinburne was often whipped at Eton and enjoyed it; he got in trouble and left before he finished. He finally failed at Oxford and departed without a degree.

[6] Georges Lafourcade, *Swinburne: A Literary Biography*, London, 1932.

[7] Letter 353 to William M. Rossetti, Aug. 21, 1905, in Edmund Gosse and Thomas J. Wise (ed.), *Complete Works of Algernon Charles Swinburne* (Bonchurch Edition), London: Heinemann, 1925, vol. 17, *Letters*, pp. 484-85:

"I don't think you ever read or heard me read any part of the more than forty-year-old book in which I enclose this note [*Love's Cross-Currents*]; but if you glance at page 215 I think you may be reminded of a young fellow you once knew, and not see very much difference between Redgie Harewood and Algie Swinburne. . . . I want you to like the presentation of Lady Midhurst—who is entirely a creature of my own invention—and of Reginald Harewood, who (though nothing can possibly be more different than *his parents* and mine) is otherwise a rather coloured photograph of

Yours,

A. C. Swinburne

[8] Letter 22 in *Love's Cross-Currents, A Year's Letters*, in Gosse and Wise, *op. cit.*, vol. 17, pp. 209-11.

Gosse says:

A certain change took place in Swinburne's character at the opening of his last year at school (1853). He became less amenable to discipline and idler in his work.[9]

It is a very common phenomenon that those who later develop antireligious tendencies have in childhood more or less bitter conflicts with parents and teachers. It was true of Shelley and his atheism was nothing more than a reaction to his father complex, and he, like Swinburne, followed the lure of pleasure without the restraint of morals; it seems, however, that, though Shelley's antagonism to his father was more bitter, his pleasure drive was more normal and uncomplicated by the sadistic, masochistic, and necrophilic tendencies of the *libido* drive in Swinburne.

How did Swinburne develop this peculiar group of abnormal symptoms?

There is much in his character and the incidents of his life to indicate that Swinburne received very little direction and wholesome criticism in the development of his personality. Later in life he could not put up with the least shadow of criticism, as the following incident shows. He was spending an evening with the Reverend William Stubbs, his tutor, later Bishop of Oxford, and read to his host and hostess the original draft of *Rosamond*.

Early in the evening Swinburne began to read, and he read the play right through. Stubbs was very much impressed with the merits of the piece, but also with its faults, and he felt obliged to say that he thought the tone of the amatory passages somewhat objectionable. He had anticipated a little scene of modest confusion, which he would have removed by praise, but what he was not prepared for was a long silent stare, followed by a scream that rent the vicarage, and by the bolt upstairs of the outraged poet, hugging his MS to his bosom. Presently gentle Mrs. Stubbs stole upstairs, and tapping at Swinburne's door entreated him to come down to supper. There was no reply, but an extraordinary noise within of tearing and a strange glare through the keyhole. All night, at intervals, there were noises in the poet's room, and the

---

[9] E. Gosse, *The Life of Algernon Charles Swinburne*, New York: 1917, p. 26.

Stubbses were distracted. In the morning Swinburne appeared extremely late, and deathly pale. Stubbs by this time very wretched, hastened to say how sorry he was that he had so hastily condemned the drama, and how much he hoped that Swinburne had not been discouraged by his criticism. The poet replied: "I lighted a fire in the empty grate, and I burned every page of my manuscript." Stubbs was horrified. "But it does not matter; I sat up all night and wrote it right through again from memory."[10]

It appears that he "learned during his early years, 'to live at large and stray at will.'"[11] Lafourcade quotes the following passage from the unpublished autobiographical "Lesbia Brandon" as descriptive of the childhood of Swinburne.

For months he lived and grew on like an animal or fruit; and things seemed to deal with him as one of these; earth set herself to caress and amuse him; air blew and rain fell and leaves changed to his great delight; he felt no want in life.[12]

Swinburne happened to be a rare type of nature that was in special need of guidance, lest he should undergo an easily possible pathological development. He was one of those individuals in whom intense stimulation of the skin, particularly when it is accompanied by stinging pain, affords a high degree of pleasurable excitement. Such a nature would be capable of endurance and suffering for noble ends far beyond the ordinary power of the common man, had the ends been outlined and a lofty idealism and strong purpose been instilled into the poetic mind of the growing child; instead, he was left "to live at large and stray at will" and then

To flush with love and hide in flowers.[13]

Some will find the union of physical pain with intense enjoyment utterly incomprehensible, but one must remember that the neurology of human beings manifests some marked differences.

For example, there is a substance[14] which to some is tasteless

---

[10] *Op. cit.*, pp. 62–63.
[11] Lafourcade, *op. cit.*, p. 22.
[12] *Ibid.*, p. 23.
[13] *Ibid.*, p. 73.
[14] Para-oxy-phenyl-thio-carbamide.

and to others intensely bitter. Individuals vary as regards the neural pathway that taste stimuli take on the way to the brain.[15]

Patients with thalamic lesions have peculiar alterations of sensibility, though I know of no case where painful stimuli became pleasant after such an injury. Thus, one lady musician after a paralytic stroke found that serious music was intolerable, owing to sensations that were produced "throughout the right side of the body."[16]

Many cases of thalamic lesions are known in which slight stimulation is excessively painful. There are also cases in which mild stimulation becomes excessively pleasurable. Thus,

A highly educated patient confessed he had become more amorous since the attack, which rendered the right half of his body more responsive to pleasant and unpleasant stimuli. "I crave to place my right hand on the soft skin of a woman. It's my right hand that wants the consolation. I seem to crave for sympathy on my right side." Finally he added, "My right hand seems to be more artistic."[17]

Such cases indicate the possibility that in the uninjured nervous systems of normal individuals there may be profound differences; it is possible, and the possibility was realized in Swinburne, that all excessive stimuli of the skin, even though accompanied by pricking, piercing, and cutting, may in certain individuals give rise to pleasure.

It is therefore easily understood that some individuals may from birth be so constituted that intense and even painful stimulation of the skin may lead to keen enjoyment.

At all events there is ample evidence to show that this was the case with Swinburne. The earliest evidence is his love of the sea. Lafourcade quotes the following passage from "Lesbia Brandon":

[15] E. von Skramlik, "Physiologie des Geschmacksinnes," in *Receptionsorgane*, Handbuch der normalen und pathologischen Physiologie (ed. by A. Bethe *et al.*), **10**[1]: 317, 1926.

[16] Henry Head, *Studies in Neurology*, London: 1920, vol. 2, p. 620.

[17] *Ibid.*, p. 561.

The scourging of the surf made him red from the shoulders to the knees and sent him on shore whipped by the sea into a single blush of the whole skin.[18]

The sensation derived from the scourging of the surf seems to be related to that of the whippings in which he took an abnormal delight when at Eton.   In perhaps the most powerful and most pathetic of all his poems, "The Triumph of Time," he thus speaks of the sea:

> O fair green-girdled mother of mine,
> Sea, that art clothed with the sun and the rain,
> Thy sweet hard kisses are strong like wine,
> Thy large embraces are keen like pain,[19]

thus suggesting the sexual component that in Swinburne became attached to his enjoyment of pain.

Before undertaking his daring but foolhardy climb of Culver Cliff, he took a dip into the midwinter sea, as he wrote, "to steady and strengthen my nerve,"[20] and even made the first attempt naked, not minding and even stimulated by the sharp cold of the wind and the cuts and bruises he suffered from the rocks.

In *Love's Cross-Currents* Reginald (of whom Swinburne wrote to William Rossetti that he was no other person than himself) carried a whip with which at times he switched his leg and later persuaded a small boy to whip him.

We do not know just when the formal sexual element came to be present in Swinburne's experience of pain.   It is already to be found in the unpublished fragment "Laugh and Lie Down," dominated by a flagellation motif and composed about

---

[18] Georges Lafourcade, *La jeunesse de Swinburne*, Paris: 1928, vol. 1, p. 51. One must not think the suggestion is here made that all who enjoy the stimulus of cold water have a fundamental masochistic trend.   When Lafourcade traces back Swinburne's masochism to the sting of the surf, he makes a suggestion only, which without further evidence, would be wholly inadequate as indicative of masochism.

[19] Gosse and Wise, *op. cit.*, vol. 1, p. 177.

[20] Leith, *op. cit.*, p. 14.

1858–1859.[21] It is manifested in "Queen Yseult," which was written in 1858, but all we now have of it was not published till 1918.

> And his kisses on her hair
> And her throat and shoulders bare
> Fierce and bitter kisses were
>
> . . . .
> And above him while she stood,
> Stains upon her red as blood;
> Then she kissed him as he would.[22]

The term "bitter kisses" has a specific meaning with Swinburne. We may look upon it as defined by the line from *Rosamond:*

> I felt your teeth come through that bitter kiss.[23]

Lafourcade blames[24] Richard Monckton Milnes, Lord Houghton, for having corrupted the mind of Swinburne. This can be true only in the sense that Milnes stimulated the already nascent sadistic-masochistic tendencies of Swinburne to their full growth.

In a letter to Milnes dated October 14, 1860, Swinburne reminds him of his promise "that I am yet to live and look upon the mystic pages of the martyred Marquis de Sade, ever since

[21] Lafourcade, *Swinburne*, pp. 81–83; *La jeunesse de Swinburne*, vol. 2, p. 128. From the fact that an author introduces sadistic, masochistic, and other abnormal personalities into his poems, one cannot conclude that the author himself was sadistic and masochistic. He may well be representing human personalities he has known and not giving expression to trends in his own character and constitution. Certainly an author cannot truly represent human nature in all the personalities he portrays and be always expressing nothing more nor less than himself. When, however, there is historical evidence, as in Swinburne's case, that an author is masochistic, various passages in his writings will not only confirm the historical evidence, but also give some idea of how the details of the picture should be filled in so as to represent the reality.

[22] Gosse and Wise, *op. cit.*, vol. 1, p. 37.

[23] *Ibid.*, vol. 7, p. 217. *Rosamond* was published in 1860.

[24] Lafourcade, *op. cit.*, vol. 1, p. 178.

which the vision of that illustrious and ill-requited benefactor of humanity has hovered by night before my eyes."[25]   In 1861 Milnes kept his promise[26] and Swinburne ever after looked upon the Marquis de Sade as his model and hero.   He commenced to conceive of himself as the poet and philosopher and advocate of vice.

Speaking of two lines in his poem "Dolores,"

> Pain melted in tears, and was Pleasure,
> Death tingled with blood, and was Life,

he added the words:

Voilà, mes amis, une verité que ne comprendront jamais les sots idolateurs de la vertu. (Here my friends, is a truth that the stupid idolators of virtue will never understand.)[27]

The poem "Dolores" is one that fully justifies his jocose estimate of his own work written as early as 1858.

I should like to review myself and say "that I have an abortive covetousness of imitation in which an exaggeration of my models—i.e., blasphemy and sensuality—is happily neutralised by my own imbecility."[28]

The poem from which he quoted in the letter to Howell is a blasphemous parody on the Mother of Sorrows, a hymn of Swinburne to the unfound goddess of his dreams, the personified harlot of pain.

> Seven sorrows the priests give their Virgin;
> But thy sins are seventy times seven,
> Seven ages would fail thee to purge in,
> And then they would haunt thee in heaven:
> Fierce midnights and famishing morrows,
> And loves that complete and control
> All the joys of the flesh, all the sorrows
> That wear out the soul.

---

[25] Gosse and Wise, *op. cit.*, vol. 18, pp. 7–8.

[26] Lafourcade, *op. cit.*, vol. 1, p. 179.

[27] Letter to Charles Augustus Howell, 1865, in Gosse and Wise, *op. cit.* vol. 18, p. 31.

[28] Letter to Edwin Hatch, Feb. 17, 1858, *ibid.*, p. 3.

> O garment not golden but gilded,
> O garden where all men may dwell,
> O tower not of ivory, but builded
> By hands that reach heaven from hell;
> O mystical rose of the mire,
> O house not of gold but of gain,
> Our lady of Pain!
>
> . . . .
>
> By the ravenous teeth that have smitten
> Through the kisses that blossom and bud,
> By the lips intertwisted and bitten
> Till the foam has a savour of blood,
> By the pulse as it rises and falters,
> By the hands as they slacken and strain,
> I adjure thee, respond from thine altars,
> Our Lady of Pain!
>
> . . . .
>
> I could hurt thee—but pain would delight thee;
> Or caress thee—but love would repel;
> And the lovers whose lips would excite thee
> Are serpents in hell.[29]

Passages like the following are so frequent in Swinburne that one can scarcely err in supposing that he not only lived out his pathological sex life in poetic dreams, but also experienced it in reality.

> And where my kiss hath fed
> Thy flower-like blood leaps red
> To the kissed place.[30]

Furthermore, it seems that Swinburne made a proposal of marriage to a young girl, Jane Faulkner, with whom he had been on intimate terms. Gosse writes:

She gave him roses, she played and sang to him, and he conceived from her gracious ways an encouragement which she was far from seriously intending. He declared his passion suddenly, and no doubt in a manner which seemed to her preposterous and violent.[31]

---

[29] "Dolores" ("Notre Dame des sept douleurs"): *op. cit.*, vol. 1, pp. 284–98.
[30] "Fragoletta": *op. cit.*, vol. 1, p. 217.
[31] Gosse, *op. cit.*, p. 82.

She broke out laughing, and Swinburne, deeply insulted, went to Northumberland and wrote "The Triumph of Time." This was about the beginning of 1863.

His poem "Anactoria" composed about the same time utters the complaint:

> Why wilt thou follow lesser loves? are thine
> Too weak to bear these hands and lips of mine?[32]
>
> ... He speaks of pain made perfect in thy lips
> For my sake when I hurt thee.[33]

It seems that Jane Faulkner actually experienced what it meant to be

> ... seamed with sharp lips and fierce fingers,
> And branded by kisses that bruise.[34]

The poem "Anactoria" demonstrates the dictum of Stekel:

The sadist fundamentally is being driven on to the utter annihilation of the love object. Every sadist properly speaking [*eigentlich*] is a murderer.[35]

The drive to murder the love object finds the following expression:

> I would my love could kill thee; I am satiated
> With seeing thee live and fain would have thee dead.
> I would earth had thy body as fruit to eat,
> And no mouth but some serpent's found thee sweet.
> I would find grievous ways to have thee slain,
> Intense device, and superflux of pain;
> Vex thee with amorous agonies, and shake
> Life at thy lips, and leave it there to ache;
> Strain out thy soul with pangs too soft to kill,
> Intolerable interludes, and infinite ill;
> Relapse and reluctation of the breath,
> Dumb tunes and shuddering tones of death.[36]

---

[32] *Ibid.*, p. 190.
[33] *Ibid.*, p. 194.
[34] "Dolores": Gosse and Wise, *op. cit.*, vol. 1, p. 292.
[35] *Störungen des Trieb- und Affectlebens*, Berlin, 1925, chap. 7, "Sadismus und Masochismus," p. 712.
[36] Gosse and Wise, *op. cit.*, vol. 1, pp. 190–91.

And then, lest we think this mere ordinary, uncomplicated, sexless revenge, he writes:

> Ah that my lips were tuneless lips, but pressed
> To the bruised bosom of thy scourged white breast!
> Ah that my mouth for Muses' milk were fed
> On the sweet blood thy sweet small wounds had bled!
> That with my tongue I felt them, and could taste
> The faint flakes from thy bosom to the waist!
> That I could drink thy veins as wine, and eat
> Thy breasts like honey! that from face to feet
> Thy body were abolished and consumed,
> And in my flesh thy very flesh entombed.[37]

And so the peculiarity of Swinburne's nervous system, which made the stimulation of the skin all the more intensely pleasurable the more it stung with the sharpness of pain, was the basis of his masochism. Sexuality was easily fused with pain, and following the lure of pleasure, he sought for pain. And so to him

> Pain melted in tears, and was Pleasure
> Death tingled with blood, and was Life.[38]

But the craving for "the sharp and cruel enjoyments of pain" led to the "acrid relish of suffering"[39] both felt and *inflicted,* and his fingers tore the flesh and his teeth marred the skin of the one he loved.

But this was not the final goal to which the lure of pleasure led him. If the sadist can kill the one he loves and derive sexual pleasure in the killing, he can keep love's revel with the dead, and cover with kisses and caresses the cold and lifeless corpse of the victim of his love. And so, Swinburne lives out in dreams the ultimate consummation of sadistic love.

I know of no evidence that Swinburne was a necrophile in reality as well as in dreams. He may merely have followed a sadistic trend to horrify his readers by reflecting in English what

[37] *Ibid.*, p. 193.
[38] "Dolores": *ibid.*, p. 289.
[39] "Charles Baudelaire" (essay): *op. cit.*, vol. 13, p. 421.

had delighted him in the abnormalities of the French.   Necrophilia, however, is most easily understood as an outgrowth of sadism, and if Swinburne was really sadistic, his own inner imaginations may well have had a necrophilic coloring.

As a matter of fact, this peculiar abnormality finds expression in more than one place in his writings.

He can see something attractive even in the dead body that is undergoing the process of putrefaction.   He thus writes of a poem of Charles Baudelaire:

> Thus even of the loathsomest bodily putrescence and decay he can make some noble use; pluck out its meaning and secret, even its beauty, in a certain way, from actual carrion.[40]

In his short story "Dead Love,"[41] he describes how the lady Yolande falls in love with the dead body of the knight who slew her husband, embalms it, and spends the night embracing and kissing the corpse.[42]

Dead love was a favorite subject with Swinburne.   A poem also bears that theme as its title, and in it he writes:

> Kiss the lips that will not move,
> Smooth the ruffled plaits of hair.

And in the strange poem entitled "The Leper" he dreams as follows:

> Yet am I glad to have her dead
> Here in this wretched wattled house
> Where I can kiss her eyes and head.
>
> . . . .
>
> Six months, and I sit still and hold
> In two cold palms her cold two feet.
> Her hair, half grey, half ruined gold,
> Thrills me and burns me in kissing it.

---

[40] Review of a volume of poems by Baudelaire, *ibid*.   This review appeared in *The Spectator*, Sept. 6, 1862 (cf. Richard Shepard Herne, *The Bibliography of Swinburne*, London, 1887, pp. 40, 7).

[41] This seems to have appeared in *Once-a-Week* 7: 432–34 (Oct. 11), 1862.

[42] Gosse and Wise, *op. cit.*, vol. 17, pp. 11–16.

Life bites and stings me through, to see
Her keen face made of sunken bones.
Her worn-off eyelids madden me,
That were shot through with purple once.[43]

Swinburne is an example of one type of reaction to the moral conflict. When one fails in the moral conflict, there are several ways of reacting to the failure. The honest and wholesome reaction is, first of all, a candid admission of the fact: the frank statement, "I did wrong," and then the resolution, "But I will do right"—followed by the effort, painful and laborious perhaps, to establish oneself on the stable foundation of a virtuous life.

But there are those who shrink from facing themselves as they really are, and so, in one way or another, they attempt to excuse and justify themselves. Some say: "I am bad, but I cannot help it"; others: "I am bad, but I don't care." The Swinburne reaction is more extreme: "I am bad, but what the common run of men call vice is the highest virtue"; and so he rationalized his vices and reinterpreted them, regarding himself as a connoisseur who prefers a bitter, pungent liqueur to an insipid mixture of sugar and water.

When we speak of Swinburne's rationalizing his vices, we use the word in a technical sense. Not all reasoning is rationalization. *Rationalization* is a term which should be confined to the spontaneous tendency of human nature to use reasoning power to justify and ennoble what is really unjustifiable and base in one's own conduct. The result of rationalization is a lofty sense of one's own personal value and the consequent blindness to moral defects.

Swinburne's rationalization of his own conduct becomes his philosophy of life. Its starting point is really his own cruel sexual love. At first the boy, who felt lonely when as a stranger in a foreign land he entered a church and watched "the old men and tiny children kneeling together" and praying, must have felt keenly when he realized that his love was more cruel than lust. And then, he commenced to question:

[43] *Op. cit.*, vol. 1, pp. 250, 253.

> Sin, is it sin whereby men's souls are thrust
> Into the pit? Yet had I a good trust
> To save my soul before it slipped therein
> Trod under by the fire-shod feet of lust.[44]
> For I was of Christ's choosing, I God's knight,
> No blinkard heathen stumbling for scant light;
> I can well see, for all the dusty days
> Gone past, the clean great time of goodly fight.[45]

But there was no sense of fidelity, and, having touched, he changed

> . . . in a trice
> The lilies and languors of virtue
> For the raptures and roses of vice.[46]

He could not face himself in honest daylight, and so he fled

> . . . from the outermost portal
> To the shrine where a sin is a prayer.[47]
> . . . .
> In a twilight where virtues are vices
> In thy chapels, unknown of the sun.[48]

and then cried to his personified sadistic ideal:

> Come down and redeem us from virtue
> Our Lady of Pain.[49]

And then he philosophized: "I am cruel," he said, "but so is nature, and nature is God, and therefore I am like unto God. The more cruel and wicked I am, the closer do I come to nature."

Nature averse to crime? I tell you, nature lives and breathes by it; hungers at all her pores for bloodshed, aches in all her nerves for the help of sin, yearns with all her heart for the furtherance of cruelty. Nature forbid that thing or this? Nay, the best or worst of you will never go so far as she would

---

[44] "Laus Veneris": *ibid.*, vol. 1, p. 152.
[45] *Op. cit.*, vol. 1, p. 154.
[46] "Dolores": *ibid.*, p. 286.
[47] *Op. cit.*, vol. 1, p. 288.
[48] *Op. cit.*, vol. 1, p. 290.
[49] *Op. cit.*, vol. 1, p. 292.

have you; no criminal will come up to the measure of her crimes, nor destruction to her seem destructive enough. . . . And what are the worst sins we can do—we who live for a day and die in a night?   A few murders, a few.[50]

The passage quoted is attributed by Swinburne to an unnamed "modern pagan philosopher," but the passage has never been identified and, as Lafourcade says, it mirrors the thought of the Marquis de Sade,[51] whose concepts Swinburne took over *in toto* and made his own.   And in the poem "Dolores" he expresses a similar thought when he writes:

> Ah where shall we go then for pastime,
> If the worst that can be has been done?[52]

Swinburne's philosophy of life was not a mere personal affair, but a doctrine that he craved to spread abroad, as is evident from the following incident.   When Watt approached the firm of Chapman and Hall concerning the publication of Swinburne's works, they offered to bring out a cheap popular edition. Swinburne was elated, and wrote to his friend Powell:

Apart from the profit and credit [arising from a 2s. edition of his works] please imagine me stalking triumphant through the land and displaying on every Hearth in every Home of my country, naked and *not* ashamed, the banner of immorality, atheism and revolution.[53]

We may now ask what was the fruit of following the lure of pleasure and developing a sadistic philosophy of vice?   Let us first look at the character of Swinburne.   We find a man who is only an overgrown conceited child, who alienates his friends, lives out the vices of which he dreams, and finally flies from the society of his fellowmen and dies in the isolation with which he surrounded himself.

[50] "William Blake": *op. cit.*, vol. 16, pp. 202–3, footnote.
[51] Lafourcade, *op. cit.*, vol. 2, p. 355.
[52] Gosse and Wise, *op. cit.*, vol. 1, p. 287.
[53] Quoted by Lafourcade, *op. cit.*, p. 257.

Gosse says:

> The thirteen last years of Swinburne's life were spent almost as if within a Leyden jar. Nothing could be more motionless than the existence of "the little old genius, and his little old acolyte, in their dull little villa." [54]

In this isolation we have no evidence of the sadism and masochism of his youth, but that at one time he lived out his vices in reality as well as in poetry is indicated by such passages as the following:

> But there can be no doubt that "the Poet" was then (1867–1872) drinking himself to death, and the way in which for about twenty years Swinburne sustained the strain of his many activities and vices is a puzzle to many doctors. [55]

His supreme conceit is evidenced by such incidents as the following:

> Meredith had recently sent Swinburne ten pounds for a poem (sans doute "Ave atque Vale" publié dans la *Fortnightly* en janvier, 1868). Meredith explained he was paying all contributors during Morley's absence. "Yes," said Swinburne, "but why ten pounds?" Meredith explained it was what he usually got for his own poems. "Yes, for yours," said Swinburne, "but for mine?" Meredith tried to point out the justice of it; what was enough for him was enough for Swinburne. Swinburne got up, came over to him and slapped his face. That was the end of their friendship. [56]

Again, when invited by Lord Houghton to meet Tennyson, Swinburne went, but after being presented, paid little attention to Tennyson and talked to other members of the company. [57]

Philosophies may be judged by their ultimate consequences. Swinburne's philosophy attempts to justify the drive to follow the lure of pleasure wherever it may lead. It is a supremely selfish drive, and an egoistic philosophy. The one he loves must bear his hands that tear the flesh and his teeth that bite and bruise. But the end of all sadism is the death of the love object, and not that merely, according to Swinburne, but the destruction of the social order and all society and, were it possible, even nature itself.

[54] Gosse, *op. cit.*, p. 279.
[55] Lafourcade, *op. cit.*, p. 156.
[56] *Op. cit.* (quoting E. R. and J. Pennell, *The Whistler Journal*), vol. 1, p. 182.
[57] Gosse, *op. cit.*, p. 139.

Could we thwart nature, then might crime become possible and sin an actual thing. Could a man but do this; could he cross the courses of the stars, and put back the times of the sea; could he change the ways of the world and find out the house of life to destroy it; could he go into heaven to defile it and into hell to deliver it from subjection; could he draw down the sun to consume the earth, and bid the moon shed fire or poison upon the air; could he kill the fruit in the seed and corrode the child's mouth with the mother's milk; then he had sinned and done evil against nature. Nay, and not then: for nature would fain have it so, that she might create a new world of things; for she is weary of the ancient life: her eyes are sick of seeing and her ears are heavy with hearing; with the lust of creation she is burnt up, and rent in twain with travail until she bring forth change; she would fain create afresh, and cannot, except it be by destroying; in all her energies she is athirst for mortal food, and with all her forces she labors in desire of death.[58]

In Swinburne this sadistic philosophy of death has its roots in a peculiarity of the nervous system which made it possible for pain to cause a strange type of sensory pleasure that in the course of adolescence became associated with sexuality. As a child, he was allowed to "live at large and stray at will," except when his life was crossed by the dominating spirit of his father, to whom he developed a strong antagonism.

Criticism he could not brook, as evidenced by the incident cited above when he left the room with a piercing scream and destroyed the manuscript in which his tutor had suggested some changes.

And so, when his own conscience spoke to him, he silenced it by a dishonest process of rationalization, which made it forever impossible for him to see himself as he was, and perpetuated in his mind the glaring falsehood which calls virtue vice and vice virtue. He covered up the horrors and cruelties of his sadism by singing of them in metric cadences of which Coventry Patmore says:

They almost satisfy the ear without any accompaniment of sound meaning, and evoke, as it were by a trick, a current of emotion that is independent of any human feeling in the poet himself.[59]

---

[58] "William Blake": cf. above.[50]
[59] Coventry Patmore, *Principle in Art*. . . . London, 1889, p. 116.

But the magic of his cadences does not in any way lessen the crime of the "bruised bosom" and the "scourged white throat" and of "dead love" and of blasphemy against God.

If we have done wrong, why lie and say it was no wrong? And if one gives expression to his innermost self in poetry, shall not the technique of the master bear witness to the truth, and not to a lie? How much more honest and more genuinely human, how far more truly ennobling than all the sadistic witchery of Swinburne are the simple lines of Newman's act of contrition!

> O holiest Truth! how have I lied to Thee!
> I vow'd this day Thy festival should be:
> But I am dim ere night.
> Surely I made my prayer, and I did deem
> That I could keep me in Thy morning beam,
> Immaculate and bright.
>
> But my foot slipp'd; and as I lay, he came
> My gloomy foe, and robb'd me of heaven's flame.
> Help Thou my darkness, Lord, till I am light.[60]

---

[60] "Evening from St. Gregory Nazianzen": *Verses on Various Occasions*, London, 1880, p. 195.

CHAPTER XIX

RELIGIOUS SUBLIMATION[1]

IT IS maintained by Jung that there is in every organism one single, fundamental energy which has various manifestations. This concept is based on an analogy drawn from physical science. Physical energy has various forms, appearing now as heat, now as movement, now as light, now as electricity, now as a chemical change. But at bottom it is all one and the same energy, and must, in the last analysis, be looked upon as that which moves a mass with a given velocity. So Jung sees in the various strivings of a human being, whether for the pleasures of the senses or of the mind, whether noble or ignoble, whether as a child or as a man, the manifestations of one and the same physical energy, the *libido* of the organism.

It has long seemed to me that one must admit that there is in human nature a driving force which, however protean its forms, never loses its identity. At the same time it appears, also, that this driving force does not exhaust the kinetic apparatus of our nature. The two steeds in Plato's chariot may have to be reduced to one that has good moods and bad moods, that may at times move along quietly, with a dignified bearing, and then again dash ahead and threaten to wreck the chariot and kill the charioteer. But whether leisurely or with dash and spirit, the one horse always moves, and when he is moving, his head must always be pointed to one of the many points of the compass, and in the normal human being, there is some kind of guidance and control which is being exercised over his movements.

The question is akin to the ancient one of the distinction between ἡδονή and εὐδαιμονία. If we grant a distinction between pleasure and happiness, then the satisfaction of *libido* in

---

[1] Reprinted with permission from *Psychoanalyt. Rev.*, vol. 5, no. 4 (Oct.), 1918.

any of its forms is the source of pleasure, but the contentment which arises from the control of *libido* is happiness.

There are several things in psychoanalytic studies which would suggest this distinction. Thus, Freud warns against what he terms *wilde Psychoanalyse*, and regards it as a serious mistake to advise the indiscriminate satisfaction of sexual cravings as a cure for unhappiness arising from an unfortunate marriage. He does not make the distinction I have pointed out, but it could well be made, and the psychoanalyst would be closer to human nature as it is, if he would keep in mind primarily the individual who exercises a guidance and control over his *libido* strivings in their multifarious manifestations.

Then, there are phenomena even in our dream life which would indicate the existence of such a guiding factor. The censor of consciousness may, after all, often turn out to be a factor distinct from *libido* in any of its manifestations.

One could approach the problem of the distinction between *libido* and control from various well recognized standpoints of the psychoanalytic school. But another and more truly empirical procedure is to analyze the facts of individual experience and see what bearing they have upon *libido* and the restrictions placed upon it by other factors in the psychophysical organism. To do this, we should be able to look at the whole life of some human being and see the operation of the *libido* and the restrictions placed upon it.

With this problem in mind, I turned to Francis Thompson and reread his great masterpiece, *The Hound of Heaven*. How luminous this poem appears when we read it from the psychoanalytical point of view, as the autobiography of the author! It is the story of the strivings of the *libido*. At first, it is described as unchecked, uncompensated, and without any sublimation. Then we see the efforts of a poetic genius to direct the *libido*, first in one channel and then in another, and finally we witness the triumph of the individual over the *libido* in a religious sublimation.

When Francis Thompson speaks, in this poem, of his flight, he describes the devious paths that he pursued, driven by the desires of the human heart. This flight is the wandering of the *libido*—a wandering experienced by all, but only by a few in the violence and intensity of the fall and resurrection of Francis Thompson. Contrasted with the blind force that drove him on, seeking freedom from the restrictions laid upon him by the moral law, is the expression of that law in his own mind, the voice of conscience, which acts as a restraining force, blocking the manifestations of the *libido*; worn out by its very wanderings, exhausted in its flight from the Hound of Heaven, it is caught in the only channel left open to it and pours itself forth in a religious sublimation.

> I fled Him, down the nights and down the days;
> I fled Him, down the arches of the years;
> I fled Him, down the labyrinthine ways
>   Of my own mind; and in the mist of tears
> I hid from Him, and under running laughter.
>   Up vistaed hopes, I sped;
>   And shot, precipitated,
> Adown Titanic glooms of chasmèd fears,
>   From those strong Feet that followed, followed after.
>
>   But with unhurrying chase,
>   And unperturbèd pace,
> Deliberate speed, majestic instancy,
>   They beat—and a Voice beat
>   More instant than the Feet—
> "All things betray thee, who betrayest Me."

The flight from the Hound of Heaven is the reaction of the poet's nature to the insistence of his environment. As a child, he had been given a religious education—first, at the little school of the Nuns of the Cross and the Passion. The voice of conscience that spoke to him was from the first a religious voice, and it never ceased to speak, even though he fled it "down the nights and down the days," and "down the arches of the years," and "down the labyrinthine ways" of his own mind.

As a child, he loved play, loved it excessively, and shut himself up in his dream world of play. He loved his little games with his sisters, but the games meant one thing to them, another to him. "My side of the game," he said, "was part of a dream scheme invisible to them."[2]

His family entertained hopes that he would one day enter the priesthood, and, with this in view, they sent him to Ushaw College. But he was one of those spirits to whom institutional life was particularly hard. He did not relish being wakened rudely from his childish dreams and sent away from the shelter of his home, where he played with his sisters and idealized and fell in love with his favorite doll.[3] At Ushaw he manifested that shut-in type of reaction which might readily have developed into a full-grown dementia praecox. In his essay on Shelley, he describes most exactly what psychiatrists will at once recognize as a typical schizophrenic reaction:

So beset, the child fled into the tower of his own soul, and raised the drawbridge. He threw out a reserve, encysted in which he grew to maturity unaffected by the intercourses that modify the maturity of others into the thing we call a man.[4]

But in describing Shelley, he was but telling what he had experienced himself.

This shut-in type of reaction is, after all, but one of the many manifestations of the *libido* at its lower levels. The individual shrinks from the activity of the conscience principle which would direct the energies of the organism away from the self to the call of common, ordinary duty. Pleasure lies in inactivity, in doing nothing useful, in not taking one's part in the world, in living a life of dreams, in loving ideals and not realities. All share in this type of reaction to some extent and during some part of their lives. It is natural to children—but they shake it off as they enter into real life. When those in whom it is

---

[2] Cf. Everard Meynell, *Life*, p. 10.
[3] *Ibid.*
[4] *Essay on Shelley*, London: Burns & Oates, 1909, pp. 33–34.

pathologically developed first come into contact with the world, they shrink back and close up like the bell animalcule when it touches a foreign object.

When Francis Thompson went to Ushaw, he experienced his first contact with the world. In a notebook, he recalls his first impression of that contact. "Fresh from my tender home, and my circle of just-judging friends, these malignant schoolmates who danced round me with mocking evil distortion of laughter —God's good laughter, gift of all things that look back to the sun—were to me devilish apparitions of a hate now first known; hate for hate's sake, cruelty for cruelty's sake. And as such they live in my memory, testimonies to the murky, aboriginal demon in man."[5]

Two of his friends who knew him intimately at school were much surprised when they learned later that he was so unhappy. His school environment was not a harsher one than that of other boys, but his nature was more sensitive, and he reacted to his surroundings by hating them and shrinking back still further into the cavern of himself.

At school, his schizophrenic tendency did no more harm than to mark him as queer and indolent. He would not study what he did not like, for his *libido* as yet did not let him out of himself. But he loved literature and excelled all others in his English composition. His parents were notified at the end of his college career that Francis had no vocation to the priesthood. His father, a successful physician, then determined that he should study medicine.

Here the conflict between his self seeking and the duties of real life first commenced to be of serious moment. He would not study, and followed his life of dreaming, reading poetry in the libraries, and visiting museums and galleries. In one of these he saw a statue, the Vatican Melpomene, and thither each evening as twilight fell, he would steal "to meditate and worship the baffling mysteries of her meaning." Much of his time was spent at the cricket field. In the evening he would often

[5] Meynell, *op. cit.* p. 18.

come home late, saying that he had been taking private instruction with one of the lecturers. It was later found that he was visiting the home of a musician, listening to him play the piano.

At about this time, his mother—shortly before her death—gave him a copy of De Quincey's *Confessions of an Opium Eater*. Introduced thus innocently to the mysteries of opium, he sought to experience himself what De Quincey described, and became an addict until the time of his awakening. After utterly failing in his medical studies, he left home and went to London, alone and penniless. This is to be explained as a further shrinking into himself. He could not bear to have those he loved look upon the ruin of his life, and so he went where no one would know and none would care. Here he became a veritable pariah, sleeping often in the open or in cheap lodging houses, doing odd jobs, trying but failing in his attempts to do business as a boot-black, spending on opium what pennies were spared by the stern demand of hunger.

During all this time, while he was following the drive of the *libido* at its lower levels, the conscience principle was not dead within him. His attitude of mind is expressed in the *Hound of Heaven*. He is flying the Divine voice of conscience. He will not turn to look though he hears the footsteps of the Master. He shrinks from conscience. He cannot obey with a half-hearted service; he must seek God as the mystic seeks Him if he will seek at all.

> For, though I knew His love Who followèd,
>   Yet was I sore adread
> Lest, having Him, I must have naught beside.

He feared lest he should in some way be driven into the conflict with his *libido*—a conflict which he had avoided from earliest childhood. It was this shrinking that made him fail in all but literature at college. He had not failed in that, because it had helped him to live on in his world of dreams. Because he would not forsake this world of dreams, he disappointed his father, refusing even to enter on a medical career, wasting his days watching cricket, devoting the twilight to amorous musings over a statue, and seeking at night to feel the expression of his pent-up self while listening to the musical productions of the classic composers. But whether he played at home or sought to bury himself in the depths of darkest London, whether in the dreams of poetry he "troubled the golden gateway of the stars, smiting for shelter on their clangèd bars," or following the *libido* drive, he clung "to the whistling mane of every wind," whether he suffered the pangs of hunger in direst poverty or sought surcease of sorrow in drugged oblivion,

> Still with unhurrying chase
> And unperturbèd pace,
> Deliberate speed, majestic instancy,
> Came on the following Feet,
> And a voice above their beat—
> "Naught shelters thee, who wilt not shelter Me."

In London he reached the lowest depths of his career. His turning point came in a very natural way—in an apparent accident of his life, which prepared him for a process of sublimation, the natural mechanism of man's elevation to higher things. His first attempt at sublimation was precipitated by an act of kindness done him by a young girl, when, exhausted with hunger, he was an outcast in the streets of London. He describes this in a little poem entitled "A Child's Kiss." He tells of his long watching through the night, and how he thought he was dying of hunger.

> Bled of strength
> I waited the inevitable last
> Then there came past
> A child, like thee, a spring flower; but a flower
> Fallen from the budded coronal of Spring.
> And through the city streets blown withering
> She passed,—O brave, sad, lovingest, tender thing!—
> And of her own scant pittance did she give,
>   That I might eat and live:
> Then fled, a swift and trackless fugitive.

Were we to judge from the poem alone, we might think that this was a single kindly act of some poor waif who shared with him her crust of bread. But from Everard Meynell's *Life*, we learn more:

> This girl gave out of her scant and pitiable opulence, consisting of a room, warmth and food, and a cab thereto. When the streets were no longer crowded with shameful possibilities, she would think of the only tryst that her heart regarded, and, a sister of charity, would take her beggar into her vehicle at the appointed place and cherish him with an affection maidenly and motherly, and passionate in both these capacities. Two outcasts, they sat marveling that there were joys for them to unbury and to share.[6]

He had not been partaking of her hospitality long when he heard that one of his poems had been published, and that the editor of *Merry England* wanted to give him constant employment. He told his outcast hostess of his success, expecting her to rejoice with him. But instead, she told him that he must go to his new-found friends, and leave her. "They will not understand our friendship," she said, and then: "I always knew that you were a genius."

And it was then that she fled "a swift and trackless fugitive." In vain he sought her at the old trystying places. In vain he haunted the streets, looking for her. In vain he put off the offer of Mr. Meynell to give him permanent employment. She was lost beneath the vast human sea of darkest London.

The loss of this trackless fugitive was the "gust of His approach" that clashed to the gates through which his lower *libido* strivings had found their outlet. They could no longer flow in the same low channels. Were it not that these channels were closed at the same time higher ones were opened, their closing might have resulted in mental disaster. But after he had sought his trackless fugitive long in vain, he allowed himself to come under the kindly saving influence of Mr. Meynell. He saw home life again, and again came in touch with innocent little children—not such as he had known in

> The places infamous to tell
> Where God wipes not the tears from any eyes.

---

[6] *Op. cit.*, pp. 81–82.

Later, recalling the memory of his outcast days, he wrote, "Think of it! If Christ stood amidst your London slums, He could not say: 'Except ye become as one of these little children.' Far better your children were cast over the bridges of London, than that they should become as one of these little ones.'"[7] What wonder that when he was thrown again with real little children, sweet and innocent and clean, with Rose and Lily and Daisy and Daisy's sister-blossom or blossom-sister Viola, he should learn to love them as he had never loved before.

> I sought no more that after which I strayed
>   In face of man or maid;
> But still within the little children's eyes
>   Seems something, something that replies,
> They at least are for me, surely for me!

The girl who had befriended him was remembered as a little child, idealized and personified in childhood. It was his first sublimation—yet still the same *libido* flowing on, no longer carrying him downward in its torrent, but floating him gently upward to a higher spiritual level. In every child he saw the face of his trackless fugitive. And when he learned to love a little child, and kissed her innocently, it seemed to him as if he kissed her who gave him of her own scant pittance that he might eat and live. She lived in childhood as he writes to his child love in the poem entitled "A Child's Kiss."

> Therefore I kissed in thee
> The heart of childhood, so divine for me,
>   And her, through what sore ways,
>   And what unchildish days,
> Borne from me now, as then, a trackless fugitive.
>
> Therefore I kissed in thee
> Her, child, and innocency,
> And spring, and all things that have gone from me,
>   And all that shall never be;
> All vanished hopes, and all most hopeless bliss,
>   Came with thee to my kiss.

---

[7] *Op. cit.*, p. 80.

These lines are but the description of the far reaching sublimation of the lower *libido* strivings in his love of childhood. Several of his choicest poems tell of his love of children. It was a love which must have endured with him to the end—though it was capable of satisfying his soul for only a very brief period. In a poem entitled "The Poppy," he tells how this beautiful and innocent sublimation commenced to crumble.

> A child and man paced side by side,
> Treading the skirts of eventide;
> But between the clasp of his hand and hers
> Lay, felt not, twenty withered years.

Suddenly the child plucks one of the poppies through which they are walking—plucks it and throws it to him.

> She turn'd with the rout of her dusk South hair,
> And saw the sleeping gipsy there;
> And snatched and snapped it in swift child's whim,
> With—"Keep it, long as you live!"—to him.

The flower of sleep, plucked by the hand of a child and given to him as a token of love to be kept as long as he lived, awakened from oblivion the memory of his withered past.

> And suddenly 'twixt his hand and hers
> He knew the twenty withered years—
> No flower, but twenty shriveled years.

The *libido* channels of those shriveled years have been blocked and the stream of desire forced upward to higher things, and now seek an outlet in the love of childhood.

> Oh! child! I love, for I love and know.

The love of the past is linked by memory to the love of the present and just at the moment when his heart is about to overflow in the channels of its sublimation, the past rises up to his mind and he realizes that he is a man and she a child, and between the two are his twenty shrivelled years; and guilt dares not seek fellowship with innocence. And then, besides, the loves he had known before were so short and fickle. Had he not known by experience

> The diverse chambers in Love's guest-hall
> Where some rise early, few sit long.

And what can be more fickle than the love of a child?

> O frankly fickle, and fickly true,
> Do you know what the days will do to you?
> To your love and you what the days will do,
> O frankly fickle and fickly true?

And then he ponders sadly over his wasted life. He thinks of others, the friends of his childhood, who did not waste their youth, whose twenty years were not withered and shrivelled, but full of days and works, fat and plump as the grains of wheat amid which the poppy—the withering flower of dreams— swayed its head. But he cannot contemplate the past without seeking compensation in the future. It is one of the necessities of the human heart to seek in some way to make good for the time and opportunities it has wasted. And so Francis Thompson sees in his own poems, which are but the expression of his agonies past and present, the means by which he is to make good his shrivelled years and stand with honor beside the friends of his youth. The very sins of the past are to be transformed into the poems of the future, which would never have been written had he not wasted those twenty years, and then tried to express his withered, withered dreams.

> I hang 'mid men my needless head,
> And my fruit is dreams, as theirs is bread:
> The goodly men and the sun-hazed sleeper
> Time shall reap, but after the reaper
> The world shall glean of me, me the sleeper.

"Of me, me the sleeper"—how pitiably this line rings when the image of the poet rises up to our minds, drugged and unconscious in darkest London.

About this time there became active another force which

helped to lead him from the lower levels of his *libido* striving. He gives us an account of this in the charming personal poem, "Manus animam pinxit." The psychoanalyst will find therein many expressions which indicate the sublimation of a merely human love and bear witness to the struggle which went on in a noble mind in its passage *per aspera ad astra.* Having loved with a carnal love, we find him in this poem painting an ideal woman to whom he cries,

> Lady, who hold'st on me dominion!
> Within your spirit's arms I stay me fast
> Against the fell
> Immitigate ravening of the gates of hell.

He feels his utter dependence upon her.

> Like to a wind-sown sapling grow I from
> The cleft, Sweet, of your skyward-jutting soul.

He begs her to be true to her soul as he is to her:

> For if that soil grow sterile, then the whole
> Of me must shrivel, from the topmost shoot
> Of climbing poesy, and my life, killed through,
> Dry down and perish to the foodless root.

He asks her, his chastest one, to take his curbed spirit and

> This soul which on your soul is laid,
> As maid's breast against breast of maid.

She has engraved her soul upon his own. Her love has made him like herself. "The copy is a painful one, and with long labor done." If she doubts, let her come and look.

> Your beauty, Dian, dress and contemplate
> Within a pool to Dian consecrate!
> Unveil this spirit, lady, when you will,
> For unto all but you 'tis veilèd still:
> Unveil, and fearless gaze there, you alone,
> And if you love the image—'tis your own.

The same *libido* which he now terms the "immitigate ravening of the gates of hell" enters this picture of his spiritualized ideal. It lends a charm to the labor of love—the transformation of his life that he may gain the respect of one who did not shrink from the depth of his degradation.   It lent a charm, a peculiar indescribable attractiveness to this "chaste and intelligential love." But it did not drive him on as the lower *libido* did only a little while before.   Then he was a passive being, incapable of any exertion.   But now he experiences something wholly new—painful and sustained effort, the domination of the *libido*.   And yet this domination, "most hardly won," by long and painful labor, is assisted by the *libido* itself, whose lower outlets are blocked and that now flows over, lending a sensual charm to his spiritualized ideal.   He was perhaps innocently ignorant of the real source and cause of the tenderness of his love and the pleasure he took in yielding to this lady the dominion of his soul.   But nevertheless he felt this charm, whether its source and origin were utterly unconscious or flittingly on the outskirts of his mind.   But this charm was not the only factor; it simply aided in a battle "most hardly won," which gave him a claim of "chaste fidelity upon the chaste."

Simultaneous, apparently, with the influence of this lady—who formed the subject of the poems entitled "Love in Dian's Lap"—there seems to have come to him the realization that the love of children could not give complete and perfect satisfaction to his human heart.   Their very innocence reproached him and brought up to his mind the memory of his withered years. The period during which he first poured out his soul in the love of little children seems to have been a short one.   It was the reaction of his mind to the beauty of a life that he felt could never be his—when he passed from the squalor of London poverty to be an honored guest in happy English homes.   But it was not long before he realized that there were many reasons why the love of children and of childhood could not give his soul that satisfaction which it craved.   This realization developed a hundred fold the feeling of guilt and unworthiness that oppressed his soul. Therefore, he utters the complaint that

> . . . just as their young eyes grew sudden fair
> With dawning answers there
> Their angel plucked them from me by the hair.

From children, he turned to Nature. Several of his poems reflect the attempt of a poet to slake the thirst of his human soul in the beauty of Nature. She was to him a personal something. "Few," he says, "seem to realize that she is alive, has almost as many ways as a woman, and is to be lived with, not merely looked at."[8] He went so far as to sleep a night in the woods that he might live with his new-found spouse. He sought to know her—but know her in a poetic fashion, and dream about her, as once he dreamed about his doll, and later of the statue in the museum with which as a boy he had fallen in love. Though he vainly boasts of his knowledge of Nature, he "could not distinguish the oak from the elm, nor did he know the names of the commonest flowers of the field."[9] What he contemplates in Nature is not science but beauties which express the subconscious yearnings of his soul.

> Love and love's beauty only hold their revels
> In life's familiar, penetrable levels.[10]

Turning then from the children of men he calls to Nature's children,

> Come then, ye other children, Nature's—share
> With me (said I) your delicate fellowship;
>   Let me greet you lip to lip
>   Let me twine with you caresses,
>   Wantoning
>   With our Lady-Mother's vagrant tresses,
>   Banqueting
>   With her in her wind-walled palace,
>   Underneath her azured dais.

---

[8] In a letter to Mrs. Meynell, *op. cit.*, p. 131.
[9] *Op. cit.*, p. 131.
[10] "Poet and Anchorite."

It was not long before he felt the coldness of Nature's response. His night in the woods seems never to have been repeated. In an essay on "Nature's Immortality," he expresses in prose his dissatisfaction with this attempt at sublimation. "You speak, and you think she answers you. It is the echo of your own voice. You think you hear the throbbing of her heart, and it is the throbbing of your own. I do not believe that Nature has a heart; and I suspect, that like many another beauty, she has been credited with a heart because of her face."[11]

In *The Hound of Heaven* the same complaint is uttered in more symbolic language. With perhaps a memory of his night spent voluntarily in the woods or perhaps of those many nights when poverty forced him to sleep beneath the stars, he says:

> Against the red throb of its sunset-heart
>   I laid my own to beat,
>   And share commingling heat;
> But not by that, by that, was eased my human smart.
> In vain my tears were wet on Heaven's grey cheek.
> For ah! we know not what each other says,
> These things and I; in sound I speak—
> *Their* sound is but their stir, they speak by silences.
> Nature, poor stepdame, cannot slake my drouth;
>   Let her, if she would owe me,
> Drop yon blue bosom-veil of sky, and show me
>   The breasts o' her tenderness:
> Never did any milk of hers once bless
>   My thirsting mouth.

Francis Thompson was slowly being made to realize that life does not consist in dreaming, and that he could not be satisfied by shutting himself up within the narrow confines of his own petty spirit. His burial in darkest London had terminated in a resurrection—a coming to life, which he had done but little to accomplish. In the depths of London he had found his child love

> Fallen from the budded coronal of spring,
> And through the city-streets blown withering.

---

[11] *A Renegade Poet and Other Essays*, Boston, 1910, pp. 95–96.

He had found her but to lose her, and be wakened suddenly by the pang of her loss from the sleep of his dream life with her. And when she remained a trackless fugitive, he could no longer hide himself in a tomb now made chilly by her absence. And so he left this tomb and came to life again. And then he sought to shrink back once more from the sunlight of real life and return to childhood in the love of children. Life brought him once more face to face with cold practical duty. It forced obligations upon him that were incompatible with the pleasures of his dreams—obligations from which all his life he had fled. By flight, however, he did not escape from the conflict going on within him, but merely changed the battlefield. In one form or another, the insistence of the real world was ever threatening to break into the citadel of his dreams and disturb the peaceful slumber of his sublimated selfishness. This insistence seemed to grow louder and louder as one attempted sublimation after another was dissipated into nothingness. It was a voice speaking within his soul. It seemed to be more than the ordinary dictates of conscience. He was literally pursued by a Divine Personality who allowed him no escape, for

> . . . if one little casement parted wide,
> The gust of His approach would clash it to:
> Fear wist not to evade, as Love wist to pursue.

Gone was the trackless fugitive—gone too the peace and joy he hoped to find in the love of childhood, in which she was personified, and when he turned to Nature, he did not even find the outlet for his affections which a poet's spirit had anticipated. There is no hope, there is no joy, there is no peace in any dream.

> Nigh and nigh draws the chase,
> With unperturbèd pace,
> Deliberate speed, majestic instancy,
> And past those noisèd Feet
> A voice comes yet more fleet—
> "Lo! naught contents thee, who content'st not Me."

The ideal of duty rises in his mind in spite of him. He has no choice. He must compare what he is with what he might have been, the waste of dreams with the accomplishment of reality, his twenty withered years with the two decades his schoolmates have made to blossom and bear fruit heavy with utility.   How utterly hopeless the present seems, how sinful the waste of the past!

> In the rash lustihead of my young powers,
>   I shook the pillaring hours
> And pulled my life upon me; grimed with smears,
> I stand amid the dust o' the mounded years—
> My mangled youth lies dead beneath the heap.
> My days have crackled and gone up in smoke,
> Have puffed and burst as sun starts on a stream.

Those who are blessed with the fruits of this world's loveliness, those who have home, place, position, and wealth enough to make the wheels of life's chariot roll on with ease, and good fame sufficient to gain the credit and applause of their own neighbors—these may find sublimations that will offer a measure of human peace and content which is illumined only by the shadow of Divinity.   But those who, like Francis Thompson, look back upon withered, shrivelled lives, who with him must say,

> My freshness spent its wavering shower i' the dust;
> And now my heart is as a broken fount,
> Wherein tear-drippings stagnate, spilt down ever
> From the dank thoughts that shiver
> Upon the sighful branches of my mind.

—for such as these there is no human consolation, there is no natural power of sublimation, there is no object on which the heart can set its affections, there is no hope of happiness, for man cannot be happy unless he loves and is loved again in return.

Who cares for the fallen creature "forlorn and faint and stark" who homeless wanders the streets, enduring "through watches of the dark the abashless inquisition of each star," who is the very "outcast mark of all those heavenly passers' scrutiny," suffering "the trampling hoof of every hour in night's slow-wheeled car"—who cares for the fallen outcast? And if he cares enough to help, can any care enough to love? But has not the outcast a human heart, and is not that heart like all human hearts that in order to be happy must love and be loved again? And so for him whose Spring has vanished utterly, whose hopes are extinguished, and whose days are told—there is none to whom he dares to turn.

It was this that Francis Thompson experienced when he felt that the unseen Christ said to him:

> Strange, piteous, futile thing!
> Wherefore should any set thee love apart?
> Seeing none but I makes much of naught? (He said),
> And human love needs human meriting:
>   How hast thou merited—
> Of all man's clotted clay the dingiest clot?
>   Alack, thou knowest not
> How little worthy of any love thou art!
> Whom wilt thou find to love ignoble thee,
>   Save Me, save only Me?

Whatever some may think of the nature of a religious sublimation, few will deny its utility, or fail to recognize that in many cases it gives the only hope of alleviation in mental difficulties where to reconcile opposing forces is impossible. To Francis Thompson final submission to the voice of conscience, the demands of reality, and the dictates of religion came as a last resort when his *libido* striving had worn itself out in every other path open to his peculiar nature.

Were we to judge him by his poem, and see him the strange, piteous, futile thing finally overtaken by the following feet of the Hound of Heaven, utterly overcome but surprised to find that his gloom, after all, is but "the shade of His hand, outstretched caressingly," we might expect a complete transformation, a conversion similar perhaps to that of St. Augustine. But no, Francis Thompson, though much changed, was no saint. The conflict between the *libido* and the spiritual ideal, though terminated in a religious sublimation, was not settled so satisfactorily that the ideal of duty triumphed wholly and forever afterwards.

In the life and poems we have just studied we see exemplified the strife between pleasure and reality which psychoanalysts term the conflict. The concept, however, is as old as human experience. Thus St. Paul wrote: "I see another law in my members, fighting against the law of my mind, and captivating me in the law of sin" (Rom. 7:23). Thus also Kant describes the conflict as the struggle between the sensory self of childhood and the intellectual self that is developed by the ideal of duty and the insistence of the categorical imperative. But only in recent times have the unconscious elements in the conflict been duly appreciated and the relation of the conflict to the neuroses detected.

Sigmund Freud gave clear expression to these ideas in 1911 in an article entitled "Formulierung über die zwei Prinzipien des psychischen Geschehens."[12]

In this article he maintains that the two principles which govern all mental phenomena are the pleasure-pain and the reality principle. Of these the most primitive is the pleasure-pain principle. The infant is governed solely by this primitive driving force. By gestures or cries he makes known his wants, and they are no sooner made known than a tender mother or attentive nurse tries to hush the crying and give the child the little pleasure that it seeks. Thus it seems to the child that it only has to wish in order to have its wants satisfied. But as life goes on it learns by one experience after another that wishes do not always come true—that it may desire and desire and desire again and still the much sought indulgence is not obtained. It is then face to face with reality. Before, the child has lived its life of whims and fancies all alone to itself. It wakens at last to the startling and bitter truth that its fancies may be unrealized, that there is a world of dreams and a world

[12] Cf. *Jahrbuch für psychoanalytische und psychopathologische Forschungen,* vol. 3, pp. 1–8.

of reality and that the two stand over against each other in irreconcilable conflict.

This realization forces a process of adaptation to the world as it is, a process in which the pleasure-pain principle commences to yield to the reality principle. Two selves commence to be built up—the ego of pleasure and the ego of reality. The pleasure ego knows nothing but wishing and the real ego looks only at utility. "Bernard Shaw," says Freud, "has well expressed the advantage that the Ego of Reality has over against the Ego of Pleasure: 'to be able to choose the line of greatest advantage instead of yielding in the direction of least resistance.' "[13]

If one is to shield himself from harm he must often give up the present pleasure for a future advantage, and here arises the strife—and here is the origin of the conflict. The primitive, unconscious strivings of the ego of pleasure demand the present pleasure without regard to consequences. The conscious demands of the ego of reality, with its insight into the future, urge the renunciation of a present gain to ward off a future calamity.

When the pleasure-pain principle cannot attain its end, because it is blocked and thwarted by the barriers and countertrends of the real world, it seeks an outlet in the world of phantasy—in plays and daydreams and vain imaginings.

When the world of reality is all too harsh and dreadful, and the constitution of the individual is unequal to the burdens thrown upon it, the reaction is extreme and we have the abnormal behavior of the neurotic.

The division Freud makes between the pleasure-pain and the reality principle is complete—if we understand by reality all that is opposed to the blind seeking of satisfaction. When, however, we commence to study the checks upon the pleasure-pain principle, we find that Freud has not in this study brought everything to light.

As the individual's life develops he often finds that the

[13] Cf. "*Man and Superman*—A Comedy and a Philosophy," *op. cit.*, p. 5.

fulfillment of his wishes is blocked by objective reality, because that which is *hic et nunc* desired is not *hic et nunc* available. Again, a wish is left unfulfilled because one has learned by experience or hearsay that it is bound up with a future evil. All this Freud recognizes, but here he stops. Now, over and above the restrictions he points out—the limitations, namely, of impossibility and/or expediency—is the restriction of the "ought." In many individuals the limitations imposed by a sense of duty are far greater and more insistent then those demanded by pure expediency and sheer impossibility. The conscience principle, therefore, is one that should be recognized and it might be conveniently distinguished from the reality principle as the subjective is from the objective.

In the concept of the conflict, the conscience principle is of supreme importance. For it often happens that there is no real conflict between desire and its mere physical fulfillment, or between desire and one's sense of expediency, but that it is mainly and above all between desire and the sense of duty.

This is the conflict that we see reflected in *The Hound of Heaven*. The soul fears that if it stops and listens to the voice of conscience it must renounce all its desires and therefore it flies. In this flight it is not merely doing what is inexpedient and foolish—or whining because what it wants cannot be had—but it is flying from the voice of God, the Designer Infinite, to Whom the soul is bound by ties of love.

It is the *libido* that drives it on, whether the soul is "shot precipitated adown Titanic glooms of chasmèd fears" or "troubles the golden gateway of the stars, smiting for shelter on their clangèd bars." While the *libido* drives, conscience calls and no matter where the *libido* may go, conscience always follows after. It is a human force divinized by union with the Deity. Hence, the ideals of duty and the apparent accidents of life concur to block the lower outlets for the *libido*, and direct it from one channel to another, until it arrives at a religious sublimation and conscience triumphs in the conquest of *libido*.

True it is that no matter what is sought, there is one common element in the seeking; whether in the depths of its degradation or in the height of its sublimation, the mind is ever aiming consciously, or unconsciously, at one and the same thing. With the Freudians, this is some aspect of the sexual. But Francis Thompson, whose mind was leavened with Thomistic traditions, regards this one thing as the good—the true good, the one Supreme Good, the Personal Ideal of the conscience principle. What man really desires is the True and Perfect Good, that which alone can fully satisfy the heart. The Infinite Good is, after all, the driving force of human nature. One seeks and seeks again and finds not till desire gives place to will and *libido* is overcome by conscience.

> "Ah, fondest, blindest, weakest,
> I am He Whom thou seekest!
> Thou dravest love from thee, who dravest Me."

Chapter XX

REINTERPRETATION AND RELIGIOUS IDEALS

No one can sail through life successfully without becoming a good psychologist, for all mental difficulties are essentially psychological problems. So, to deal with vital problems successfully is good psychology; and to allow oneself to become ensnared in the meshes of sorrows and trials and disillusionments and disappointments is plain downright bad psychology. He, therefore, who triumphs over his troubles is a good psychologist, and he who meets with shipwreck in managing his own mind in the storms of life is a poor skipper and a bad psychologist. I would not be so extreme in the extension of this proposition as to maintain that there are no storms so violent but that a good skipper can always weather them, and that there are no sorrows so deep but that a good psychologist can rise above them. But in the present order of things, the waters of life are crowded with untrained sea captains, and many of the wrecks, perhaps most, could be prevented by the use of good psychology in the storms through which we must necessarily sail.

What do we mean by shipwreck on the sea of life? A broken home is always a shipwreck. One who is permanently discontented has suffered shipwreck. One who develops the settled conviction that other people are down on him, who becomes sour, cynical, morose, quarrelsome, critical, or abusive to those with whom he comes in contact, is stranded on a desert island from which escape is well nigh impossible.

What, on the other hand, constitutes good seamanship on the ocean of life? Peace, happiness, and good fellowship; friendliness, and free, frank, cordial relationship with all we meet; joy in living and hope for eternity: all this is the fruit of a prudent management of our affairs in virtue of good psychological insight and in obedience to the dictates of reason, illumined, as it will be, by that true Light which enlighteneth every man who cometh into the world.

It is very important for mental hygiene that we realize that the strings of our destiny are in our own hands, and that no blind fate cuts through the strands of our mental health with the shears of a fatal heredity or the steel of the mechanics of the unconscious.

Realizing, therefore, our personal responsibility for good seamanship on the waters of life, we turn naturally to the experience of others, that we may learn the art that we must ply or suffer the consequences of mental shipwreck. This docility, this willingness to learn by the example of others, is an integral part of that prudence which is essential to good seamanship in the affairs of life.

All lives speak to us by their successes and their failures. All examples of handling the difficulties of life are instructive, for we, too, must in due season be confronted with the same or with similar problems.

With these considerations in mind, I turned to the works of Joyce Kilmer in the hope of finding in the writings of a poet some light on the way in which the trials of life may be met.

It is not to be supposed that any one character will exhibit all or even many of the successful methods of handling life's difficulties, nor all the types of failure that we may meet with in the shipwrecks of life. It is probable that characters differ by the dominance of certain mechanisms and drives over the many others that are possible in a human being. It is because this is so that one character differs profoundly from another. To some extent this dominance may depend on the original constitution of the individual, and in some degree it may result from voluntary adoption and practice. The relative importance of nature and nurture is still an unsolved problem, but we can be fairly sure that nurture plays an appreciable role, and it is with this that we are concerned when we study the life history of another human being in order to get light on the management of the difficulties with which we are and will be confronted.

In Joyce Kilmer one finds two mental mechanisms standing out above others. These are overcompensation, and what might be termed reinterpretation. Of these two, reinterpretation is the characteristic trait of Joyce Kilmer, and the chief source of success in the management of his own difficulties, and, therefore, the most important lesson that we are to learn from the story of his life and the poetry and prose he has left to posterity.

Overcompensation is a mechanism with which we are all familiar, though most people have not known it by name. Tell a child he is too weak to accomplish some little task, and he is likely to show you by a supreme effort that he can not only do what you said he could not, but also much more. Children who are too weak to shine in athletics are sometimes driven to outshine all others in their studies. Adler has made the drive to overcompensate for defects the basis of all superiority. It is a psychological factor of some importance in all actual excellence, but it is evidently not the only element and must have as its foundation some positive ability of value in the line in which one finally determines to succeed and surpass.

The taunting of his companions seems to have spurred Joyce Kilmer to show them that he was by no means a personality to be despised. This led him to overcome his initial failure in book learning and stand at the head of his class.

In Holliday's memoir we find the following incident:

"He didn't altogether fit in somehow, couldn't find himself, was somewhat of an outsider among the juvenile class, he was required to fight other boys a good deal, he evidenced a pronounced inability to comprehend anything at all of arithmetic; and somewhere between eight and twelve (so the report goes) he contracted a violent passion for a lady, of about thirty-five, who was his teacher at school; a passion which endured for a considerable time, and became a hilarious legend among the youth about him of jocose humor.

"It is told that at 'Prep' School when this goal seemed rather unlikely of his attainment, he made up his mind to stand at the head of his class, and with something like the later Kilmerian exercise of will he accomplished his purpose."

This spurt did not last long, for "his University life seems to have been in outward effect, fairly normal. There is no evidence that he shone particularly, and none that he failed to shine."[1]

Not all are able to overcompensate. It implies the metal of which heroes are made, strength of will, and the ability to undergo hardship for the sake of an ideal. This character trait, the drive to show others what you can do when they commence to taunt you, was in a measure responsible for his death.

For a while he had worked in the Adjutant's Office, having special charge of recording and reporting statistics. Then he was no longer ("thank God") doing statistics. Someone over there had said that he had a "bullet-proof job." "I had one, but succeeded, after two months intriguing in getting rid of it. . . . At that time I was just an office hack—now I am a soldier, in the most fascinating branch of the service there is—sheer romance, night and day—especially night." He had become attached to the regimental intelligence section, working as an observer—"very amusing work," "wonderful life," "'the finest job in the army."[2]

"Fascinating job," "sheer romance," "amusing work" were terms by which he hid the real danger of his duty when writing to his wife. Its real nature was prowling about the woods locating the exact position of the enemy's machine guns. On July 30, 1918, having discovered that the woods into which

[1] Cf. *Joyce Kilmer*, ed. with Memoir by Robert Cortes Holliday, New York: G. H. Doran, pp. 20–21.

[2] *Op. cit.*, p. 191.

his regiment was about to advance, harbored a nest of the enemy's machine guns, he was sent ahead with a patrol to discover their exact position.   When later his regiment advanced, Joyce Kilmer was found "lying as if still scouting," but with a bullet through his brain.

Is Joyce Kilmer to be blamed for getting rid of his bullet-proof job and entering the most dangerous branch of the military service when at the front in time of war?   Not unless it is wrong for one to risk his life in the service of his native land. Though our mental mechanisms may drive us on, so long as reason shows us that the end to which they drive is essentially good, we are justified in yielding to the impulses of our nature. Furthermore, the hand of God guides the destiny of our lives. Greater love than this no man knows than that a man lay down his life for his friends.   Sacrifice is the crown of life and civic martyrdom was the reward of a poet who served God and his country by word and deed.

What he wrote of Rupert Brooke can be reuttered of himself:

> In alien earth, across a troubled sea,
> His body lies that was so fair and young.
> His mouth is stopped with half his songs unsung;
> His arm is still, that struck to make men free.
> But let no cloud of lamentation be
> Where, on a warrior's grave, a lyre is hung.
> We keep the echoes of his golden tongue.
> We keep the vision of his chivalry.
>
> So Israel's joy, the lovliest of kings,
> Smote now his harp, and now the hostile horde,
> Today the starry roof of Heaven rings,
> With psalms a soldier made to praise his Lord,
> And David rests beneath Eternal wings,
> Song on his lips, and in his hand a sword.

Reinterpretation, as we have said, is the most characteristic trait in Joyce Kilmer's character.   The following incident is typical of what I mean by reinterpretation.

"At the death of James Whitcomb Riley, Kilmer hurried to the Catskills for his interview with Bliss Carman. On his way back to the City, by way of his home at Mahwah, he dashed with his usual impetuosity in front of the moving train he was seeking to board, was knocked down and hurled or dragged a considerable distance, and taken to the Good Samaritan Hospital at Suffern, New York, with three ribs fractured and other injuries; when wiring immediately to New York for his Secretary, he dictated an interview as engaging and as full of journalistic craft as any he ever wrote. . . .

"I did not see Kilmer at this time myself, but I have an idea that, when he had relieved his mind of the anxiety concerning his article, he entered into the spirit of his experience with much relish. It isn't every day that one gets hit by a train, nor everybody that has three ribs broken. Exhilarating kind of thing, when you see it that way! I remember one time when I was practically in the hospital myself he went to a good deal of trouble to come to see me. He seemed to admire my predicament very much, and beaming upon me, remarked in high good humour that it must be an entertaining thing to be so completely at the mercy of circumstances over which you had no control."[3]

Most people do not react to broken ribs or broken noses or broken anything in that kind of a way. When anything is broken, it is just simply smashed, and that is all there is to it. It is a calamity to be "cussed" at or cried about, but who is he who can rise above broken bones or broken dishes or broken finances and see in it an exhilarating kind of thing. And yet it is possible "when you see it that way." Such is the lesson of Joyce Kilmer. When next we are in the hospital or in jail, perhaps, or in any kind of predicament, let us see if we cannot reinterpret and find it an "entertaining thing to be so completely at the mercy of circumstances over which we have no control."

[3] *Op. cit.*, pp. 43-44.

Holliday tells us: "When confronted with some financial dilemma, he was fond of declaring 'The demand creates the supply. A sound economic principle.' He seemed to crave serious responsibilities and insistent obligations as some men crave liquor; and he grew more rosy as this increased."

Again we learn from Holliday: "In 1913 Kilmer's daughter Rose, nine months of age, was stricken with infantile paralysis. During the course of his stay with me that day he said several times, 'Well, there are lots of people worse off than I am.' This idea, too, it was apparent, he felt he must hold before him. And then, with his amazing and unconquerable *flair* for life, he launched upon the theme that this was a 'very interesting disease!' and he elaborated the thought that an infirmity of the body frequently resulted in an increased vitality of the mind."[4]

It is very important that a poet or anybody else, for that matter, should not develop a condition in which he thinks highly of himself and despises others.

There are two ways of averting this. The first is to elevate our conception of others to the plane on which we ourselves live, or hope to live. In this way we commence to appreciate the value of the lives of those we meet in the humbler occupations of life. The true worth of a man does not lie in what he does, but in how he does it. This is a most important lesson for us to learn, and if all this world would learn it, it would contribute much to the peace and happiness of society.

The second way is to see our own faults, which, perhaps, we have glossed over so that they look like virtues, and humble ourselves to the level of those whom the world is likely to despise. Both methods require considerable ability of interpretation and reinterpretation, and both are exemplified in the poetry of Joyce Kilmer.

Reinterpretation, by which the poet sees a value in one of the most commonplace activities of life, which seems of all things

[4] *Op. cit.*, p. 51.

perhaps the least poetical, is exhibited in Kilmer's poem on a delicatessen shop.

> Well, it is true he has no sword
>   To dangle at his booted knees.
> He leans across a slab of board,
>   And draws his knife and slices cheese.
>
> He never heard of chivalry,
>   He longs for no heroic times;
> He thinks of pickles, olives, tea,
>   And dollars, nickels, cents and dimes.
>
> His world has narrow walls, it seems;
>   By counters is his soul confined;
> His wares are all his hope and dreams,
>   They are the fabric of his mind.
>
> Yet—in a room above the store
>   There is a woman—and a child
> Pattered just now across the floor;
>   The shopman looked at him and smileᴅ.
>
> For, once he thrilled with high romance
>   And turned to love his eager voice.
> Like any cavalier of France
>   He wooed the maiden of his choice.
>
> And now deep in his weary heart
>   Are sacred flames that whitely burn.
> He has of Heaven's grace a part
>   Who loves, who is beloved in turn.
>
> And when the long day's work is done
>   (How slow the leaden minutes ran!)
> Home, with his wife and little son,
>   He is no huckster, but a man!
>   . . . .
> And in his little shop, who knows
>   What bitter games of war are played?
> Why, daily on each corner grows
>   A foe to rob him of his trade.
>
> He fights, and for his fireside's sake;
>   He fights for clothing and for bread;
> The lances of his foemen make
>   A steely halo round his head.

He decks his window artfully
He haggles over paltry sums.
In this strange field his war must be
And by such blows his triumph comes.
. . . .

This man has home and child and wife
And battle set for every day.
This man has God and love and life;
These stand, all else shall pass away.

O Carpenter of Nazareth,
Whose mother was a village maid,
Shall we, Thy children, blow our breath
In scorn on any humble trade?

Have pity on our foolishness
And give us eyes, that we may see
Beneath the shopman's clumsy dress
The splendour of humanity!

Reinterpretation, which humbles the personality and makes the poet see a failing he is likely to gloss over, is given to us in his poem, "The Big Top."

The boom and blare of the big brass band is cheering to my heart
And I like the smell of the trampled grass and elephants and hay.
I take off my hat to the acrobat with his delicate, strong art,
And the motley mirth of the chalk-faced clown drives all my care away.

I wish I could feel as they must feel, these players brave and fair,
Who nonchalantly juggle death before a staring throng.
It must be fine to walk a line of silver in the air
And to cleave a hundred feet of space with a gesture like a song.

Sir Henry Irving never knew a keener, sweeter thrill
Than that which stirs the breast of him who turns his painted face
To the circling crowd who laugh aloud and clap hands with a will
As a tribute to the clown who won the great wheel-barrow race.

Now, one shall work in the living rock with a mallet and a knife,
And another shall dance on a big white horse that canters around a ring,
By another's hand shall colours stand in similitude of life;
And the hearts of the three shall be moved by one mysterious high thing.

For the sculptor and the acrobat and the painter are the same.
   They know one hope, one fear, one pride, one sorrow and one mirth,
And they take delight in the endless fight for the fickle world's acclaim;
   For they worship art above the clouds and serve her on the earth.

But you, who can build of the stubborn rock no form of loveliness,
   Who can never mingle the radiant hues to make a wonder live,
Who can only show your little woe to the world in a rhythmic dress—
   What kind of a counterpart of you does the three-ring circus give?

Well—here in a little side-show tent today some people stand,
   One is a giant, one a dwarf, and one has a figured skin,
And each is scarred and seared and marred by Fate's relentless hand,
   And each one shows his grief for pay, with a sort of pride therein.

You put your sorrow into rhyme and want the world to look,
   You sing the news of your ruined hope and want the world to hear;
Their woe is pent in a canvas tent and yours in a printed book.
   O, poet of the broken heart, salute your brothers here!

So Kilmer humbles himself for the craving for sympathy and praise which personal experience made him recognize in himself. The drive to interpret and reinterpret made him find in the side show of a circus its counterpart of himself.

Joyce Kilmer's interpretations and reinterpretations were not mere poetic dreams, but actual mental mechanisms which enabled him to see something good or beautiful or amusing and interesting in the midst of harrowing experiences.

In a letter to his wife, he says: "I am having a delightful time out here—absolutely beautiful country and very nice people."[5]   In another letter he writes:

"A terrible thing, this war, what with a pine forest to live in, all the latest novels to read, and bridge every evening. And now I am preparing for a short week-end in a nice small city, an hour's walk through the forest and across the mountains. It is a lovely forest in which to wander of a June day—so deliberately European—a forest whose tall evergreen trees and smooth

[5] Nov. 24, 1917: *op. cit.*, vol. 2, p. 167.

brown floor suggest all the folk tales I ever heard your dear voice beautify for our children's delight."[6]

This was certainly not the ordinary reaction of the "dough-boy" to the rain and mud of sunny France.

That there was much genuine hardship in his life in France is evidenced by the simple incident described in the opening lines of his essay, "Holy Ireland."

"We had hiked seventeen miles that stormy December day— the third of a four day journey. The snow was piled high on our packs, our rifles were crusted with ice, the leather of our hob-nailed boots was frozen stiff over our lamed feet. The weary lieutenant led us to the door of a little house in a side street. . .we at once climbed to the chill attic, our billet, our lodging for the night. First we lifted the packs from one another's aching shoulders; then, without spreading our blankets we lay down on bare boards."[7]

But Kilmer did not allow himself to take the ordinary view of the American doughboy. He forgot about the cold, the fatigue, the miserable billets. He refused to interpret the unhappy and miserable world in which he lived at its face value. To do so would have overwhelmed him with sadness. He had to see it in a new light. It must have a value. And so he delighted in the contact with human nature that his army experience forced upon him.

However useful reinterpretation may be as a temporary mechanism, it must be regarded as a defense reaction against the realization of the bitterness of the trials and sorrows of life, which, in itself, is inadequate and superficial.

We cannot always conceive of all sorrows as exhilarating experiences when we "see it that way." No defense reaction can be more than a temporary makeshift. The skeleton in the closet will finally rattle its bones till we must hear. The door will finally be opened and the misery of our inner life be revealed to our conscious gaze.

[6] June 1, 1918: *op. cit.*, vol. 2, p. 220.
[7] *Op. cit.*

Reinterpretation must ascend from superficial trivialities to the realization of essential and eternal values. It thus grows from a defense reaction to a most valuable type of sublimation. And it is precisely this that we see in the mechanism of reinterpretation as developed in the mind of Joyce Kilmer.

One day, when overwhelmed by almost hopeless difficulties, he sat down and wrote his poem "Thanksgiving," which expresses the blind confidence of the soul in God, Who does nothing without reason and Who in wisdom and love chastens the soul that is dear to him.

> The roar of the world is in my ears
> Thank God for the roar of the world!
> Thank God for the mighty tide of fears
> Against me always hurled!
>
> Thank God for the bitter and ceaseless strife,
> And the sting of His chastening rod!
> Thank God for the stress and pain of life,
> And oh, thank God for God!

The distinctly Christian interpretation of suffering, particularly physical pain, by an association of our own pain and sorrow with the passion of Christ, appears in the poem he entitled "Meditatio Militis" which was published under the title "Prayer of a Soldier in France."

> My shoulders ache beneath my pack
> (Lie easier, Cross, upon His Back).
>
> I march with feet that burn and smart
> (Tread, Holy Feet, upon my heart).
>
> Men shout at me who may not speak
> (They scourged Thy back and smote Thy cheek).
>
> I may not lift a hand to clear
> My eyes of salty drops that sear.
>
> (Then shall my fickle soul forget
> Thy agony of Bloody Sweat?)

My rifle hand is stiff and numb
(From Thy pierced palm red rivers come).

Lord, Thou didst suffer more for me
Than all the hosts of land and sea.

So let me render back again
This millionth of Thy gift. Amen.

Such thoughts as these make it possible for Christian faith to find a holy joy in all trials and sufferings, no matter what they may be. In such moments one who knows what it is to love Christ may with joyful resignation repeat with this poet-soldier in France:

Lord, Thou didst suffer more for me
Than all the hosts of land and sea.

So let me render back again
This millionth of Thy gift. Amen.

Let us now consider a few practical possibilities that we may see how, in some way, we may profit by the poetry and example of Joyce Kilmer. Let us suppose that where you work a new head of your department enters upon his office. You have heard that he is cross and cranky, and you find out to your dismay that this is the case, that he is even capable of "cussing" people out at times, and, what is worse, that you in particular are in closest contact with him, and the usual buffer of his impossible temper.

It is time for reinterpretation. What a delightful old gentleman, what a lot of interesting moods he has! What an exhilarating thing to be really "cussed" at in loud and stentorian tones! How stimulating to have a real psychological problem to be solved every single day of your life!

You are in the Army or Navy or in the government service, or your husband gets a job in a far-off country, and you hear that you will have to move to the Desert of Sahara, Timbuktu, South Africa, or Tierra del Fuego. You commence to get downhearted, as you think of forsaking old associates, living among strangers, and meeting new and unheard-of difficulties. It is time for reinterpretation. It is not everybody who gets the opportunity to go on a long sea voyage. What a delightful thing to see a new country! How interesting to meet new people, to learn about human nature, etc.

You are taken sick and have to go to the hospital. It isn't everybody that gets a chance to have his breakfast served to him in bed in the morning and then roll over and sleep as late as he pleases.

And so for every calamity, there are always two ways of looking at it, and we should learn to glean whatever may be humorous and pleasant in our unfortunate circumstances. But should this at times become too shallow, or wholly impossible in the severe storm that threatens to overwhelm us, then our minds must turn to the cross of Christ.

> Lord, Thou didst suffer more for me
> Than all the hosts of land and sea.
>
> So let me render back again
> This millionth of Thy gift. Amen.

Let us now quote two passages from the letters of Joyce Kilmer which indicate that shortly before his death he had attained to an appreciation, at least, of the mystical ideal.

"I have written very little—two prose sketches and two poems since I left the States—but I have a rich store of memories. Not that what I write matters—I have discovered since some unforgettable experiences, that writing is not the tremendously important thing I once considered it. You will find me less a bookman when you next see me, and more I hope a man. Pray for me, my dear Father, that I may love God more and that I may be unceasingly conscious of Him—that is the greatest desire I have."[8]

In one of his last letters he wrote to Sister M. Emerentia

[8] May 6, 1918, to Father Garesché, S. J.: *op. cit.*, vol. 2, p. 119.

of St. Joseph's College, Toronto, Ontario: "Pray that I may love God more. It seems to me that if I can learn to love God more passionately, more constantly, without distractions, that absolutely nothing else can matter. Except while we are in the trenches I receive Holy Communion every morning, so it ought to be all the easier for me to attain this object of my prayers. I got Faith, you know, by praying for it. I hope to get love the same way."[9]

I call special attention to the words "that I may be unceasingly conscious of Him. . . . It seems to me that if I can learn to love God more passionately, more constantly, without distractions, that absolutely nothing else can matter." Poetry alone would not have given to this soldier in France this hope for the actual realization of the mystical ideal. There is no indication in the *Memoir* or his letters of the way in which these aspirations arose in his soul. But they were evidently present some months before his death.

This ideal of unceasing awareness of the presence of God is the goal of true mysticism, sought for by many, attained by only a few. It is not meant for the cloistered nun alone, but for all who live earnestly in accordance with the ideals of their baptism. It can be attained by those living and working in the world. A poor woman taking care of her large family of children, and neglecting none of the duties which that implies, could nevertheless write: "All this week I have been able to pray incessantly, except when I slept, and I have wished that I could be awake to Christ through the night instead of sleeping." How far Joyce Kilmer realized his ideal before he laid down his life for his country, we do not know, but we can feel sure that one who attained faith by prayer and asked that charity might be granted by Him Who gave faith, was not left unheard.

The answer to this prayer is the secret of Joyce Kilmer's bravery. Father Duffy, the chaplain of his regiment, said

[9] *Op. cit.*, vol. 1, p. 101.

of him: "He was absolutely the coolest and most indifferent man in the face of danger I have ever seen." He was brave because in danger he was in very truth not alone. The unseen presence of Divinity did not forsake him in the hour of duty. And so he wrote, with no mere poetic figure of speech, but with all the reality of one who had enjoyed in some measure the mystic experience:

> Who fights for Freedom, goes with joyful tread,
> To meet the fires of Hell against him hurled,
> And has for Captain Him whose thorn-wreathed head
> Smiles from the Cross upon a conquered world.

Let us who are still captivated with the visible things of this world learn the lesson. The eye is not satisfied with seeing, nor the ear with hearing. The human mind was made to live in conscious union with Eternal Truth. Let us no longer seek to satisfy the yearnings of the soul with the lust of the flesh and the lust of the eyes and the pride of life. "Let not these occupy my soul; let God rather occupy it, who made these things very good indeed, yet He is my good, not they" (St. Augustine, *Confessions*, X, 51, Pusey's translation).

And so we go about our work in the world. We endure hardships patiently. We give up our own way in order to be kind and helpful to others, bearing all and suffering all, reinterpreting our trials in the light of eternal truths, until that which is perfect shall come, and that which is in part shall be no more, and we attain to the substance of things to be hoped for and the vision of things that appear not.

INDEX OF AUTHORS

INDEX OF SUBJECTS

328